DISCARDED
UNIVERSITY OF WINNIPEG
LIBRARY
515 PORTAGE AVENUE
WINNIPEG, MAN. R3B 2E9

CONTROL OF
ENERGY METABOLISM

A Colloquium on Metabolic Control
Johnson Research Foundation
Philadelphia, May 20, 1965
and A Symposium on Control of Energy Metabolism
Philadelphia, May 21, 1965
in celebration of
the Bicentennial of the University of Pennsylvania School of Medicine

University of Pennsylvania

School of Medicine

QP
171
.C48

CONTROL OF ENERGY METABOLISM

EDITED BY

BRITTON CHANCE RONALD W. ESTABROOK

JOHN R. WILLIAMSON

JOHNSON RESEARCH FOUNDATION, SCHOOL OF MEDICINE
UNIVERSITY OF PENNSYLVANIA, PHILADELPHIA, PENNSYLVANIA

ACADEMIC PRESS · NEW YORK · LONDON · 1965

Copyright © 1965, by Academic Press Inc.
ALL RIGHTS RESERVED.
NO PART OF THIS BOOK MAY BE REPRODUCED IN ANY FORM,
BY PHOTOSTAT, MICROFILM, OR ANY OTHER MEANS, WITHOUT
WRITTEN PERMISSION FROM THE PUBLISHERS.

ACADEMIC PRESS INC.
111 Fifth Avenue, New York, New York 10003

United Kingdom Edition published by
ACADEMIC PRESS INC. (LONDON) LTD.
Berkeley Square House, London W.1

Library of Congress Catalog Card Number: **65-27786**

First Printing, 1965
Second Printing, 1967

PRINTED IN THE UNITED STATES OF AMERICA.

Participants

AUGUSTIN BETZ, *Botanisches Institut der Technischen Hochschule, Braunschweig, Germany*

R. H. BOWMAN, *Department of Physiology, Vanderbilt University, Nashville, Tennessee*

THEODOR BÜCHER, *Physiologisch-Chemisches Institut der Universität München, München, Germany*

ERNEST BUEDING, *Department of Pathobiology, School of Hygiene and Public Health, The Johns Hopkins University, Baltimore, Maryland*

BRITTON CHANCE, *The Johnson Research Foundation, University of Pennsylvania, Philadelphia, Pennsylvania*

CARL F. CORI, *Department of Biological Chemistry, Washington University School of Medicine, St. Louis, Missouri*

WILLIAM H. DANFORTH, *Department of Internal Medicine, Washington University School of Medicine, St. Louis, Missouri*

ROBERT E. DAVIES, *School of Veterinary Medicine, University of Pennsylvania, Philadelphia, Pennsylvania*

DAVID EPEL, *Hopkins Marine Station, Pacific Grove, California*

RENÉ FRENKEL, *The Johnson Research Foundation, University of Pennsylvania, Philadelphia, Pennsylvania*

DAVID GARFINKEL, *The Johnson Research Foundation, University of Pennsylvania, Philadelphia, Pennsylvania*

ERNST HELMREICH, *Department of Biological Chemistry, Washington University School of Medicine, St. Louis, Missouri*

WALTER HEMPFLING, *The Johnson Research Foundation, University of Pennsylvania, Philadelphia, Pennsylvania*

BENNO HESS, *Max-Planck Institut für Ernährungsphysiologie, Dortmund, Germany*

JOSEPH J. HIGGINS, *The Johnson Research Foundation, University of Pennsylvania, Philadelphia, Pennsylvania*

RICHARD D. KEYNES, *Agricultural Research Council, Institute of Animal Physiology, Babraham, Cambridge, England*

DAVID M. KIPNIS, *Metabolism Division, Department of Medicine, Washington University School of Medicine, St. Louis, Missouri*

MARTIN KLINGENBERG, *Physiologisch-Chemisches Institut der Universität Marburg, Marburg/Lahn, Germany*

EDWIN G. KREBS, *Department of Biochemistry, University of Washington School of Medicine, Seattle, Washington*

SIR HANS KREBS, *Department of Biochemistry, University of Oxford, Oxford, England*

HENRY A. LARDY, *Institute for Enzyme Research and Department of Biochemistry, University of Wisconsin, Madison, Wisconsin*

OLIVER H. LOWRY, *The Edward Mallinckrodt Department of Pharmacology, Washington University, St. Louis, Missouri*

JOHN M. LOWENSTEIN, *Graduate Department of Biochemistry, Brandeis University, Waltham, Massachusetts*

TAG E. MANSOUR, *Department of Pharmacology, Stanford University School of Medicine, Palo Alto, California*

CYRIL L. MOORE, *Department of Neurology, Albert Einstein College of Medicine, Bronx, New York*

H. E. MORGAN, *Department of Physiology, Vanderbilt University, Nashville, Tennessee*

ARTHUR B. PARDEE, *Department of Biology, Princeton University, Princeton, New Jersey*

JANET V. PASSONNEAU, *Department of Pharmacology, Washington University School of Medicine, St. Louis, Missouri*

DIRK PETTE, *Physiologisch-Chemisches Institut der Universität München, München, Germany*

KENDALL PYE, *The Johnson Research Foundation, University of Pennsylvania, Philadelphia, Pennsylvania*

HOWARD RASMUSSEN, *Department of Biochemistry, University of Pennsylvania, Philadelphia, Pennsylvania*

IRWIN A. ROSE, *The Institute for Cancer Research, Philadelphia, Pennsylvania*

JAY TEPPERMAN, *State University of New York, Upstate Medical Center, Syracuse, New York*

KOSAKU UYEDA, *Department of Biochemistry, Public Health Research Institute of the City of New York, Inc., New York, New York*

JOHN R. WILLIAMSON, *The Johnson Research Foundation, University of Pennsylvania, Philadelphia, Pennsylvania*

RAY WU, *Department of Biochemistry, Public Health Research Institute of the City of New York, Inc., New York, New York*

Preface

One of the foremost problems challenging biochemists today is the understanding of integrated metabolic systems as functional units within the cell, and the factors which influence and control them. The major pathways of metabolism in such systems have been established over the past thirty years, and the University of Pennsylvania has been fortunate to be a contributor to many important aspects through some of its distinguished faculty, such as Otto Meyerhof, W. C. Stadie, and D. Wright Wilson. It is fitting that an evaluation of the present status of the field be made during this 200th anniversary of the founding of the School of Medicine at the University of Pennsylvania.

Present knowledge of the dynamics of cellular metabolism is based largely upon an extension of the basic principles of physical chemistry as applied to enzyme reactions in solution. The establishment of current hypotheses spans the metamorphosis from classic studies with single enzymes to the understanding of the mechanism of integrated enzyme reactions. The ability to approximate concentrations of enzymes and substrates along various pathways of metabolism now leads to more accurate formulations of the dynamics of these pathways, and offers better opportunities for a more intensive study of computer models.

Scientific investigation into a new area of study often arises from the development of a new technique, as exemplified by studies of metabolic control, beginning with the purification and crystallization of many of the enzymes of the glycolytic pathways and the intensive study of their properties. In particular, wider recognition of the many facets controlling enzyme activity provides a basis for new ideas about the control of metabolism in multi-enzyme sequences. The ability to perform rapid and highly accurate assays of minute concentrations of intermediates of metabolism with sampling methods that "stop the biological process in its tracks" provides the key to much-needed data within the cell.

Patterns of metabolite concentration reveal control sites or "crossover points" during transitions which vary the flow rate of metabolites through the system. Methods which allow the continuous monitoring of metabolite changes in cells and tissues, give key information about the application of chemical methods to the study of the kinetics of metabolite changes. Thus, critical times in metabolic transitions can be established so that one can assess not only the extent to which intermediates are changing but also the times at which intermediates are changing most rapidly. It is apparent that future thinking must recognize the growing significance of the transient response of an enzymatic system, rather than accept the static picture presented by a restricted view of the steady state or equilibrium properties of the system.

Many problems confront us; our knowledge of enzymes is far from complete, particularly in understanding their response to different control chemicals. Our assays of metabolites are imperfect and our methods for stopping biochemical reactions in some cases are too slow. Of prime difficulty is the estimation of the localized concentrations of enzymes and substrates in their appropriate places in the cell. In addition, the failure to appreciate the complexity of the intracellular milieu, when extrapolating from test tube to the intracellular environs of enzymes, restricts our knowledge. When these questions are answered, exact simulation of the complete systems by computers will be possible, giving a clear understanding of the applicability of physical-chemical principles to the control of multi-enzyme systems. Furthermore, the supervisory control of hormones on the systems will still need further study and ultimately computer simulation.

The success of the present volume resides with the contributors—all recognized authorities in the field of cellular metabolism. Their examination in depth of many provocative hypotheses serves as the foundation for the illuminating discussions. Any failure of the volume resides with the organizers, whose enthusiasm encouraged general discussion of the many facets of cell metabolism, thereby restricting the detailed evaluation of newly developed and promising hypotheses. The balance between success and failure will be determined by its usefulness to investigators and students interested in the area of regulation of cell metabolism. It is hoped that this interim report on the current status of a rapidly developing area of research will serve to stimulate further interest in the intricate mechanisms of cellular dynamics.

The Editors are grateful to Miss Judith Anderson for her devotion and skill in performing the monumental, and often frustrating, task of assisting them in producing this volume. Appreciation and thanks are due also to the typists and especially to Mrs. Lilian Chance, who supervised the transcription and preliminary editing of the Colloquium proceedings.

The Editors also wish to express their appreciation to the Smith, Kline and French Laboratories, in particular to Dr. A. E. Heming, for their financial support which allowed the participation of our foreign colleagues.

THE EDITORS

November 1, 1965

Table of Contents

LIST OF PARTICIPANTS v

PREFACE vii

CONTROL CHARACTERISTICS OF ENZYMES AND ENZYME SYSTEMS *IN VITRO*

Opening Remarks 3
B. CHANCE

Introductory Remarks 5
H. A. KREBS

I. Theoretical Aspects of Control Properties in Enzyme Systems

The Respiratory Chain as a Model for Metabolic Control in Multi-Enzyme Systems 9
B. CHANCE

Dynamics and Control in Cellular Reactions 13
J. J. HIGGINS

II. Computer Studies

Computer Based Analysis of Biochemical Data 49
D. GARFINKEL

Discussion: BÜCHER, ROSE, CHANCE, CZERLINSKI, HESS, SALGANICOFF

III. Phosphofructokinase: Its Purification, Crystallization, and Kinetic Properties

Phosphofructokinase 63
O. H. LOWRY

Purification and Properties of Rabbit Skeletal Muscle Phosphofructokinase . 65
E. G. KREBS AND A. PARMEGGIANI

Phosphofructokinase from Rabbit Muscle 69
H. A. LARDY

Some Properties of Fructose-6-Phosphate Kinase from Rabbit Skeletal Muscle 71
D. PETTE AND H. W. HOFER

Multiple Forms of Heart Phosphofructokinase 81
T. E. MANSOUR

On the Mechanism of Inhibition and Activation of Phosphofructokinase in Novikoff Ascites Tumor Cells 87
R. Wu

Control Properties of Phosphofructokinase from *Saccharomyces cerevisia* . . 97
C. L. Moore, A. Betz, and B. Chance

A Computer Simulation Study of the Metabolic Control Behavior of Phosphofructokinase 101
D. Garfinkel

Summary 105
O. H. Lowry

ENZYME CONTENT, SUBSTRATE AND COFACTOR AVAILABILITY, AND CATION TRANSPORT AS FACTORS IN METABOLIC REGULATION

IV. Enzyme Profile Patterns and Reconstituted Systems

Enzyme and Metabolite Profiles 111
B. Hess and K. Brand

Enzyme Profile and Beef Heart Supernatant Fraction 123
R. Frenkel

Comment 125
R. W. Estabrook

Coordinated Stimulation of Hexokinase and Phosphofructokinase by Phosphate in a Reconstituted System of Glycolysis 127
K. Uyeda and E. Racker

A Reconstituted Enzyme System 139
A. Betz

Discussion: Hess, Bücher, Chance

V. Control in Single-Cellular Systems Due to P_i or ADP Availability

Control Characteristics of the Adenine Nucleotide System 149
M. Klingenberg

ADP and P_i Control in Ascites Tumor Cells 157
P. K. Maitra and B. Chance

The Control of Hexokinase in Ascites Tumor Glycolysis 177
I. A. Rose

On the Control of Glycolysis in Novikoff Ascites Tumor Cells 187
R. Wu

The Control of Glycolysis in Yeast 193
E. K. Pye

Discussion: Hess, Chance, Rose, Lowry, Krebs, Bücher, Wenner, Garfinkel, Moore, Lowenstein

VI. The Role of Cations in Metabolic Control

Cation Flux Across the Mitochondrial Membrane as a Possible Pacemaker of Tissue Metabolism 209
H. Rasmussen and E. Ogata

A Role of Sodium and Potassium in Metabolic Control 217
R. D. Keynes

The Role of Na^+ and K^+ on α-Aminoisobutyric Acid Transport in Striated Muscle 221
D. M. Kipnis

Discussion: Bücher, Lardy, Keynes, Chance, Kipnis, Pressman, Salganicoff

VII. Control Due to Changes of Enzyme Content

On Transitory and Periodic Systems in Bacteria 239
A. B. Pardee

On the Direction of Pyridine Nucleotide Oxidation-Reduction Reactions in Gluconeogenesis and Lipogenesis 245
H. A. Lardy

On the Biochemical Imprinting of Metabolic Experience in Liver Cells . . 249
J. Teppperman and H. M. Tepperman

Adaptive Behavior of Citrate Cleavage Enzyme 261
J. M. Lowenstein

Some Aspects of Metabolic Control in the Fertilization Transition of Sea Urchin Eggs 267
D. Epel

Discussion: Bücher, H. A. Krebs, Chance, Klingenberg, Lardy

CONTROL OF METABOLISM IN INTACT TISSUES

Introductory Remarks 283
C. F. Cori

VIII. Regulation of Glycolytic Activity in Smooth and Skeletal Muscles

Activation of Glycolytic Pathway in Muscle 287
W. H. Danforth

The Response of the Glycolytic System of Anaerobic Frog Sartorius Muscle to Electrical Stimulation 299
E. Helmreich, W. H. Danforth, S. Karpatkin, and C. F. Cori

Some Biochemical Properties of Intestinal Smooth Muscle in Relation to the Physiological Actions of Epinephrine 313
E. Bueding and E. Bülbring

Discussion: Berry, Davies

IX. Regulation of Metabolism in Brain

Effects of Altered Brain Metabolism on the Levels of Krebs Cycle Intermediates 321
N. D. Goldberg, J. V. Passonneau, and O. H. Lowry

Discussion: H. A. Krebs, Passonneau, Lowenstein, Chance

X. Regulation of Glycolytic Activity in Heart Muscle

Metabolic Control in the Perfused Rat Heart 333
J. R. Williamson

Regulation of Glucose Transport 347
H. E. Morgan, J. R. Neely, J. P. Brineaux, and C. R. Park

Fatty Acid Induced Alterations in Citric Acid Cycle Intermediates . . . 357
R. H. Bowman

Discussion: Hempfling, Olson, Morgan, Hess, Williamson, Bücher, E. Krebs, Mansour, Lowry, Chance, Helmreich, Danforth, Davies

BICENTENNIAL LECTURES ON CONTROL OF ENERGY METABOLISM

Energy Transformation in the Generation of Bioelectricity 375
R. D. Keynes

Control of Energy Metabolism. Bioenergetics of Muscular Contraction . . 383
R. E. Davies

Hemoglobin-Free Perfusion of Rat Liver 393
R. Scholz and Th. Bücher

Control of Energy Metabolism in Mitochondria 415
B. Chance

Index 437

CONTROL CHARACTERISTICS OF ENZYMES AND ENZYME SYSTEMS *IN VITRO*

OPENING REMARKS

Britton Chance

The third Colloquium at the Johnson Research Foundation addresses itself today to the topic of Control of Energy Metabolism, a new and rapidly developing field, and one which is quite appropriate to the interest of the Johnson Foundation in particular, and to the Medical School as a whole, which this year celebrates its Bicentenary. Three notable workers in the field of metabolism have been honored members of its faculty -- D. Wright Wilson, William C. Stadie and Otto Meyerhoff. Their work sets standards that we have since striven to emulate.

This Colloquium of the Johnson Foundation differs somewhat from the distinguished tradition organized by Dr. Bronk in the 1930's where leaders in the field of physiology, particularly A. V. Hill, E. D. Adrian, and the great chemist Irving Longmuir, presented a series of outstanding lectures on their special interests. Now we tend more toward an exchange of ideas among a group of experts. Each one of you here has something special to contribute to our ideas on metabolic control. But the one who has contributed most in the past and who continues to be a leader in experimentation and in scientific thought in the field of metabolic control is Sir Hans Krebs, Chairman of the Department of Biochemistry at Oxford University. Those who know and study his works have the greatest respect for him as an experimentalist and synthesizer of new ideas in modern biochemistry. It gives me great pleasure to introduce the chairman of this portion of the symposium, Sir Hans Krebs.

INTRODUCTORY REMARKS

Sir Hans Krebs

The only thought I want to express to the organizers of this meeting, above all to Dr. Chance, but also to Dr. Estabrook and Dr. Williamson, is our thanks for bringing us together under such pleasant circumstances.

There is really not much to say by way of introduction. As Dr. Chance has said, we all know each other; it is almost like coming to a family gathering. In view of the very rapid development of the field in which we are interested, gatherings at frequent intervals are of the greatest value to all of us a and to our work. I for one, never fail to go away from this type of meeting without feeling very much stimulated, and without having been fairly criticized, and without having learned a great deal. Attending such a Colloquium feels like going to school again.

To the arrangers we are truly grateful, and I am sure, from what I have gathered in the informal discussions last night and this morning, that I am speaking for all of us who have come here.

I

Theoretical Aspects of Control Properties in Enzyme Systems

THE RESPIRATORY CHAIN AS A MODEL FOR METABOLIC CONTROL IN MULTI-ENZYME SYSTEMS

Britton Chance

Johnson Research Foundation
University of Pennsylvania
Philadelphia, Pennsylvania

A useful point of departure for a discussion of the control properties of the multi-enzyme system of glycolysis is, interestingly enough, the respiratory chain itself. The control properties of this system, although poorly understood insofar as chemical mechanisms are concerned are remarkably simple and straightforward. While both glycolysis and respiration involve multi-enzyme systems of many interacting components, the significant difference is without doubt, the structural orientation in the mitochondrial system and the lack of it in the glycolytic system. If indeed, nature has evolved simplicity from complexity in metabolic control we may regard the glycolytic system as being more primitive than that of respiration, and consequently we may be able to learn more from her later works than from her earlier ones. And of particular importance is the fact that when the respiratory chain evolved, each component was given a different color—a matter of the greatest convenience in this study of the individual components _in situ_.

Oxidative phosphorylation exemplifies idealized control characteristics for multi-enzyme systems. First, the control characteristics are sharp; half maximal effect for ADP control requires 20 μM. Second, ADP control acts simultaneously at three sites in the chain. Third, the control is rapid. The half-time with ADP control is 30 msec at 33°; this is the same order as the time required for a single turnover of members of the respiratory chain. Fourth, the pool sizes are small; many components bear a 1:1 stoichiometry with respect to one another. Where large pools are found in DPNH and ubiquinone, they appear to be on a side pathway in which the steady state is maintained through the expenditure of high energy intermediates. Fifth, the respiratory chain functions with an orderly sequence of steady-state oxidized-reduced levels implying a uniform distribution of velocity constants throughout the chain. Many of these properties are described elsewhere (1) but one is so vital to a discussion of metabolic control in multi-enzyme systems that it needs to be reiterated here. A method of determining the site of an inhibitory interaction with the system, and its relationship to the location of sites of the control of electron transfer is afforded by the crossover theorem. This theorem, derived from a study of the respiratory chain, has provided a method for identifying control sites in multi-enzyme systems, particularly where exact reconstruction of the activity in the intact system by summation of its purified components is impracticable. This theorem is best demonstrated as control of electron transfer at a single site.

Accumulation-depletion phenomena in inhibited electron flow. Antimycin-A. The inhibitors acting upon the respiratory chain at single sites are indicated in Figure 1. Those that act at the cytochrome b sites are particularly useful for a demonstration of steady-state changes following inhibition of electron transfer in the respiratory chain.

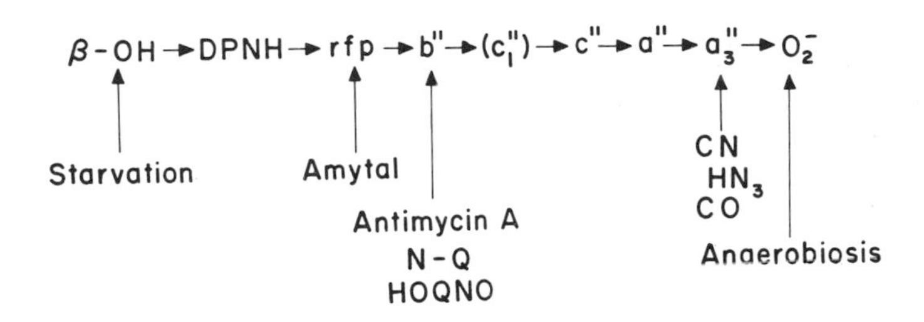

Figure 1. Sites of action of inhibitors of the respiratory chain (MD 47).

It is apparent from the diagram that a slowing of electron flow from substrate to oxygen would cause the accumulation of reduced cytochrome b and the depletion of reduced cytochrome c.

This is indicated spectroscopically in Figure 2; a peak corresponding to the accumulation of reduced cytochrome b and a trough corresponding to the depletion of reduced cytochrome c is recorded by a wavelength scanning spectrophotometer.

ADP-depletion. Although the respiratory chain is controlled simultaneously at three sites, usually only one of these sites is identified under a particular condition of dehydrogenase or oxidase activities. In Figure 3, we show an accumulation-depletion phenomena in pigeon heart mitochondria for the trans-

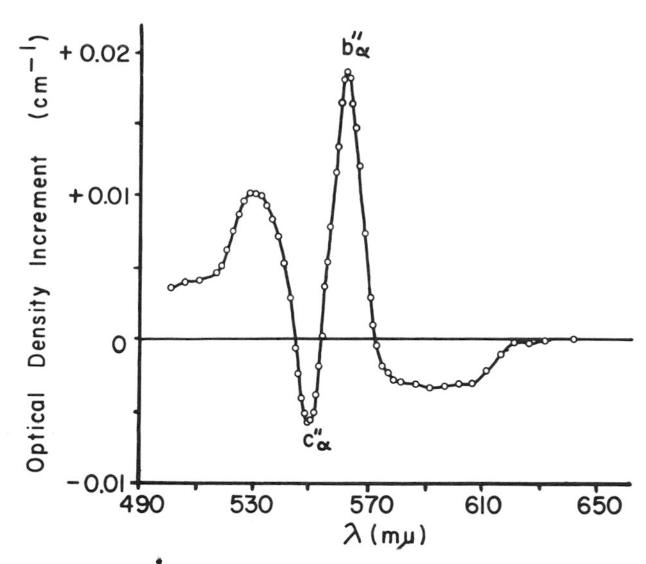

Figure 2. Crossover point between cytochromes b and a, caused by addition of antimycin-A to phosphorylating mitochondria (460 B 3 II).

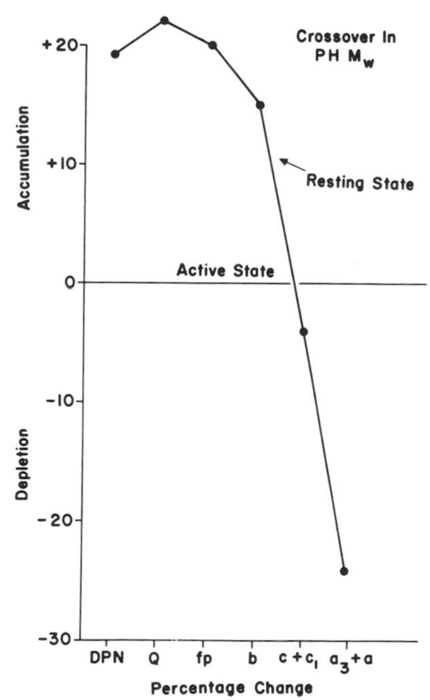

Figure 3. Accumulation-depletion phenomenon in pigeon heart mitochondria caused by exhaustion of added ADP. The names of the respiratory components are listed on the abcissa and the percentage change of the steady-state on the ordinates (MD 171).

ition from the active state to the resting state (3-4), which in many respects resembles that due to Antimycin-A in Figure 2. The reduced forms of DPNH, quinone, flavoprotein, and cytochrome b accumulate while those of the reduced forms of cytochromes $c + c_1$ and $a + a_3$ are depleted.

This chart, which we will call a crossover diagram, indicates a site of inhibitory interaction of ADP with the respiratory chain. For purposes of the discussion which will follow, the crossover theorem may be stated to form a simple sequence of reactions:

$$(A \xrightarrow{E_1} B \xrightarrow{E_2} C \xrightarrow{E_3} D \xrightarrow{E_4} E)$$

(i.e., without feedback). If, by some means, the steady-state flux is decreased with consistent increases (+) and decreases (-) in the steady-state levels of the intermediates, then a (+ , -) pair in the sequence of changes is called a crossover point and can only occur at a site of interaction. A (- , +) pair is called a reverse crossover and can occur anywhere between two crossover points; a reverse crossover does not indicate a site of interaction. It should be further emphasized that while a crossover point always indicates a site of interaction the converse is not true; a site of interaction does not always give rise to a crossover point.

The above theorem is extremely useful because of its simplicity and because of the simplicity of the graphical representation such as that shown in Figure 3, and also because of the clear cut nature of the site identifications. The situation may be more complex in multi-enzyme systems which involve branched chain and feedback interactions. The limitations of the crossover theorem under these conditions is a topic which needs further investigation.

Numerous diagrams will be presented in this volume from which crossover points may be identified. As in the case of the respiratory chain, more than one control site may be involved, even though only one crossover point is identified. Generally data on metabolic control identify only one of the possible control sites in an enzymatic sequence. The variation of conditions in the glycolytic systems in order to identify all control sites is a topic which is just beginning to be given detailed consideration.

REFERENCES

1. Chance, B., and Williams, G. R., Advances in Enzymology and Related Subjects, Vol. XVII (F. F. Nord, ed.) Interscience, New York, 1956, p. 65.

DYNAMICS AND CONTROL IN CELLULAR REACTIONS [+]

Joseph Higgins

Johnson Research Foundation, University of Pennsylvania
Philadelphia, Pennsylvania

I. Introduction

The modern description of the cell as developed over the last half century is well known. Briefly: the sequences of metabolic reactions catalyzed by a number of enzymes; the synthesis of these enzymes under genetic control; the diffusion of chemicals in subcellular compartments and the diffusion of nutrients into the cell. Much effort has gone into this description and still much more is needed. However, it is largely a static description, and biological phenomena manifest themselves in a dynamic sense--with cell division, controlled absorption and rejection of substances, and changes in the various chemical concentrations with time and position. It appears appropriate to term the study of such changes as _cellular dynamics_; and, in view of the thousands of chemicals involved, to recognize it as the many body problem of biology. The basic differential equations of motion may be derived by application of the diffusion laws, the law of Guildberg and Waage, and similar relationships to the various chemicals involved.

Analogies to other dynamical systems, as exemplified by electronics and mechanics should not be surprising. They reside in the general properties of the simultaneous, nonlinear, ordinary and partial differential equations which describe all these systems. Over the last fifteen years the application of mechanical and electronic analogies has introduced many new concepts such as energy transfer, control and feedback. Such concepts, though fruitful, have generally been introduced and utilized in a qualitative and vague manner. At this stage, it seems necessary to make these concepts more precise in order to attack the general problem of cellular dynamics.

+ This work was supported by grants from the Public Health Service (GM 12202) and the Office of Naval Research (N,ONR-551 (15).

II. Analysis of Cellular Dynamics - Time Scale Reduction

A. Simple Chemical Systems. One of the major practical points in any many body problem is the reduction of the system to fewer variables. One such reduction, long known and explicitly pointed out for biological and chemical problems by Lotha (1), Prigogine (2), and Goodwin (3), is based on the differences in the time scale for various reactions. While not generally appreciated, the difference in time scales or, as termed herein, the characteristic times, form the actual basis for the steady state approximation.

In general, the motion of a system can frequently be resolved into distinct states. Starting from some arbitrary state requiring specification of the initial conditions, the system moves, within a characteristic time, to a new state of motion which approximately obeys a reduced set of equations and can be specified by a reduced set of initial conditions. That is, the number of independent dynamical variables required to describe the motion is reduced. A measure of the time required for the systems to change from one state of motion to another is called the characteristic time (τ), and is usually taken as the time required for the system to approach within one half of the new state of motion.*

The analysis of the simple reaction $A \rightleftarrows B$, in which, unless otherwise stated, the law of Guildberg and Waage is assumed to apply, is shown in Figure 1, together with the kinetic curves (concentration vs. time) and the phase plane description of the motion. The phase plane is developed by taking any two of the dynamical variables (such as a and b) as the axis. The values of these variables at any time, t, then mark a point in the plane, and the entire motion for all values of t describes a curve in the plane.

It will be noticed that in the zero state of motion, two differential equations are required and two independent initial conditions must be specified to describe the motion. In the characteristic time ($\tau = \frac{1}{k_1 + k_{-1}}$), the motion changes to a new state (in this case the near equilibrium state) which can be described by algebraic equations and requires

* In the sense of relaxation time. Thus, the system is within 1/4 of its final value in 2τ, 1/8 in 3τ, and in general, $1/2^n$ in $n\tau$. Exact values of characteristic times are frequently difficult to compute, but usually only the order of magnitude is important.

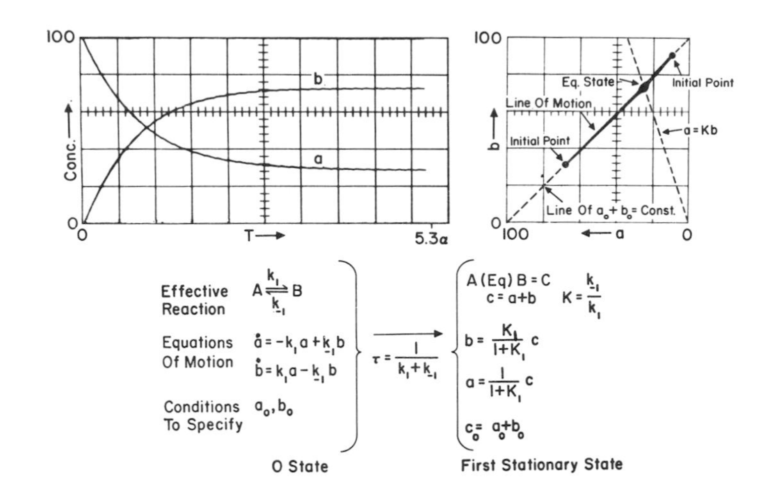

$$A \underset{k_{-1}}{\overset{k_1}{\rightleftharpoons}} B \qquad \dot{a} = -k_1 a + k_{-1} b \qquad \dot{b} = k_1 a - k_{-1} b \qquad a_0, b_0$$

$$\tau = \frac{1}{k_1 + k_{-1}}$$

$$A\,(Eq)\,B = C \qquad c = a + b \qquad K = \frac{k_{-1}}{k_1} \qquad b = \frac{K_1}{1+K_1}c \qquad a = \frac{1}{1+K_1}c \qquad c_0 = a_0 + b_0$$

Figure 1. Dynamical analysis of reaction $A \rightleftharpoons B$. Kinetics (upper left diagram); phase plane (upper right). Note reduction of equations and initial conditions.+

the specification of only one quantity ($c_o = a_o + b_o$). In mathematical terms, the equilibrium state is termed a limit point of the motion as can be seen from the phase plane diagram.

The differences in the dynamical states of motion are reflected in the chemical character of the reaction and a notation which indicates such changes is useful. Thus, A (eq) B is used to describe two chemicals which are in essential equilibrium. Since they are then dynamically equivalent to one chemical++, they may be replaced by a newly designated chemical (such as c).

\+ Computer solutions in this and other figures in the text were obtained on the Johnson Foundation Electronic Analog Computer, Mark II (13), with the technical assistance of Mr. Gus Rangazas.

++ The emphasis here is placed on the dynamical equations for the reaction rather than the stoichiometry. For example, if a above were measured, there would be an apparent discrepancy in the stoichiometry indicating the existence of some other form of a. Nevertheless, under the equilibrium constraint, the equations of motion could be entirely expressed without consideration of b.

It is convenient and useful to represent the motion in terms of a dynamical state level diagram as in Fig. 2. The ordinate is $\omega = 1/\tau$, where τ is the characteristic time for a given dynamical state. The ordinate is usually given a logarithmic scaling so that linear differences provide ratio of frequences. Each line on the graph represents a distinct dynamical state and can be described by the character of the chemical reactions for that state. Note that for a closed system, the equilibrium state has $\omega = -0$.

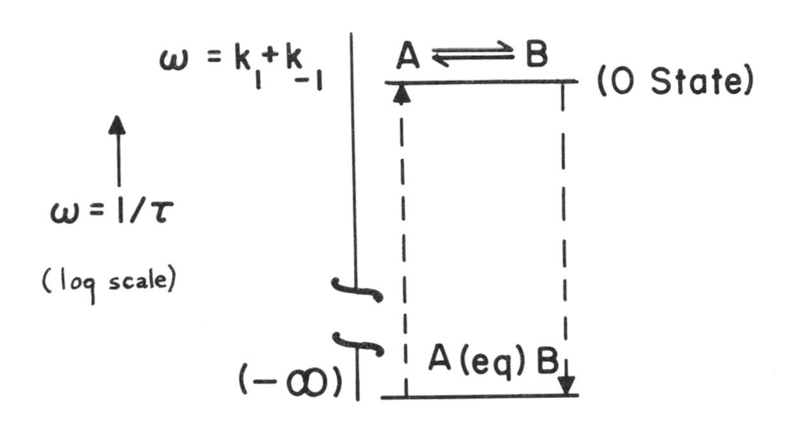

Figure 2. Dynamical state level diagram for the reaction A ⇌ B. Arrows indicate excitation and return to equilibrium state.

Consider now the case where the system is initially at equilibrium, but open to the extent that a and b are allowed to change ,due to varying inputs. If the changes in a and b are slow, as in a reversible process, the equation a=Kb will remain approximately valid and the motion would lie along the equilibrium line shown in the phase plane of Fig. 1. However, if a is changed very fast so that the frequencies (ω) involved in the change become comparable to ω_0, then the equation a = Kb will break down and the motion must be described in terms of the complete set of equations (A ⇌ B). Such an effect can be described as the excitation of the dynamical substructural (in this particular example A ⇌ B is the substructure of the reaction A(eq)B). The dotted arrow in Figure 2 illustrates the effect of a sharp impulse to the equilibrium system (such as $a \longrightarrow a + \Delta a$). The system is excited and returns to the approximate equilibrium state within a time of order τ . It may be noted here that the extent to which the equation a = Kb is approximately valid depends on the ratio of the characteristic time ($\tau_o = \frac{1}{k_1 + k_{-1}}$) to the characteristic time involved in the slow changes of a and b. Thus, it should be written as

$$a \overset{o}{=\!=} Kb\ (\omega_o)$$

to indicate that it is only approximately valid and that the extent of its validity depends on the changes in a and b having frequencies much less than ω_o.

As a second example consider the system:

$$A \underset{k_{-1}}{\overset{k_1}{\rightleftharpoons}} B \underset{k_{-2}}{\overset{k_2}{\rightleftharpoons}} C$$

whose analysis, kinetics and phase plane plot are shown in Figure 3 for the condition $k_1 + k_{-1} \gg k_2 + k_{-2}$. Under this

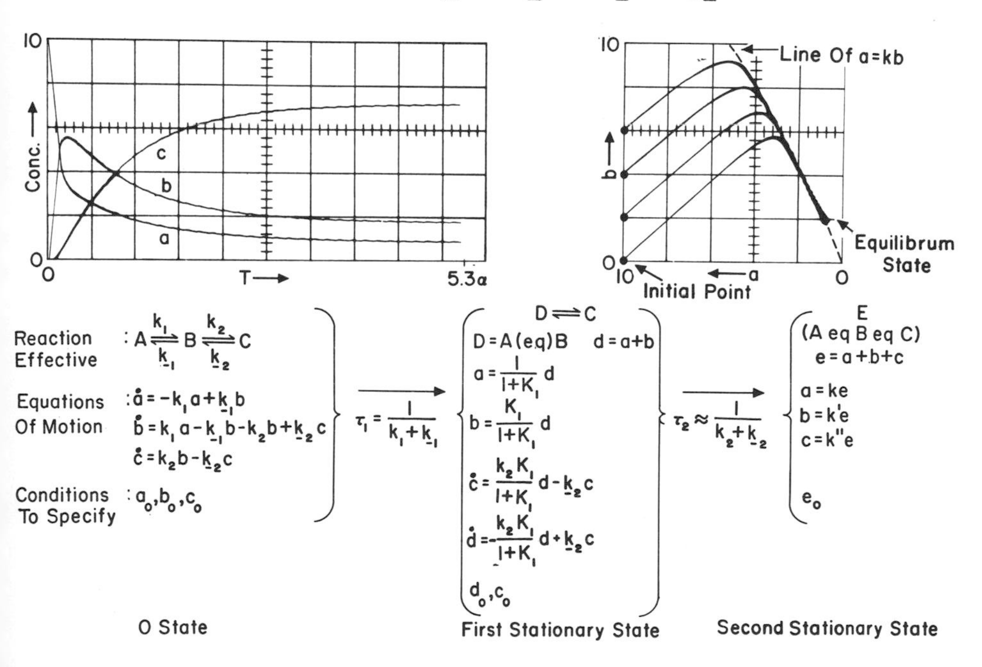

Figure 3. Dynamical analysis of reaction A⇌B⇌C. Kinetics (upper left diagram); phase plane (upper right). Note reduction of equations and initial conditions.

condition, it is well known that the motion can be taken as a rapid equilibration of A and B followed by a slow equilibration with C to the complete equilibrium state. To realize this, one calculates the characteristic frequency for the first reaction ($\omega_1 + k_1 + k_{-1}$) and the second reaction ($\omega_2 = k_2 + k_{-2}$). So long as the ratio of frequencies $(\frac{\omega_1}{\omega_2})$ is very large, the motion can be described as a rapid transition toward the limit line ($a = K_1 b$), and then a slow transition approximately along the limit line to the final limit point (the equilibrium state) as can be seen in the phase plane diagram. Each dynamical state requires fewer independent initial conditions to be specified; the complexity of the equations of motion and the associated chemical character are similarly reduced.

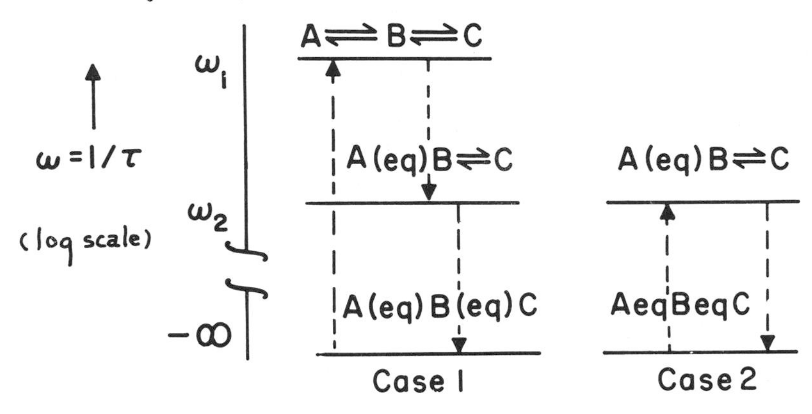

Figure 4. Dynamical state level diagram for the reaction A⇌B⇌C. For Case 1, the arrows indicate the effective motion for strong excitation of A. Case 2 indicates motion for weak excitation of A.

A dynamical level diagram for this system is depicted in Figure 4. In case 1, the system is started in the equilibrium state (ground state) and excited to the upper state by a sharp pulse (of say, a) returning to the middle level in a time of order τ_1, and to the lower level in a time of order τ_2. In the second case (2), the change in a is introduced more slowly (of order ω_2) and the system is only excited to the middle level, decaying back to the ground state in a time of order τ_2.

The breakdown of the dynamical motion into particular states and the character of such states depends on the various parameters (such as the rate constants) which enter into the equations. Some typical effects of such parameters are illustrated in Figure 5 for the system A⇌B⇌C. As the

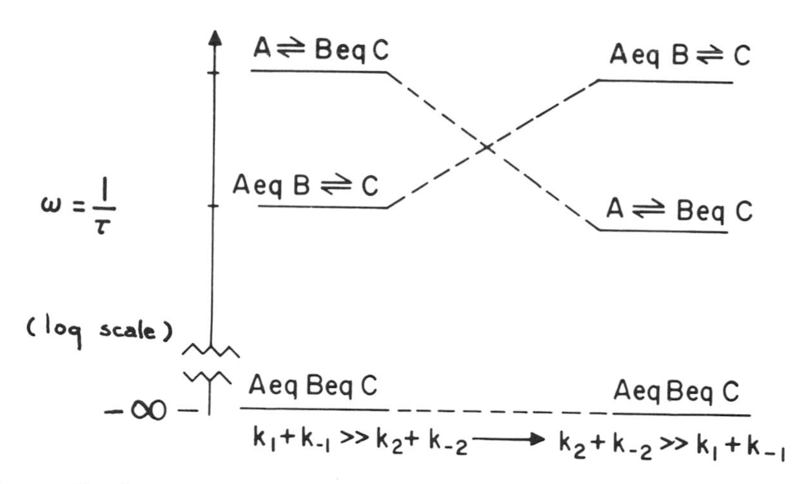

Figure 5. Dynamical state level diagram for the reaction $A \rightleftharpoons B \rightleftharpoons C$ illustrating dependence of dynamical levels on the structural control variables--in this case, the rate constants.

rate constants are varied from $k_1 + k_{-1} \gg k_2 + k_{-2}$ to $k_1 + k_{-1} \ll k_2 - k_{-2}$, the fast and slow reactions (as defined by their characteristic times) reverse their position on the level scheme.

Under other conditions of the parameters, stationary states+ rather than equilibrium states will play a major role in the resolution of the motion. The analysis of a simple enzyme reaction illustrates such dynamical states, as shown in Figure 6. The motion is resolved into a transition, with a characteristic time ($t_{1/2\ on}$), to the steady state; and the decay of the steady state to the final equilibrium state with a characteristic time $t_{1/2\ off}$ ++. The extent to which the steady state motion approximates the line of stationary states (i.e., $\dot{p} = 0$ exactly) depends on the ratio of $t_{1/2\ off}$ to $t_{1/2\ on}$, the approximation being better the larger the ratio.

\+ Equilibrium states can, of course, be considered as a special case of stationary states.(2)

++ It may be noted that the characteristic time for subreactions in a complex scheme are defined as the time it takes these reactions alone to make the transition to a new set of values as required by the overall motion. (5)

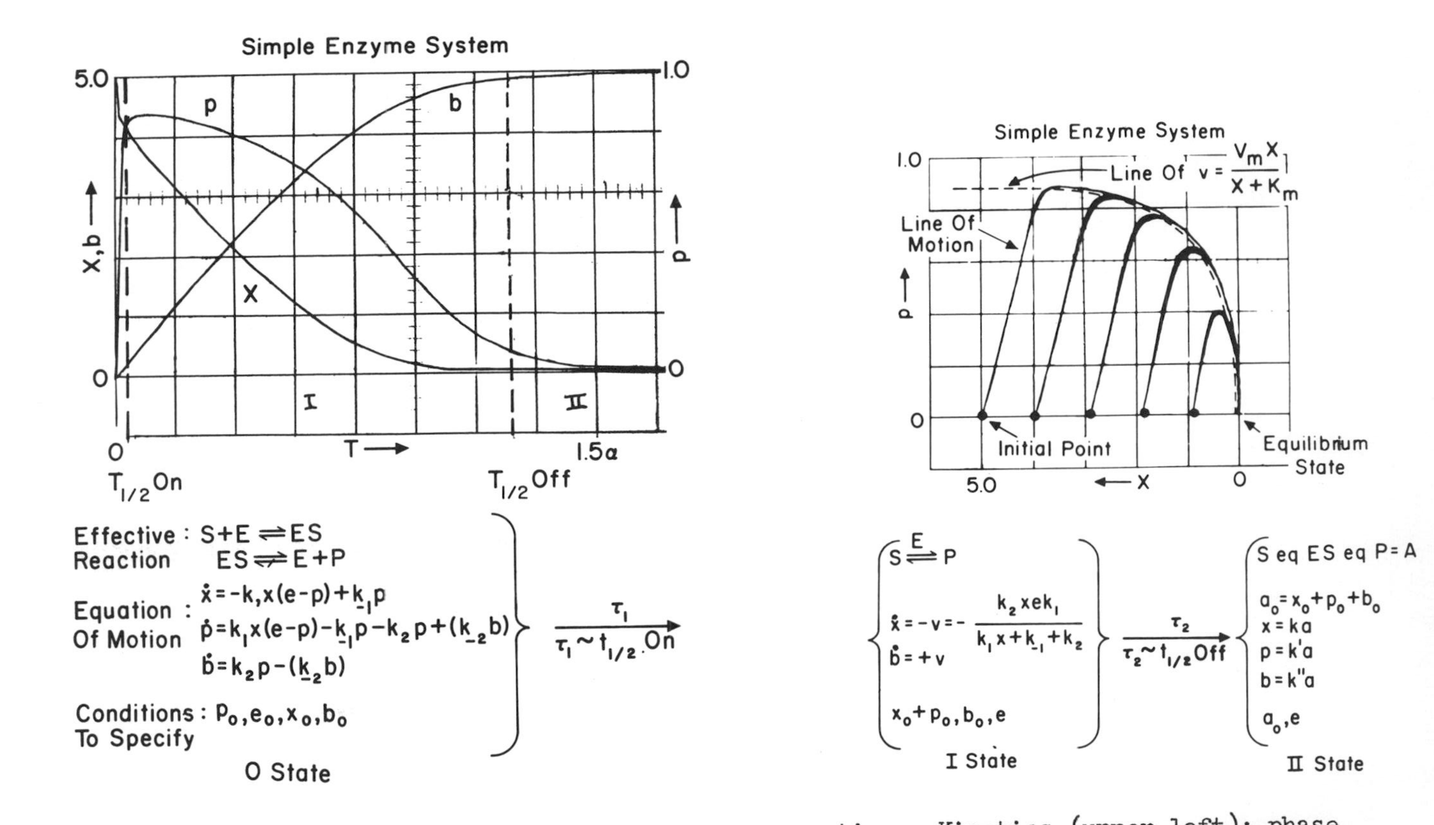

Figure 6. Dynamical analysis of the simple enzyme reaction. Kinetics (upper left); phase plane (upper right). Region I is the steady state region and closely approximates the line of stationary states.

Values for these quantities can be given (4) as

$$t_{1/2 \text{ on}} \sim \frac{1}{k_1 x + k_2 + k_{-1}}$$

$$t_{1/2 \text{ off}} \sim \frac{k_1 x + k_2 + k_{-1}}{k_1 k_2 e} = \frac{x + Km}{Vm}$$

$$\text{where } Km = \frac{k_2 + k_{-1}}{k_1} \text{ and } Vm = k_2 e$$

and it can be shown that the ratio satisfies (5)

$$t_{1/2 \text{ off}} \Big/ t_{1/2 \text{ on}} > 4 \frac{x}{e} \quad \text{for } x > e$$

(values of the ratio typically range from 10^2 to 10^4 for the enzymes in the metabolic pathways.) The fact that the characteristic times depend on the concentrations as well as the rate constants is a typical result for bimolecular reactions, and the breakdown into dynamical states requires certain limitations (such as $x > e$)$^+$. It should also be emphasized that for the simple enzyme reaction, the characteristic time for changes (Δx) in the substrate are of the order of Δx, that is

$$t_{1/2 \text{ off}} \sim \frac{\Delta x}{Vm} \quad (\text{for } x > Km)$$

reflecting the fact that the rate (v) is essentially independent of the substrate concentration (x). A dynamical level diagram for this system is shown in Figure 7.

The applicability of the various reduced equations, such as the equilibrium or stationary state relationships, depends only on the ratio of characteristic frequencies involved in the actual motion to the characteristic frequencies associated with these dynamical states. So long as this ratio is small, the higher dynamical states will remain unexcited and the reduced equations of motion will apply. For example, the steady state equation for an enzyme system (Michaelis-Menton

+ A more careful analysis of such systems is discussed elsewhere. The subtle points involved need not be considered here since for most enzyme reactions under typical circumstances, the condition $x > e$ is satisfied. In general, it is necessary to examine each dynamical state for temporal consistency.(5)

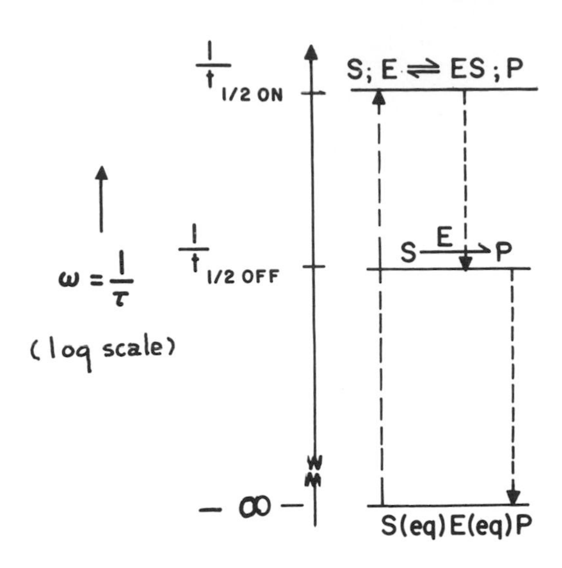

Figure 7. Dynamical state level for the simple enzyme reaction.

equation) can be applied even though the intermediate ([ES] = p) is changing or even oscillating in time, so long as the frequencies involved are much less than the characteristic frequency for the steady state equation; thus, the steady state does not require that the intermediate be steady in time.

B. Analysis of Cellular Motion. A rough level diagram for the cell is depicted in Figure 8, and is arranged according to typical values for the characteristic frequencies of the various states of motion. At any given level, all the variables well below that level can be approximated as constant and are referred to as the structural control variables (abbreviated SCV) for that level, since they determine the character of the dynamical equations (as previously seen for the rate constants, i.e., temperature dependence). The variables well above the given level can be referred to as "hidden variables," since they will not generally be excited and consequently their effects not realized; such variables are said to lie in the dynamical substructure of the given level.

At the upper levels, various basic physical and physical chemical laws are expected to apply to the equations of motion.

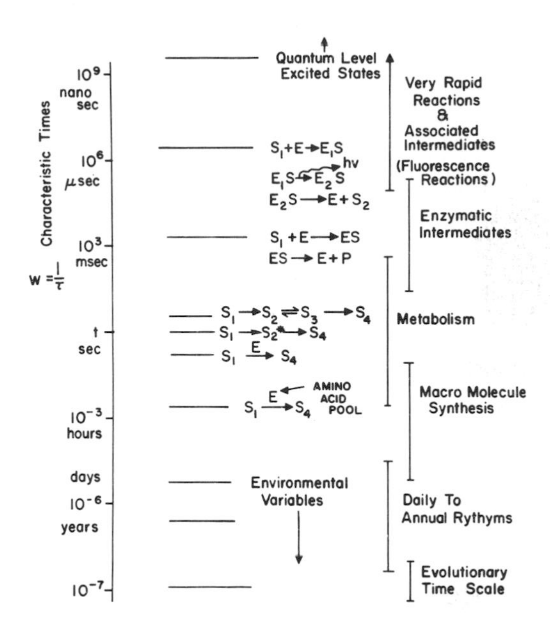

Figure 8. Dynamical spectrum for cellular changes: rough diagram of dynamical states influencing cellular motion.

Thus, at the very upper levels, the laws of quantum mechanics should be applied. At the level of enzymatic intermediates it is usually assumed that the law of Guildberg and Waage should apply. At each level, the equations of motion are usually taken to represent a reduced form of the equations applying to the preceding level. Thus, in principle, the law of Guildberg and Waage can be derived from the laws of Quantum Mechanics. Similarly, the equations of motion at the metabolic level are derived from the application of the law of Guildberg and Waage to the various enzymatic interactions.

While the interrelationships between the various levels are of considerable importance scientifically and afford a deep insight into the detailed nature of the interactions, they can frequently be ignored at any given level of interest.[+]

+ For example, it may be noted that a very sharp temperature jump (as in temperature jump experiments) would excite all levels; and if the various intermediates could be detected, would lead to an exceedingly complex description for even relatively simple reactions. However, most of the complexities would not be relevant to biology *per se*, since under normal circumstances their effects would not be exhibited.

The dynamical equations for some particular level can in practice be determined experimentally without regard to those substructures which are not normally excited+. While the basic physical laws place some restriction on the types of dynamical equations which can be expected, these restrictions are quite weak at the level of metabolism, and consequently virtually any form of dynamical motion can result. Figure 9 indicates some possible kinetics which can be realized under stationary state conditions. The motion can be unbounded or bounded. The variables may have a constant value in time (as under equilibrium conditions) or they may change periodically or even non-periodically.

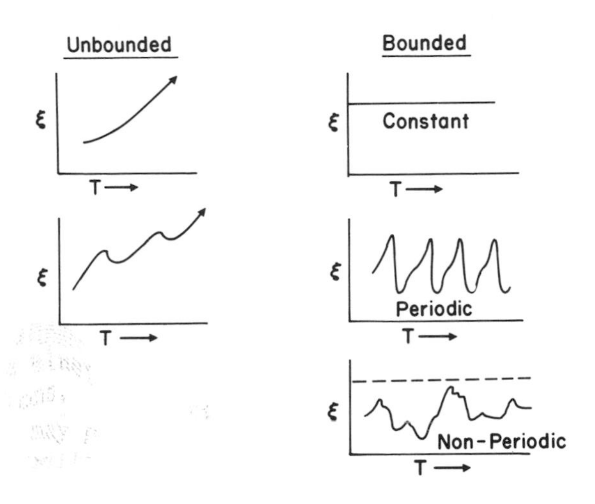

Figure 9. Typical stationary state motions. Note that virtually any type of motion is possible at the metabolic level ranging from unbounded to bounded, constant, oscillatory or non-periodic.

III. Dynamical Characteristics and Their Use

A. Typical Characteristics. As just remarked, with respect to any given dynamical level, we do not need to concern ourselves with the entire set of equations describing the

+ In fact, the delineation of the substructure is usually based on such studies as can be seen for an enzymatic reaction. The overall rate law for an enzymatic reaction was first developed experimentally; and then, based on the assumption that the chemistry should obey the law of Guildberg and Waage, the detailed nature of the intermediate formation was postulated. It was only later that sufficiently sharp excitations were applied to study such reactions directly.

very far removed substructure (high upper levels). Thus, at the metabolic level, the description of the reactions can usually ignore the enzymatic intermediates since these will not normally be excited. Consequently, we may concentrate on the dynamical characteristics (i.e., rate laws) for the chemicals of interest. It may be noted that while the basic laws of physical chemistry--such as the law of Guildberg and Waage--would be expected to apply directly to the chemical substructure level, the lower levels (such as the metabolic level) may satisfy a variety of different rate equations.

Some typical dynamical characteristics (rate laws) for the metabolic level are given below. The substructure reactions are also noted in order that the particular laws may not be though devoid of chemical interpretation and to provide some insight into the interrelationships between the two levels[+].

Finally, an equivalence notation for chemical reactions, is further developed here, as much as possible in accord with common usage already found in the literature. However, since many of the properties of chemical systems are more directly associated with the shape of the dynamical characteristics than with the detailed equation, it is convenient to have the notation reflect such emphasis.

1. First Order Rate Law - Simple Reaction

   a. Reaction Designation[++]: $S \xrightarrow{k} P$

   b. Rate Law $v = kx$ (see Figure 10A, curve I)

   c. Typical Subreaction - itself

   d. Notation: Reaction designation will usually refer to a straight line

2. Second Order - Self-Activation

   a. Reaction Designation $S + S \xrightarrow{k} P$

   b. Rate law: $v = kx^2$ (see Figure 10A, curve II)

[+]For purposes of relating the substructure reactions to the net reactions, the Guildberg and Waage law is assumed.

[++]In specific examples, the k in $S \xrightarrow{k} P$ may be supressed if there is no chance for confusion with the notation given in section IV.

2. continued

c. Typical Subreaction - itself

d. Equivalence Relation

$$S + S \longrightarrow P \equiv S \xrightarrow[k]{\text{act}} P$$

e. Notation: The notation $S \xrightarrow[k]{\text{act}} P$ is used to designate any specific rate law such that

$$\frac{\delta^2 v}{\delta x^2} > 0$$

3. Simple Enzymatic Reaction

a. Reaction Designation: $S \xrightarrow{E} P$

b. Rate Law: $v = \dfrac{Vm\ x}{x + Km}$ (see Figure 10B)

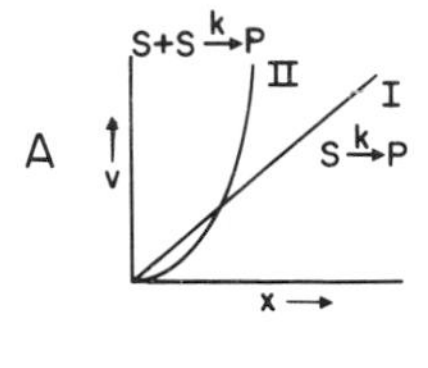

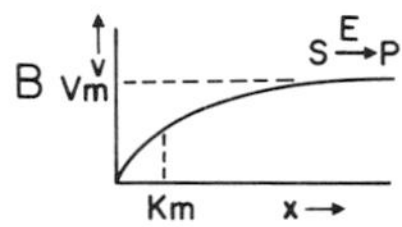

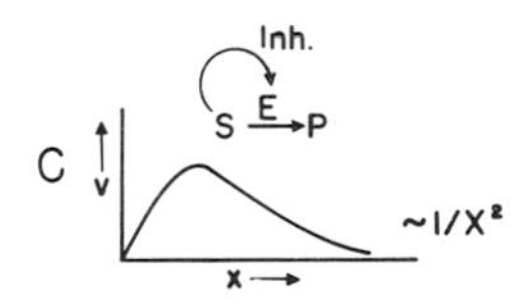

Figure 10. Dynamical characteristics for simple reactions.

c. Typical Subreaction

$$S + E \underset{k_{-1}}{\overset{k_1}{\rightleftharpoons}} ES \quad \text{where } Vm = k_2 e$$

$$ES \xrightarrow{k_2} E + P \qquad Km = \frac{k_2 + k_{-1}}{k_1}$$

d. Equivalence Relation

$$S \xrightarrow{E} P \equiv S \xrightarrow[k]{\text{inh(o)}} P$$

The fact that an enzyme reaction may be considered inhibitory relative to a simple reaction (1) is evident from the graphs (Figure 10B and 10AI). The inhibitory aspect can also be recognized in subreaction form as:

$$S \xrightarrow{[E]} P \qquad\qquad v = k_2 q$$

$$\underset{q}{S + E} \underset{k_{-1}}{\overset{k_1}{\rightleftharpoons}} \underset{p}{ES} \qquad\qquad (q + p = e)$$

where the net flux (v) is taken as proportional to the concentration (q) of free enzyme. The second reaction indicates that the free enzyme is inhibited by the substrate (x). The Michaelis Menton relation

$$v = \frac{Vm\ x}{x + K_I} \quad \text{where } Vm = k_2 e$$

is easily obtained.

e. Notation: The notation $S \xrightarrow[k_2]{\text{inh(o)}} P$ indicates zero order inhibition defined as having (1) $\frac{\partial^2 v}{\partial x^2} < 0$, (2) $\frac{\partial v}{\partial x} > 0$ for all x and (3) a finite maximum rate (Vm), that is a shape similar to that for a simple enzyme.

4. Substrate Inhibited Enzyme (Site Inhibition)

a. Reaction Designation: $S \overset{\text{inh(s)}}{\underset{}{\xrightarrow{E}}} P$

4. continued

b. Rate Law:

$$v = \frac{Vm\ x}{x + Km} \cdot \frac{K}{K + x} \qquad \text{(see Figure 10C)}$$

c. Typical Substructure

$$S + E \underset{k_2}{\overset{k_1}{\rightleftharpoons}} ES \qquad Vm = k_2 e \qquad Km = \frac{k_2 + k_{-1}}{k_1}$$

$$ES \xrightarrow{k_3} E + P \qquad\qquad Vm = \frac{k_{-4}}{k_4}$$

$$S + E \underset{k_{-4}}{\overset{k_4}{\rightleftharpoons}} E^+ \qquad \text{(inactivation site)}$$

$$S + ES \underset{k_{-4}}{\overset{k_4}{\rightleftharpoons}} ES^+$$

d. Equivalence relation

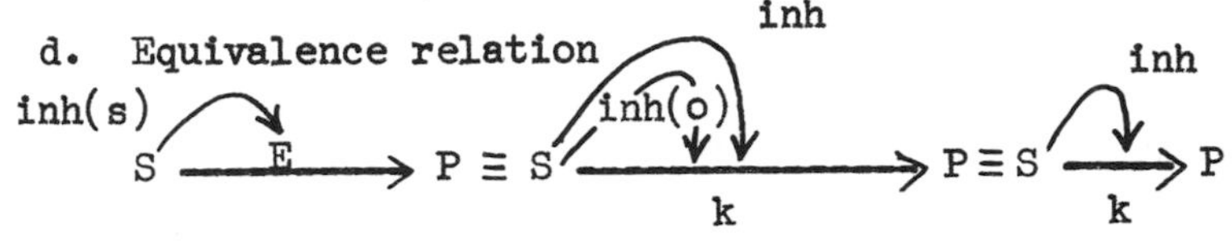

e. Notation: The first equivalence follows from the equivalence relation derived in (3). The second $S \xrightarrow[k]{inh} P$ is considered to represent first order (or greater) inhibition and requires that (1) $\frac{\partial^2 v}{\partial x^2} < 0$, (2) $\frac{\partial v}{\partial x} = 0$ for some finite value of x and (3) $v \rightarrow 0$ as $x \rightarrow \infty$; that is, a typical inhibition type characteristic.

The following cases illustrate the resultant equivalence, in certain specific cases, of apparently different mechanisms.

5. Substrate Activation of Simple Enzyme via Intermediate

a. Reaction Designation $S \xrightarrow{E} P$ (act(ES))

b. Rate Law $v = \dfrac{k_2 e x}{1 + Km} = kx$

c. Substructure

$$S + E \underset{k_{-1}}{\overset{k_1}{\rightleftharpoons}} ES \qquad Km = \frac{k_2 + k_{-1}}{k_1}$$

$$S + ES \xrightarrow{k_2} E + P$$

d. Equivalence Relations

$$S \xrightarrow{E} P \text{ (act(ES))} \equiv S \xrightarrow{k} P \text{ (inh(o), act(ES))} \equiv S \xrightarrow{k} P$$

6. Substrate Inhibited Enzyme - Substrate goes on wrong way.

a. Reaction Designation $S \xrightarrow{E} P$ (inh(E))

b. Rate Law $v = \dfrac{Vm' \; x}{x + Km'}$

c. Substructure:

$$S + E \underset{k_{-1}}{\overset{k_1}{\rightleftharpoons}} ES \qquad Vm' = \frac{Vm}{1 + \frac{Km}{K}} \qquad Vm = k_2 e$$

$$ES \xrightarrow{k_2} E + P \qquad Km' = \frac{Km}{1 + \frac{Km}{K}} \qquad Km = \frac{k_{-1} + k_2}{k_1}$$

$$K = \frac{k_{-3}}{k_3}$$

$$S + E \underset{k_{-3}}{\overset{k_3}{\rightleftharpoons}} ES$$ (substrate went on the wrong way)

6. continued

d. Equivalence Relation

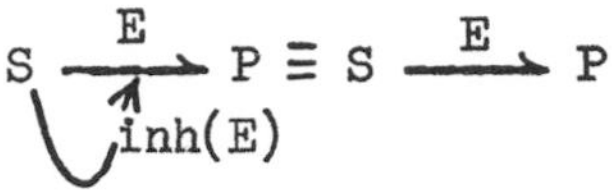

$$S \xrightarrow[\text{inh}(E)]{E} P \equiv S \xrightarrow{E} P$$

The relation is obtained from the fact that the designation, $S \xrightarrow{E} P$, does not, in itself, refer to the particular values of Vm and Km.

The examples (5 and 6) can be considered as simply additional examples of substructure reactions for the dynamical characteristics of 1 and 3 respectively. The existance of such equivalence makes it obvious that the detailed nature of the reaction substructure can not be determined from analysis of the steady state (4). The substructure must be excited if the detailed character of the reaction is to be determined.

Dynamical characteristics for reactions involving two distinct chemicals such as $S + A \longrightarrow P$ basically require a three dimensional plot, but can be treated as in Figure 14. Similarly, reversible reactions such as $\underset{(x)}{S} \rightleftharpoons \underset{(y)}{P}$ can be treated with three dimensions, by plotting the net flux ($v = kx - k'y$) as a function of x and y. A flux surface is then obtained which, for a simple reaction, reduces to a plane passing through the origin. The reversible case can also be treated in two dimensions as indicated in Figure 14, but in general, such situations become geometrically complicated and require an analytical approach.

B. <u>Use of Dynamical Characteristics to Determine Reaction Character</u>. The use of the dynamical characteristics to determine the stationary state character of the reaction has been previously pointed out by Chance (6). The technique is relatively straightforward for sequential reactions.

For example, given the sequences of simple reactions

$$\underset{x_0}{[S_0]} \xrightarrow{0} \underset{x_1}{S_1} \xrightarrow{1} \underset{x_2}{S_2} \xrightarrow{2} \underset{x_3}{S_3} \xrightarrow{3} \underset{x_4}{S_4} \xrightarrow{4} P$$

where $v_i = k_i x_i$ and $\overline{x_0}$ is the structural control variable, the entire set of dynamical characteristics can be plotted on the same graph as shown in Figure 11. The different x_i are plotted on the abscissa and do not need to have the same scale, while the net flux (v_i) is plotted on the ordinate and must have the same scale for all the subreactions.

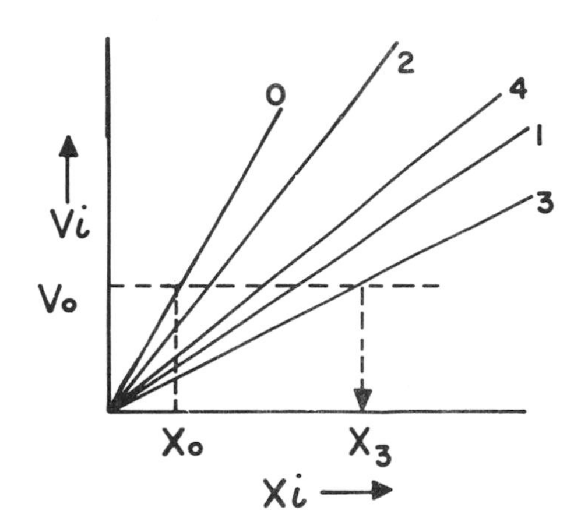

Figure 11. Use of dynamical characteristics to determine stationary state for sequential reactions.

As indicated on the graph, a value of the (SCV) $\overline{x_o}$ is chosen and the value of v_o is determined through the intersection with the 0 curve. Since the flux through all reaction steps must be the same in the stationary state (for this type of system), a line is drawn through the v_o. The intersection of this line with the other dynamical curves determines the values of the dynamical variables, x_i (as indicated for x_3).

It may be noted that this simple system of sequential reactions is extremely well behaved. Any value of x_o or v_o leads to an intersection with all the dynamical characteristics of the other intermediates. Since the stationary state flux (v) is entirely determined by x_o, and its dynamical characteristic, the stationary state character of the net reaction is then

$$[S_o] \xrightarrow{0} P \qquad\qquad v = k_o \overline{x_o}$$

A second example involving a sequence of simple enzyme reactions is illustrated in Figure 12.

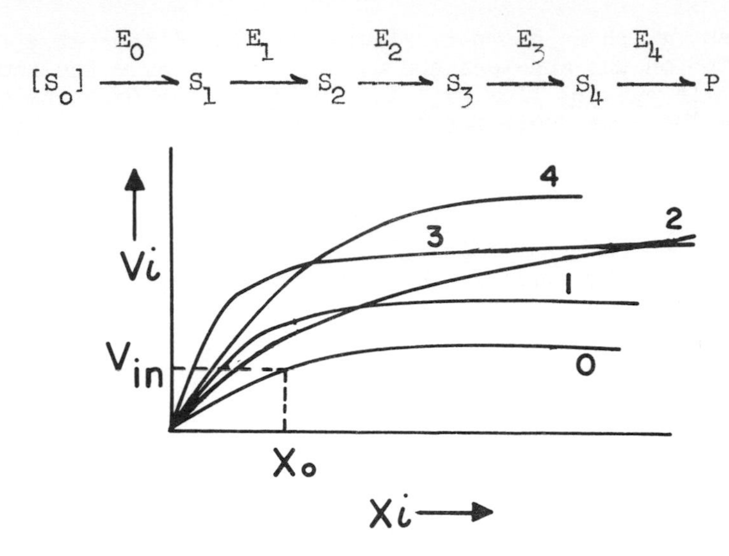

Figure 12. Use of dynamical characteristics to determine stationary state for sequential reactions ($Vm_o < Vm_i$).

Using the same technique, one finds that the net reaction is characterized as

$$[S_o] \xrightarrow{E_1} P \qquad v = v(E_0) = \frac{\overline{x_o}\ Vm_o}{\overline{x_o} + Km_o}$$

Thus, in this case, where $Vm_o < Vm_i$ (i)= 1, 2, 3, 4), the system is again well behaved as a function of $\overline{x_o}$ and the net flux is determined by the first step.

An example which illustrates the dependence of the reaction character on the SCV is obtained when the Vm's for the different enzymes in the above sequence are ordered as in Figure 13A. The value x_o* is determined by the intersection of the lowest Vm (in this case Vm_1) with the 0 characteristic.

Applying the same technique, one finds that the net reaction character can be defined as

$$[S_o] \xrightarrow{E_o} P \quad \text{for } \overline{x_o} < x_o^*$$

but for $x_o > x_o^*$ there is no longer an intersection with the v_3 characteristic and the reaction character changes to

$$S \xrightarrow{E_o} \begin{cases} \nearrow S_3 \\ \searrow^{Vm_3} P \end{cases} \qquad \text{for } \overline{x_o} > x_o^{+}$$

for which

x_1 and x_2 are constant and determined by v_o

x_3 is continually increasing at a rate $(v_o - V_{m3})$

x_4 is determined by the interaction of v_{m3} and the v_4 characteristic

P is produced at a rate v_{m3}.

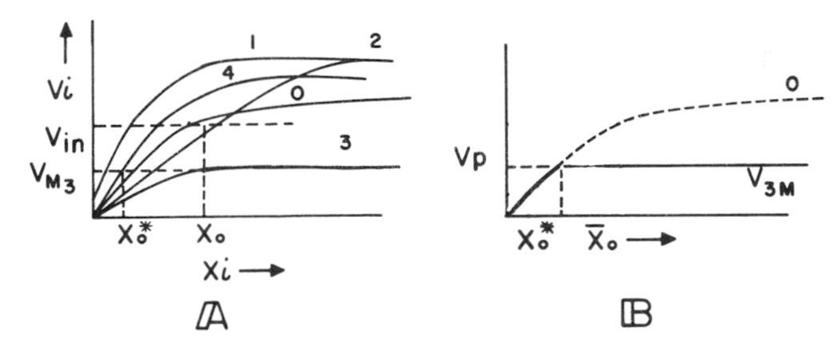

Figure 13. Use of dynamical characteristics to determine stationary states and chemical character for sequential enzyme reactions ($Vm_3 < Vm_i$). (A) Analysis, (B) net reaction flux (v_p) as a function of $\overline{x_o}$.

The net flux for production of P as a function of $\overline{x_o}$ is shown in Figure 13B. The dependence of the dynamical and chemical character of the stationary state on the SCV is clearly evidenced by this example.

The case of sequences of reversible reactions can be treated in three dimensions as the intersection of planes and surfaces. It may be noted here that the case of a sequence of simple reversible reactions ($A \rightleftharpoons B$) is well behaved for all values of the (SCV), a result due to the planar structure of the dynamical characteristics.

III. Control

The significance and meaning of the Structural Control Variables in determining the character of the stationary state is clear from the previous section. It should be borne in mind that control is a relative concept and requires clear and precise definition as to what is controlling what and in what respect. With this is mind, a definition of flux control can be attempted.

A. Flux Control. In general, the flux through a given reaction sequence will depend on a number of parameters (the SCV) such as the rate constants, enzyme concentrations, and various substrates ($\overline{x_o}$). Since "control" is normally used in the sense of "to effect," it is useful to take some function of the change in flux for a given change in one of the SCV as a measure of the control strength. Thus,

$$\text{if } v = f(\alpha_1, \alpha_2, \alpha_3, \ldots) \qquad \alpha_i \equiv \text{SCV}$$

Then

Control Strength

$$C = \begin{cases} \dfrac{\partial v}{\partial \alpha_i} \\ \text{or} \\ \dfrac{\partial \ln v}{\partial \ln \alpha_i} = \alpha_{i_{R_v}} \end{cases}$$

Either the partial derivative (ratios of change) or the reflection coefficient (4,7) (ratio of relative changes) can be used as a measure of control strength+. The latter quantity has some advantages in that it is dimensionless and particularly suited to irreversible reactions.

The control strengths for the different SCV can then be ordered according to which is larger such as:

+The apparent arbitrariness in the definition of control strength is easily understood. It resides in the difficulties of finding a common basis for comparing changes in the different types of parameters. Such a basis should take account of the typical changes which the different variables may take in the actual system. Thus, if some enzyme typically changes by ten times the amount of another in a particular system, it may exert the dominant influence on the flux even though the control strength as defined above might be less. In such cases, corrected measures of control strength should be used.

$$C_{\alpha 1} > C_{\alpha 3} > C_{\alpha 2} > C_{\alpha s}, \text{ etc.}$$

While generally, the control strengths may be of comparable magnitude, it frequently happens that one particular control strength will be many times greater than the others. In such cases, that variable can be said to have control of the flux relative to the other variables. Such relative dominance of control can be realized by the control ratio

$$r_{ij} = \frac{C_{\alpha i}}{C_{\alpha j}}$$

If $r_{ij} > 10$, then $C_{\alpha i}$ has control relative to $C_{\alpha j}$.

It should be noted that the values, and hence the ordering of the control strengths depends on the values of the parameters (the SCV) themselves. Consequently, control dominance may change with different values of the SCV.

An example of the control analysis is given for two simple reactions. For the reaction

[S] x, [A] y $\xrightarrow{E}$ P

with the possible substructure

$$S + E \xrightarrow{k_1} ES$$

$$A + ES \xrightarrow{k_2} E + P$$

where $v = \dfrac{k_1 k_2 \bar{x} \bar{y} e}{k_1 \bar{x} + k_2 \bar{y}}$

the dynamical characteristics are shown in Figure 14. One readily finds

$$r_{xy} = \frac{x_{R_v}}{y_{R_v}} = Km \ y/x \qquad \text{where } Km = \frac{k_2}{k_1}$$

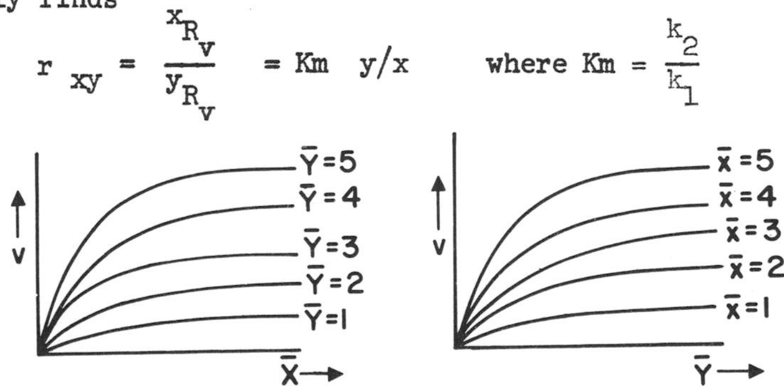

Figure 14. Dynamical characteristics for system with two substrates (or, in general, two variables).

A relative control plane diagram for this reaction is shown in Figure 15. The axes of the plane are the values of $\overline{x}$ and $\overline{y}$ and each point in the plane can be marked by a value of r_{xy}. The plane is then divided into regions of $r_{xy} > 10$, and $0.1 < r_{xy} < 10$, and $r_{xy} < 0.1$, and the regions can then be characterized according to whether S or A is in control.

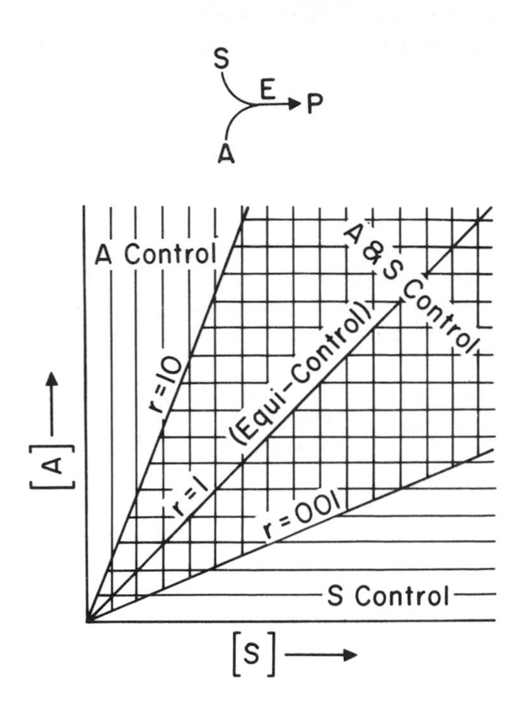

Figure 15. Relative control plane for reaction indicated with rate law given in text (page 35).

As a second example, consider the same type of reaction, but with the different dynamical characteristics and subreactions as shown.

S, A $\xrightarrow{E}$ P

with

$$S + E \longrightarrow ES_1$$
$$A + ES_1 \longrightarrow ES_2$$
$$ES_2 \longrightarrow E + P$$

and where

$$v = \frac{Vm\ x\ y}{xy + ky + k'x}$$

In this case, the absolute control plane (not the relative control plane) is plotted as shown in Figure 16 with each point in the plane being given a value of both ${}^{x}R_v$ and ${}^{y}R_v$. The plane is then divided into regions according to whether ${}^{x}R_v$ is greater or less than 0.1[+] and similarly for ${}^{y}R_v$.

For purposes of notation, a slash through the reaction arrow is used to indicate that a particular variable is not in control of the flux, as indicated in Figure 16.

While the control plane was developed with the variables considered as SCV ($\bar{x}$ and $\bar{y}$), it is also possible to consider the given reaction as a subreaction of a larger system. In that case, the variables x and y will become dynamical variables and undergo some stationary state motion. If the control plane is simultaneously interpreted as a phase plane, the motion can be plotted directly on top of the control regions as indicated by the dashed lines in Figure 16.

Such analysis provides another basis for reducing the complexity of the equations of motion. One first assumes that certain variables are not in control of the flux in particular reaction steps, treating those variables as constants in the rate laws for those steps (but only those steps). The approximate equations of motion are then solved and the motion examined in the control plane. If the resulting motion is such that the original assumptions as to flux control are still satisfied then the assumptions are considered consistent[++]. This approach may reasonably be called the Self Consistent Control Approximation. For example, the upper dashed line in Figure 16 is consistent with the assumption that the flux is independent of [S]; while the lower dashed line requires that both variables be considered.

[+] The value of 0.1 is arbitrary and attention must be paid to the effect of small changes in v as well as the typical excursions for the variables x and y.

[++] A second order perturbation analysis should also be carried out to determine the validity of the first approximation.

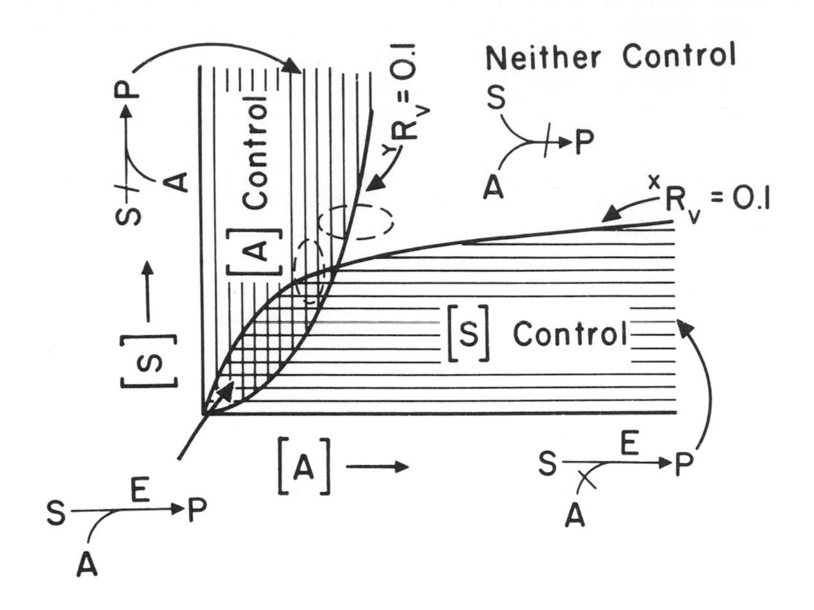

Figure 16. Absolute control plane plot for two substrate reactions with rate law given in text (page 36). Explanation is dashed lines is also given in text.

B. Rate Controlling Steps. The concepts of rate controlling and rate limiting steps in a sequential reaction, and the interrelationships to fast and slow steps, while intuitively appreciated, has led to some confusion in the literature.

Consider a reaction $[S_o] \longrightarrow P$ with the flux[+] $v = v(\alpha)$ $\alpha \equiv$ all SCV, and having a sequential substructure of the form

$$[S_o] \underset{}{\overset{0}{\rightleftharpoons}} S_1 \overset{1}{\rightleftharpoons} S_2 \overset{2}{\rightleftharpoons} S_3 \overset{3}{\rightleftharpoons} S_4 \overset{4}{\rightleftharpoons} P$$

where each step has a flux $v_i \equiv v_i(\alpha_i; x_i)$, with $a_i \equiv$ SCV for that step (such as k_i, e_i, Vm_i) and the dynamical variables, x_i. In a normal (constant) stationary state the dynamical variables adjust themselves so that all steps in the sequence will have the same flux $v_i = v$. Consequently, no one step can be considered as rate limiting, and the use of such terms must be carefully interpreted. It is preferable to refer to a "rate controlling" step. Using the previous definition, we

[+]The reaction designation $S \longrightarrow P$ (without a k) is used to indicate a general reaction with any type of rate law.

UNIVERSITY OF WINNIPEG LIBRARY 515 PORTAGE AVENUE WINNIPEG, MAN. R3B 2E9

can calculate the control strength as $\frac{\partial v}{\partial [v_i]}$ where $[v_i]$ must be interpreted as a specific rate (not the actual rate) in the sense of $\frac{\partial v}{\partial \alpha}$. The choice of α_i should be such that v_i is proportional to α_i +. For enzymatic reactions, a natural choice for $[v_i]$ is e_i, and provides a convenient experimental method for the study of rate control in extracts: namely, by adding an amount of enzyme Δe_i and determining Δv. In this manner the control strengths can be evaluated and ordered. Again, there need not be any great difference in the control strengths implying that no one step has dominant rate control. However, in cases where such disparity does exist, it is reasonable to refer to the step with the very large strength as the rate controlling step.

The relationship of the rate controlling step to the fast and slow steps (defined through the values of the characteristic times) is easily demonstrated. The net flux v is linked to the disappearance of $\overline{x_o}$ (which is not actually allowed in the stationary state). We consider a virtual change in $\overline{x_o}$ to $\overline{x_o} + \overline{\Delta x_o}$ and compute Δv as well as Δx_i. The characteristic times τ_i for each step are then defined as the time for reaction (i) alone to make the transition Δx_i. In general, one finds that

$$\text{order } \tau_i \quad = \quad \text{order } C_{(v_i)}$$

and that the relative magnitudes of the τ_i are of the same order as the relative magnitudes of the $C_{[v_i]}$. Consequently, we may conclude that ++

$$\text{Slow step} \equiv \text{Rate Control Step}$$

As a specific example, we consider the sequential enzyme system examined previously (with the dynamical characteristics of Figure 13A).

$$[S_o] \xrightarrow{v} P \qquad\qquad v = v[e_i]$$

$$[S_o] \xrightarrow{E_0} S_1 \xrightarrow{E_1} S_2 \xrightarrow{E_2} S_3 \xrightarrow{E_3} S_4 \xrightarrow{E_4} P$$

+Special variables λ_i may be introduced into the rate equations just for the purpose of taking such specific derivatives. Thus, if the actual equation is $v_i = v_i(\alpha_i, \chi)$ we set $v'_i = \lambda_i v_i$. Then $v_i = v'_i(\lambda_i = 1)$. Calculate $v' = v'(\lambda, \alpha)$ and hence $v = v'(\lambda = 1)$. Then $\left(\frac{\partial v}{\partial [v_i]} \equiv \frac{\partial v'}{\partial \lambda_i}\right)_{\lambda_i = 1}$

++This statement is valid in specific instances, and appears to be generally valid, but there may be exceptional cases.

Calculation of the control strengths $C_{[v_i]} = \dfrac{\partial v}{\partial e_i}$ yields

$$C_{[v_o]} = \text{finite},\; C_{[v_i]} = 0 \text{ for } i = 1,2,3,4 \;(\text{for } \overline{x_o} < \overline{x^*})$$

which is obvious from the fact that the equivalent reaction is

$$[S_o] \xrightarrow{E_o} P \qquad (\text{for } \overline{x_o} < \overline{x^*})$$

Calculation of τ_i yields

$$\tau_o = \infty; \quad \tau_i = \text{finite } (i = 1,2,3,4) \;(\text{for } \overline{x_o} < \overline{x^*}$$

(Recall that the first step must have $\tau_o = \infty$ by definition of a SCV ($\overline{x_o}$).) It is evident that the first step is the slow step and also the rate controlling step.

In the case of $\overline{x_o} > \overline{x^*}$, the reaction splits into

$$[S_o] \xrightarrow{v'} \;\cdot\; \begin{cases} \xrightarrow{v''} S_3 \\ \xrightarrow{v} P \end{cases}$$

and there are actually three different rates (v', v", v) to consider. It is easily shown that

$$\frac{\partial v'}{\partial e_o} = \text{finite}, \quad \frac{\partial v'}{\partial e_i} = 0 (i = 1,2,3,4)$$

$$\frac{\partial v''}{\partial e_o} = \text{finite}, \quad \frac{\partial v''}{\partial e_3} = \text{finite}, \quad \frac{\partial v''}{\partial e_i} = 0 \;(i = 1,2,4)$$

$$\frac{\partial v}{\partial e_3} = \text{finite} \quad \frac{\partial v}{\partial e_i} = 0 \;(i = 0,1,2,4)$$

The relative values of the τ_i are depicted on the dynamical level design shown in Figure 17. The fact that τ_3 becomes infinite for $\overline{x_o} = \overline{x^*}$ is recognized in that $\Delta x_3 = \infty$ and, for an enzymatic reaction $t_{off} \sim \Delta x$. The close relationship between the rate controlling step and the slow step is again evident.

Thus, for $\overline{x_o} > \overline{x^*}$ the results can be summarized by stating that the rate v' is controlled by the step 0, the rate v" is controlled by both 0 and 3, while the rate v is controlled by 3 alone

This example also provides an illustration of control transfer as a function of the SCV. The production of P is first under control by e_0 (for $\overline{x_0} < \overline{x^*}$) and then shifts to control by e_3 (for $\overline{x_0} > \overline{x^*}$).

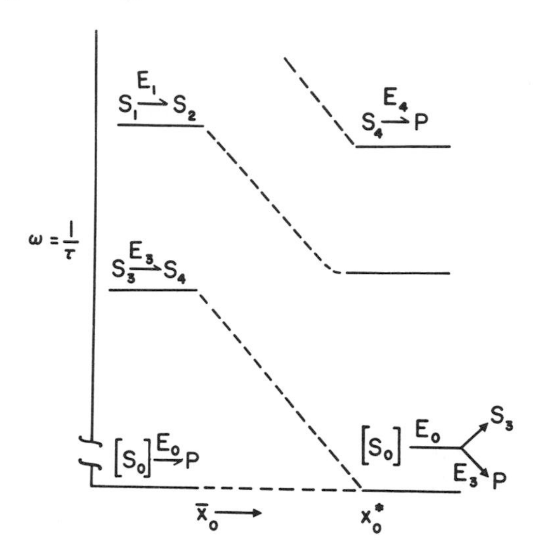

Figure 17. Dynamical level diagram showing effect of increasing $\overline{x}_0$ on the characteristic frequencies. (For sequential reaction $[S_0] \longrightarrow P$.

The concept of rate control can easily be extended to rate control by a subsystem of reactions rather than just one step. The procedure is essentially the same.

IV. Feedback

The number of distinct dynamical states and the character of these states are closely related to the feedback properties of the reaction mechanism. Such properties are easily recognized by the use of net flux diagrams.

It may be noted that in this discussion act and inh are used in a very general sense--namely, that

$$\text{act} \Rightarrow \frac{\partial v_i}{\partial x} > 0, \text{ while } \text{inh} \equiv \frac{\partial v_i}{\partial x} < 0$$

Thus, for the mechanism

$$\xrightarrow{v_1} \underset{x}{S} \xrightarrow[v_2]{\text{act}}$$

$$\frac{dx}{dt} = v_{net} = v_1 - v_2 \qquad \text{and} \qquad \frac{\partial v_{net}}{\partial x} < 0$$

Note that the simple reaction $S \xrightarrow{k} P$ can be considered as activational in this general sense $\left(\frac{\partial v}{\partial x} > 0\right)$.

The net flux diagram then appears as

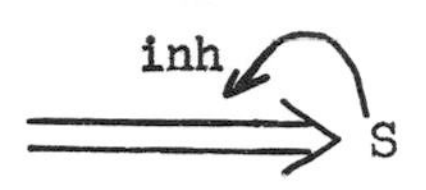

The mechanism

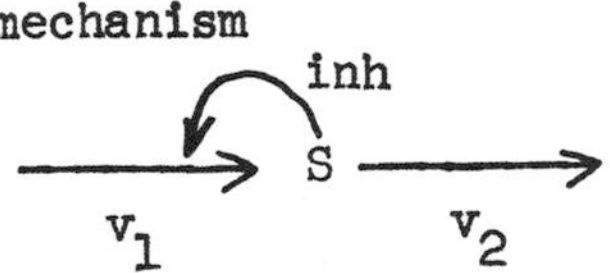

also yields a net flux diagram of the same form, namely

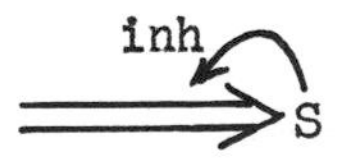

The essential equivalence of forward activation or back inhibition is evident. When the net flux diagram occurs as shown the variable is said to have negative feedback since it acts to inhibit its own net production. In general, such systems are well behaved and exhibit a high degree of stability[+].

A second case arises for the mechanisms

$\longrightarrow S \longrightarrow$ (inh) or $\longrightarrow S \longrightarrow$ (act)

which both possess the net flux diagram

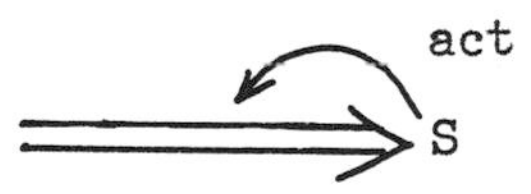

The equivalence of forward inhibition and back activation is evident, and the variables are said to exhibit positive feedback. Such mechanisms, when involved with other reactions, usually lead to a variety of dynamical states having unbounded or oscillatory kinetics.

When there are several variables in the system, the net flux

[+] A general discussion of stability (9) and its relation to control and feedback in chemical systems is given elsewhere.

diagrams will, in general, be cross-coupled. Thus, the simple reaction

$$A \underset{k'}{\overset{k}{\rightleftharpoons}} B$$

yields a net flux diagram

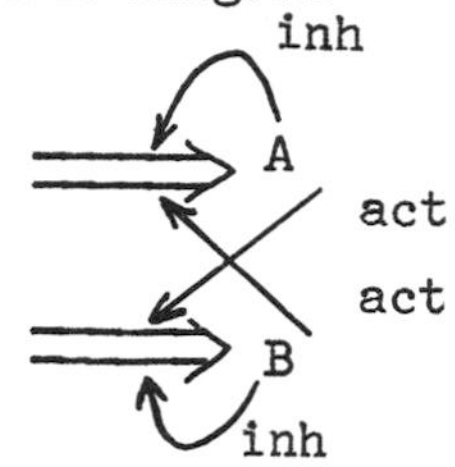

and the resultant stability and non-oscillatory character of the motion is easily demonstrated. On the other hand, the mechanism

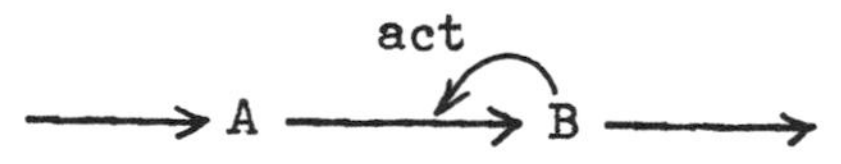

has a net flux diagram

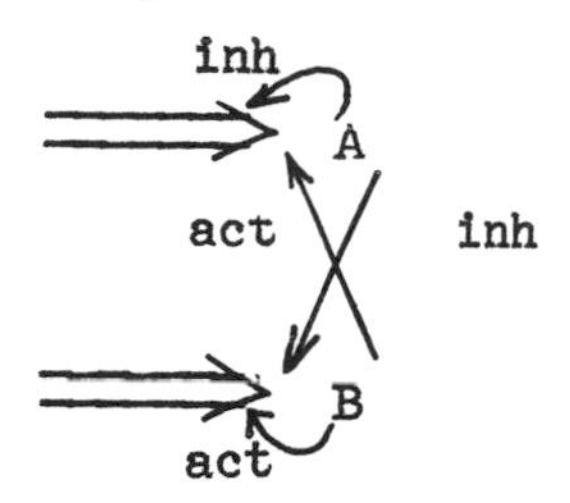

Such a diagram generally indicates the possibility of oscillatory motion and multiple dynamical states (10), (depending on the nature of the inhibition and activation). An example of such a system (11), involving the fact that the enzyme phosphofructokinase is activated by its product (FDP), is shown in Figure 18 together with computer solutions. The structural control variable (GLU) is allowed to change slowly and the system passes through the oscillatory region as shown in the kinetics. A control plane, typical of such systems, is shown in Figure 18. The detailed analysis of the net flux diagrams is discussed elsewhere (10).

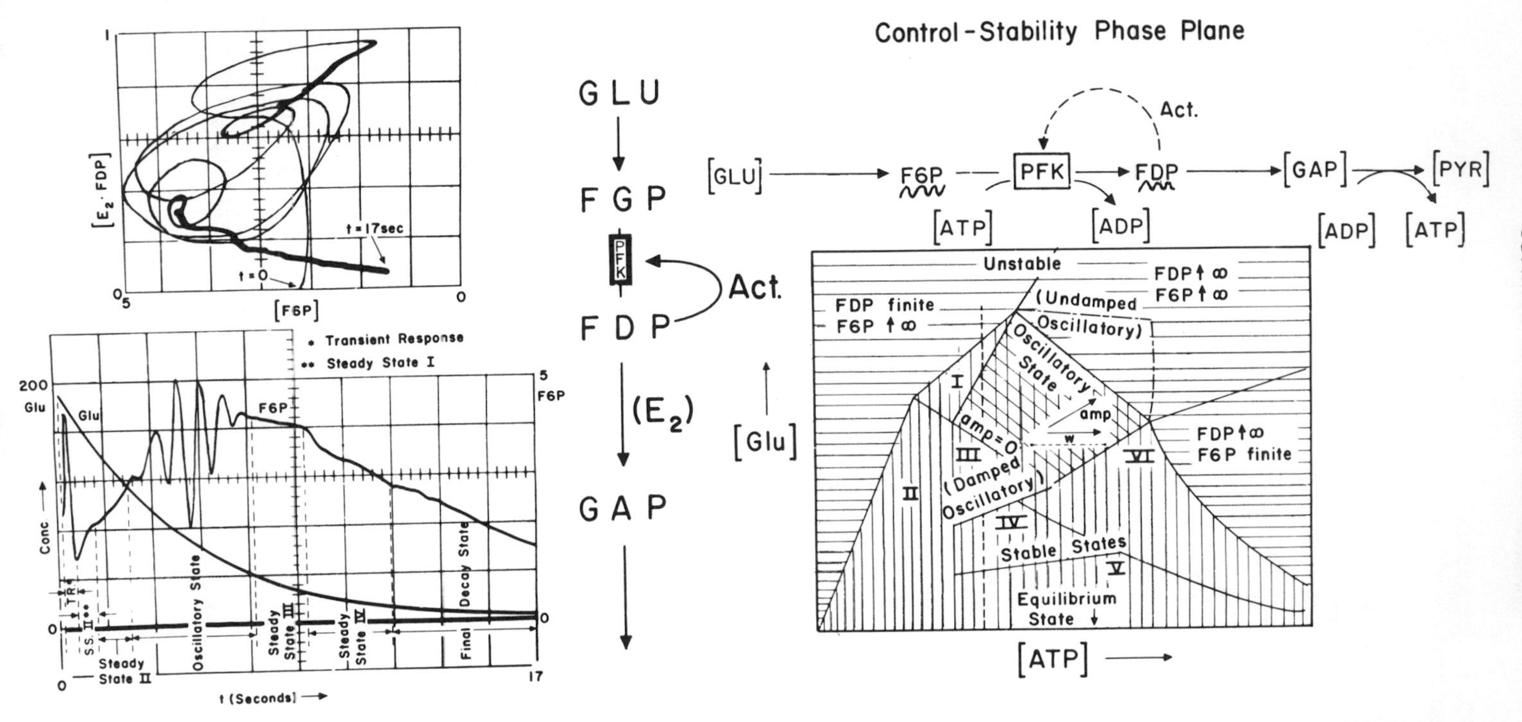

Figure 18. A) Kinetics and phase plane plot for oscillatory mechanism based on FDP activation of PFK. Note passage of system through oscillatory region as the GLU (in SCV) is allowed to change slowly.
B) Typical type of control plane diagram for such oscillatory system showing dependence of the dynamical state character on the SCV (in this case GLU and ATP).

Discussion and Summary

Most of the results brought out in the preceding analysis have been intuitively and in some cases quantitatively realized by many others. The main intention of this paper has been to develop these ideas to the point where they may provide a more analytical basis and a broader viewpoint for the future development and understanding of cellular dynamics. However, it seems worthwhile to reemphasize some of these results, in particular as they apply to metabolic control.

It is hoped that more investigators may take advantage of various types of graphs presented here in regard to the expression of their data. A plot of v vs x (dynamical characteristics) is generally more useful for dynamical and control considerations than the Lineweaver-Burke plot of (1/v vs 1/x) or other types. Such types are important in determining the enzymatic reaction substructure but difficult to utilize directly for metabolic control studies. Multiple substrate systems are perhaps best plotted as shown in Figure 14.

The somewhat frequent finding that certain metabolic intermediates maintain a constant ratio is only indicative of the fact that they are engaged in fast reactions. If the constant value of the ratio is the same as the equilibrium constant then these intermediates are engaged in a fast (i.e., high characteristic frequency) equilibration reaction; if the constant ratio is different from the equilibrium constant, then such intermediates are probably engaged in a fast stationary state reaction. Since the rate controlling steps are generally associated with the slow reactions, it may be concluded that reaction steps having the associated intermediates in a constant ratio can not be rate controlling steps (at least in the sense developed in this paper). As a minor point, it also seems preferable to replace the words "rate limiting" with the words "rate controlling," which is more literally related to the sense of usage.

In regard to the theoretical aspects, further studies are required to integrate the concepts of feedback and control with the energetic and synthesizing reactions of the cell, particularly with respect to the ability of the cell to turn these reactions on and off in accordance with external and internal demands. It may be hoped that such studies will not only enable us to understand what we already know about cellular reactions, but also direct the nature and interpretation of new experiments.

REFERENCES

1. Lotka, A.J., Elements of Mathematical Biology, Dover Publications, Inc., New York (1956).

2. Prigogine, I., Thermodynamics of Irreversible Processes, Interscience Publishers, New York (1955).

3. Goodwin, B.C., Temporal Organization in Cells, Academic Press, New York (1963).

4. Higgins, J.J., A Theoretical Study of the Kinetic Properties of Sequential Enzyme Reactions, Ph.D. Dissertation, University of Pennsylvania (1959).

5. Higgins, J.J., (in preparation).

6. Chance, B., In Symposia on Quantitative Biology, Biological Lab, Cold Spring Harbor L.I., New York, Vol. XXVI (1961).

7. Higgins, J.J., Ann. N.Y. Acad. Sci., 108(1),305,321 (1963).

8. Higgins, J.J., (in preparation).

9. Higgins, J.J., (in preparation).

10. Higgins, J.J., (in preparation).

11. Higgins, J.J., Proc. Nat. Acad. Sci., 51(6),989 (1964).

12. Higgins, J.J., Ann. N.Y. Acad. Sci., 115(2), 1025 (1964).

II

Computer Studies

COMPUTER-BASED ANALYSIS OF BIOCHEMICAL DATA[+]

David Garfinkel

Johnson Research Foundation, University of Pennsylvania
Philadelphia, Pennsylvania

The analysis of complicated biochemical systems is possible as well from the starting point of the experimental data as from the first physical principles, as Dr. Higgins has done. The "computer-based analysis" of my title does not include such procedures as the statistical evaluation of experimental data, which is usually feasible, although more difficult, without a computer. However, two types of analysis of biochemical data are now feasible through proper use of computers which are almost impossible without them. These are the analyses of transient changes in time and of inhomogeneity in space in biochemical systems.

It is most common to analyze biochemical systems by drawing conclusions from steady state data. In our first effort to simulate a biochemical system that was complex enough to be biologically meaningful, the ascites tumor cell system (1), we found it easy to simulate a steady state based on endogenous metabolism. Furthermore, when we added glucose to our ascites cell model, we had no difficulty in getting it to go to another steady state with the appropriate levels of intermediates. Probably either steady state could have been represented in hundreds of plausible ways. However, the transient changes during the transition between steady states, although more difficult to represent, also yielded results of correspondingly greater value than the simple steady state analyses. I suspect that this is rather typical; one would expect that metabolic control would manifest itself clearly in the rapid changes occurring in the transition from one steady state to another than in the steady state itself. With some experimental support, one can readily argue that a given steady state is caused by any one of a number of factors, and some such arguments have become recurring themes in the literature. Such an argument for control during a transient is subject to at least two additional constraints - the direction of change of a supposed control substance and the time duration of its

[+]Supported by PHS FR-15.

changes.

There are also transient biochemical effects that have been well studied, and one in particular - the changes resulting from muscle stimulation - will be treated at some length in this symposium (see below, p. 383). The extreme case in this direction is that of glycolytic oscillation, which is a continuous transient state; although not yet analyzed in great detail, this offers great promise in elucidating the control mechanisms of glycolysis.

We have been working on the computer simulation of glycolysis in ascites tumor cells for some years, and have accumulated considerable data on the problem. It is well-known that on adding glucose to ascites cells in the endogenous state, there is an immediate pile-up of glucose-6-phosphate (G-6-P) that falls again and subsequently rises; ADP rises and falls while ATP inversely falls and rises; AMP follows ADP, but with smaller amplitude of change. The rate of glucose uptake is fairly constant for some time, then slows down quite drastically, and remains fairly constant at this lower level thereafter. These changes begin within a second of the glucose addition, and continue for 30 to 60 seconds (depending on the temperature).

Several explanations based on control by a single chemical have been proposed for this process. Hexokinase is the control point most immediately apparent, but there are at least six substances which may control hexokinase; the two substrates, ATP and glucose - and since glucose does not enter the ascites cell freely, as shown by Dr. Cori and his associates (2), one must also take account of the system which brings it into the cell; the inhibitors ADP, AMP, and G-6-P, and P_i which partially protect hexokinase against the effects of G-6-P. One must consider two structural factors in hexokinase control as well. Hexokinase is known to be reversibly associated with the mitochondria, which then shrink and swell during this process (3). All eight parameters change rapidly, and in ways so complex that the situation probably cannot be handled intuitively. It is, however, accessible to computer simulation.

In effect, one constructs a model of the hexokinase with its associated chemicals, checking that each one of these has the appropriate effect on the model and, hopefully that they interact correctly with each other. The entire system can then be allowed to vary, and the model examined either for control by one chemical at any given time or for the ways in which all the chemicals involved share the control among themselves. Figure 1 gives an example of the order of complexity of the problem; even so, it is too simple, having been

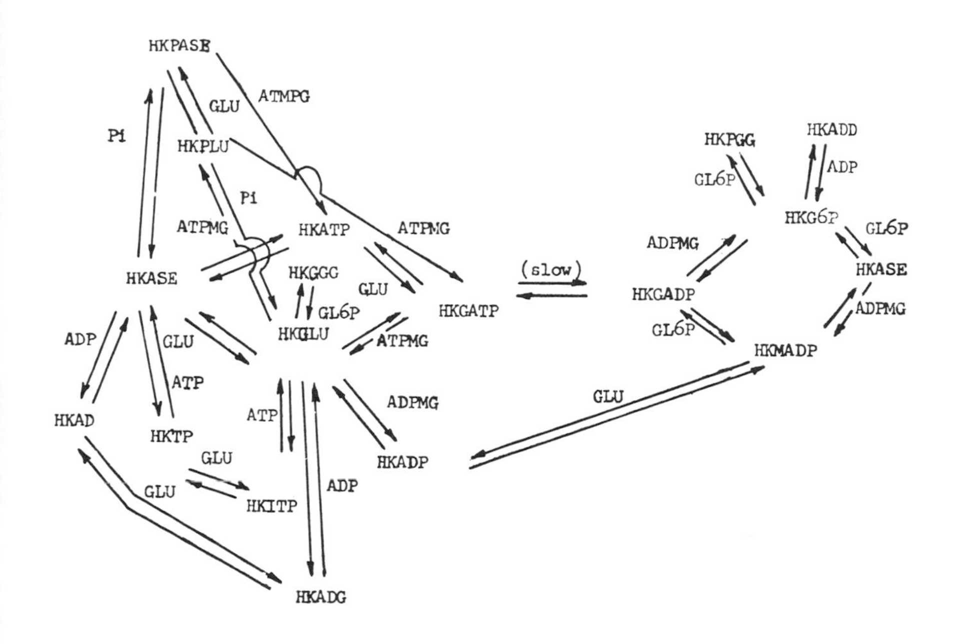

Figure 1. Scheme of ascites hexokinase model.

drawn before we became aware of the importance of AMP in this process. I fear that a real enzyme would look like this (or even worse) when considered in detail, rather than like the simple cases described by Dr. Higgins.

Figure 2 shows the results of combining such a model of hexokinase with suitable models for PFK, mitochondrial metabolism, and so on. Here again G-6-P piles up and falls off, ADP piles up and starts back down, cytoplasmic ATP falls off, while mitochondrial ATP (not shown) piles up, so that the sum of the two is about as observed for the total. The "HKGATP" curve represents the activity of the hexokinase; it is actually the concentration of the active complex in this model, and falls with time, although not following the straight line abruptly switching to another straight line which is observed for glucose uptake. While I would not claim that this is a satisfactory representation of the system, it at least takes us part of the way and offers the possibility that the other elements of the system may be added to give the complete picture.

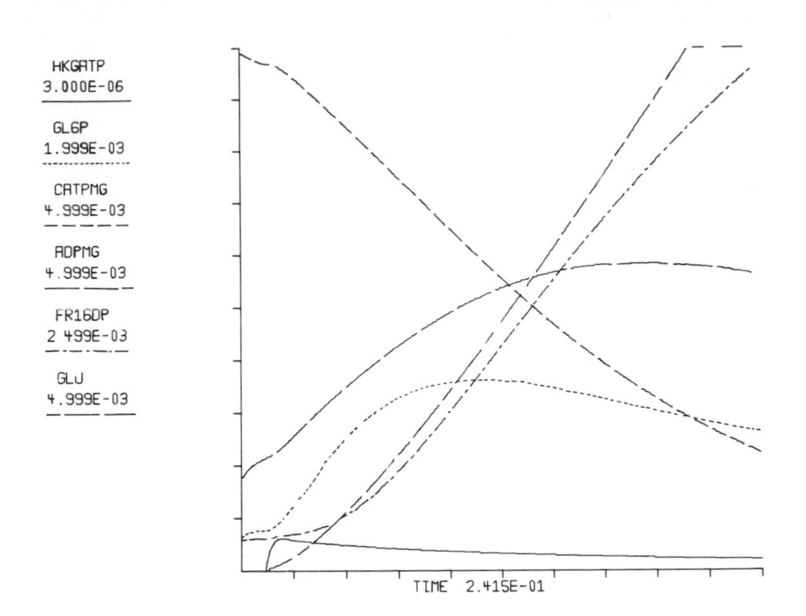

Figure 2. Plot of concentrations against time for ascites hexokinase model (total time actually 24.15 sec). Curves are identified by line quality, the scale factor being given in FORTRAN format ($E - 3 = 10^{-3}$).

A second phenomenon which may be represented by computer simulation is that of inhomogeneity in space, or compartmentation. In the above hexokinase model, ATP seems to be compartmented between the cytoplasm and the mitochondria. Compartments can range in size all the way from a collection of organs (such as the body muscle mass) through a single organ such as the brain, through subsections of organs and individual cells right down to cellular substructures such as mitochondria and other organelles, through substructures within substructures, and all the way to individual enzymes. A family of enzymes fastened to a membrane, as in the oxidative phosphorylation system, is again inhomogeneous, and cannot be treated as if the members were free in solution. At the extreme are enzyme systems in solution but so intimately associated that they also cannot be considered as acting freely; for example, aldolase and triose-phosphate-isomerase seem to interact in such a way that triose-phosphate-isomerase does not exert as much activity as would be expected from measuring the gross amount present in the cell.

Nearly all these situations have been represented by computer models, or have been analyzed by some kind of mathematical method. Much of the existing compartmentation theory has been developed to deal with the situation of numerous compartments of a single substance. It is now possible, conversely, to deal with a few compartments involving a great many substances. The metabolism in the brain of the dicarboxylic amino acids and the compounds related to them provides an example.

In this system, the compounds involved (glutamic acid and its derivatives, asparic acid, the Krebs cycle intermediates, etc.) seem from experimental evidence to be compartmented. This can be studied by introducing appropriate radioactive labels in a variety of places (e.g., glutamate may be injected into the cerebrospinal fluid or into the blood, the resulting experimental distribution of the label being quite different in the two cases), or it may even be perturbed simultaneously with labeling, as by ammonia intoxication. The resulting data may then be simulated, taking from the literature known chemical concentrations, enzyme profiles, etc.

Simulation of this system requires simultaneous consideration of compartmentation at virtually all the levels mentioned above, from the entire organ (owing to the presence of the "blood-brain barrier" the brain is definitely a compartment unto itself) through the intercellular space (which is continuous with the cerebrospinal fluid), through the cells themselves (brain contains many cell types, and it has apparently been possible to localize some of these into definite compartments), through subcellular organelles like nerve endings and their enclosed mitochondria, down to apparent associations of enzymes (i.e., there appears to be a close association of transaminase with some enzyme capable of removing the amide group of glutamine equilibrates with α-ketoglutarate much faster than it could if glutamate formed in the process had to equilibrate with the glutamate pool). Some problems may involve more than one level of compartmentation; glutamic-oxaloacetic transaminase is by far the most active enzyme considered in the model, yet the reaction catalyzed by this reaction is not in equilibrium, either in the whale brain or in any subcompartment described in this study.

It was possible to construct a model which quantitatively accounted for nearly all the experimental data; an overall diagram is shown below. On collating the properties of one of the subcompartments in this model, including its complement of enzymes and apparent permeabilities to various compounds, they were found to match one of the known cytological structures, the nerve-ending fraction. On collating more data it has apparently been possible to say how this compartmentation functions biochemically, what physiological function its presence serves, and how it may be deranged by some disease conditions.

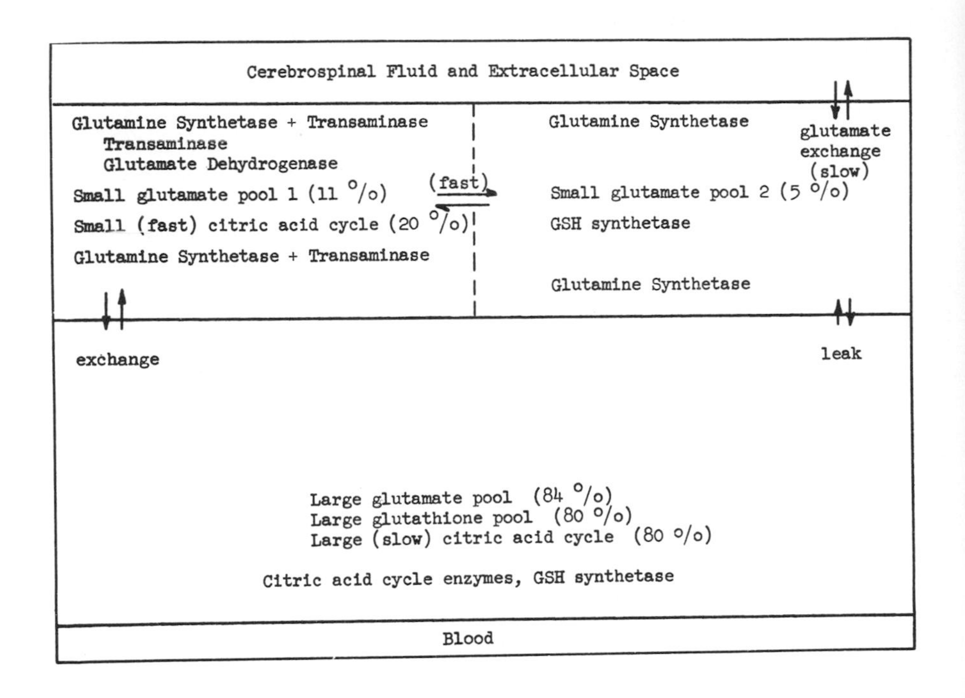

I suspect that the combination of analyses of biochemical transients in time and inhomogeneities in space will be required for a complete picture of anything as complicated as a biochemical system having biological meaning.

REFERENCES

1. Garfinkel, D., and Hess, B., J. Biol. Chem., 239, 971 (1964).

2. Crane, R. K., Field, R. A., Cori, C. F., and Roberts, M. L., J. Biol. Chem., 224, 649 (1957).

3. Packer, L., and Golden, R. H., J. Biol. Chem., 235, 1234 (1960).

DISCUSSION

Bücher: I would like to make two observations which might expand on Dr. Chance's contribution.

My first point is an additional interpretation of the physiological meaning of multiple control in a metabolic chain, which we call the aspect of "functional readiness" (Bücher, Th., and Rüssmann, K., Angew. Chemie, Int. Ed., 3, 426 (1964)). Let us consider a tissue where metabolic flow changes by orders of magnitude, for example, the glycolytic chain of skeletal muscle at rest and during activity. If you have only one control point at the beginning of the chain, the effect of "switching out" at rest would be a depletion of all intermediary metabolites below this point in the chain. Now if we "switch on" to activity, with its needs for a flux 100-1000 times greater than that required at rest, a rather long lag phase would ensue until the appropriate steady-state is achieved. Instead, by multiple site control, a homeostasis of intermediary metabolite concentrations is ensured along the entire lower portion of the glycolytic chain. Thus when there is a need for a sudden increase of activity, as in the performance of muscular work, any major lag phase in the production of glycolytic ATP is avoided. This is one point about the physiological meaning of the multiple control of a chain, especially of one which has feedbacks built in.

The second point concerns the application of the "crossover theorem" as an indicator of control sites in systems of high complexity, as extra-mitochondrial metabolism. This theorem was originally concerned with the respiratory chain. Let us compare two couples, for instance, reduced cytochrome c and oxidized cytochrome c, and the tissue content of F-6-P and FDP. The difference between these pairs is that the total amount of cytochrome c is constant in all states of the respiratory chain, while the total amount of F-6-P + FDP in the glycolytic system is subject to wider variations, due to the switching on and off at control sites upstream and downstream of PFK, for example, at hexokinase.

In order to handle the more complex situations, we must consider the term Γ/K_{app}, where Γ is the mass action ratio of the system calculated from the tissue content of the reactants, and K_{app} is the thermodynamic equilibrium constant of the system.

(see Williamson, p.333).

Rose: I'd like to make two points expanding on what Dr. Chance has said about glycolysis: one on the multi-site control, and one on crossover points.

Another candidate for multi-site control in glycolysis that may be of significance is inorganic phosphate. We know that P_i overcomes the effect of G-6-P as an inhibitor of hexokinase; we know that it stimulates ATP inhibited PFK. We also know from the work of Spolter et al., (Spolter, P., Adelman, R. C. and Weinhouse, S., J. Biol. Chem., 240, 1327 (1965)) that it increases the K_m of FDP for aldolase; and we know that it also affects pyruvate kinase. So there are several key points at which P_i can either stimulate by overcoming inhibition or itself can cause inhibition through an effect on K_m.

This brings me to the second point, namely crossover points. The effect of phosphate on aldolase could be that it raises the K_m for FDP and causes the aldolase to operate at a higher steady-state level of FDP, which causes a greater stimulation of PFK, producing a procession of effects all along the chain that could very well be initiated by phosphate changes. The fact that an affector would change the K_m of a substrate for an enzyme makes it quite difficult to apply the crossover point hypothesis generally to a multi-enzyme system, since, in the particular case I mentioned where the P_i might cause a large rise in the FDP level, this, rather than the increased rate of PFK, would be the cause of the large rise of FDP levels in the steady-states. This change could be reflected all along the line.

Chance: With respect to Dr. Rose's first point, we agree that both ADP and phosphate can be candidates for a multi-site control. Indeed, as Hess now suggests, FDP as well can be a candidate for multi-site control. It was our purpose to point out that multi-site control has advantages over single-site control.

With respect to the crossover points, you have proposed that an inhibitory effect on aldolase (a phosphate-controlled rise of K_m) will activate flux through the whole system by raising the level of FDP, and point to this as a difficulty in determining a crossover point. The phenomenon that you describe is termed by us a "reversed crossover", namely, when there is an accumulation-depletion phenomenon upon an increase of flux. Our original comment to this point is relevant: Lemma No. 4 of the crossover theorem indicates "a + to - change (reversed cross-over) does not identify an interaction site." (Chance, B., Holmes, W., Higgins, J., and Connelly, C. M., Nature, 182, 1190

(1958)). The fact that crossover points may not be demonstrable for a given set of conditions or indeed that reversed crossover points may be observed should not discourage the use of this theorem in determining control sites; insofar as I know there is no other method than the crossover approach for the identification of the control sites without perturbing the system, which in itself may vitiate the purpose of the experiment.

Czerlinski: I have only a small remark for Dr. Garfinkel, who reported on the natural overall enzyme system, and for Dr. Higgins, who mentioned one case of limiting enzyme systems, those containing irreversible steps. The other limiting case would be that of consecutive reversible steps with appropriate differences in the individual time constant (s). It is of considerable advantage then, to apply chemical relaxation techniques.

It is interesting to realize that the derivations of the equations for the two limiting cases are somewhat similar. In the investigation of the chemical relaxation of consecutive processes, each individual step may be considered, such as the i-th step in

$$\text{fast} \quad \cdots \rightleftharpoons Y_i \underset{k_{-i}}{\overset{k_{+i}}{\rightleftharpoons}} Y_{i+1} \underset{k_{-(i+1)}}{\overset{k_{+i+1}}{\rightleftharpoons}} \cdots \quad \text{slow}$$

The basic relation is the same as that of Dr. Higgins' for consecutive irreversible steps: $k_{+i} \gg k_{+i+1}$. In the time range of k_{+i} (with $k_{+i} \approx k_{-i}$ for purposes of detectability), all reactions left of the step with k_i may be considered in equilibrium, and all reactions right of the step with k_i may be considered as non-existing (kinetically only ! See J. Theoret. Biol., 7, 463 (1964)). In this respect the treatment of chemical relaxation is quite similar to the treatment given by Dr. Higgins for consecutive irreversible steps. But chemical relaxation permits the same treatment, if any or all of the steps are bimolecular. Reversible steps in front of an irreversible step can also easily be treated this way.

Hess: I would like to point to a new type of control pathway which might be important for the problem of physiological readiness which has been discussed by Dr. Bücher. In glycolysis the problem is how the overall pathway can be activated in a very short time. We recently found in yeast a control which is "forward" control, a coupling forward along the chain. When glycolysis is activated, the initial turnover wave proceeds to the level of PFK and causes an accumulation of FDP, and as we have recently found, activates pyruvate kinase.

TABLE I

FDP-Activation of Yeast-Pyruvate-Kinase

FDP [μM]	Activity [μmole x min^{-1} x mg^{-1}]
-	2.0
20	2.0
40	25.0
60	37.0
80	53.0
100	54.0

Exp. 172/5/65 (Hess, Brand, and Gey)
Unpublished experiments

Table I demonstrates the strong activation of yeast-pyruvate-kinase of Saccharomyces carlsbergensis by FDP at pH 6.5. The half-maximal activation of the experiment demonstrated in Table I is in the range of between 20 and 40 μM (i.e., $.3 \times 10^{-4}$). More recently, experiments under different conditions have shown that the half-maximal activation can be shifted to the range of from $.3 \times 10^{-4}$ to 1×10^{-3}, a wide range. This forward-control is very efficient because pyruvate kinase will already be activated when a flux increase is initiated along the pathway and finally reaches the pyruvate kinase level. Such a mechanism is important, especially in yeast, where no significant branching of the glycolytic pathway occurs and accumulation of triose phosphate and FDP must be avoided. We also understand that it is difficult to detect a crossover at the pyruvate kinase level if such an activation is operating. However, this mechanism is important for the generation of oscillation in glycolysis.

Salganicoff: I would like to draw attention to another factor that may complicate the problem of metabolic control even more. This is the presence of isoenzymes in similar substructures of the same organ.

We were able to separate the mitochondria of the nerve ending fraction (Subfraction C) of the brain from the free mitochondria of neuronal and glial origin (Subfraction E) of the same organ (Salganicoff, L., and De Robertis, E., J. Neurochem., 12, 287 (1965)). The action of aspartic and glutamic acids on the γ-aminobutyric transaminase of both types of mitochondria shows that while these amino acids do not interfere with the activity of the enzyme in free mitochondria, they inhibit the same activity in the nerve ending mitochondria. This finding suggests that there are two isoenzymes of γ-aminobutyric transaminase leading to a regulatory mechanism between the content of dicarboxylic amino acids and γ-aminobutyric acid in nerve endings.

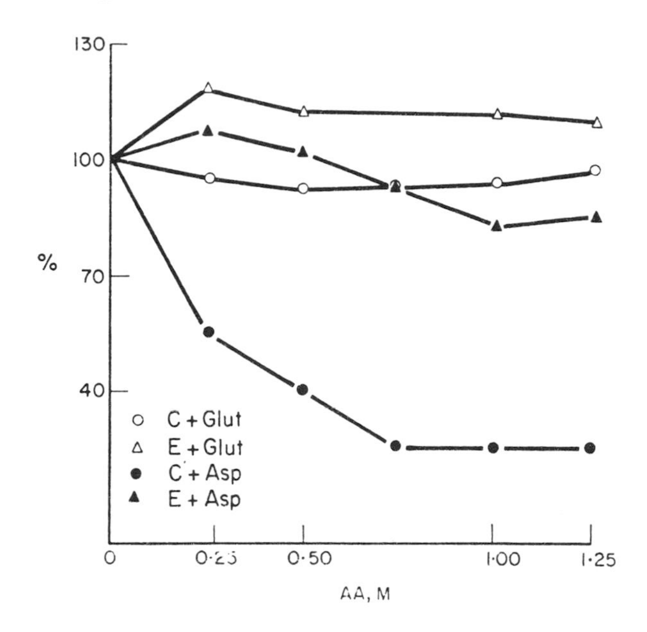

Figure 1. Action of aspartate and glutamate on GABA-AT in subfractions C and E. Portions having a similar activity were incubated in the presence of increasing concentrations of these amino acids. In all cases, 0.25 M-GABA was used as a substrate. Results are expressed in percentage activation or inhibition taken as 100 per cent of the control without the addition of aspartate or glutamate. (Courtesy J. Neurochem., 12, 301 (1965)).

III

Phosphofructokinase: Its Purification, Crystallization, and Kinetic Properties

PHOSPHOFRUCTOKINASE*

Oliver H. Lowry

The Edward Mallinckrodt Department of Pharmacology
Washington University, St. Louis, Missouri

The mission of this panel is to discuss the properties of phosphofructokinase (PFK) which must surely be one of the most complicated enzymes alive. It has been suggested that we try to see whether any of the complex kinetic properties of PFK might be explained by presently known physical or structural properties and (since I believe structural information will not be very complete) to speculate as to what kind of structural properties might be required to explain the kinetic behavior.

May I begin by describing the major kinetic properties of mammalian PFK. As Lardy and Parks showed, it is inhibited by ATP (1). It is also inhibited by citrate (2-4) and to a lesser degree by Mg. On the other hand PFK is activated or deinhibited by 4 groups of substances represented by NH_4^+ (2,5), P_i, 5'-AMP, and fructose-6-P (2). There is strong evidence that each of these acts at a different site on the molecule since they are all synergistic in their actions and the dissociation constant of each is either not changed or is decreased by the other three substances. K^+ activates in a manner similar to that of NH_4^+ but to a lesser extent. ADP and 3',5'-cyclic AMP activate presumably at the same site as AMP. Fructose diphosphate, which is one of the most potent activators, has not been studied as thoroughly, so that it is not yet possible to say whether it acts at the same site as one of the other activators.

In considering possible structures that might provide the kinetic properties of PFK it is important to have in mind the fact that citrate and ATP are synergistic in action. Each lowers the apparent inhibitor constant of the other. It is also necessary to realize that fructose-6-P is antagonistic to both citrate and ATP; it raises the apparent inhibitor constants for both. Finally, increases in ATP, at least, increase the dissociation constants for NH_4^+, AMP and P_i.

A minimal model appears to demand 2 substrate sites, 2 and probably 3 inhibitor sites, plus 4 activator sites.

Furthermore, the sites must be arranged in such a way that 1) occupation of an inhibitor site makes the other inhibitor site more accessible and the activator sites less so, and 2) occupation of an activator site makes the other activator sites more accessible and the inhibitor sites less so.

REFERENCES

1. Lardy, H.A., and Parks, R.E., Jr., in O.H. Gaebler (Editor), Enzymes: Units of Biological Structure and Function, Academic Press, New York, 1956, p. 584.

2. Passonneau, J.V., and Lowry, O. H., Biochem. Biophys. Res. Comm., 13, 372 (1963).

3. Parmeggiani, A. and Bowman, R.H., Biochem. Biophys. Res. Comm., 12, 268 (1963).

4. Garland, P. B., Randle, P.J. and Newsholme, E.A., Nature, 22, 169 (1963).

5. Muntz, J.A., and Hurwitz, J., Arch. Biochem. Biophys., 32, 137 (1951).

* Hess: Since this meeting was held, we have realized that in 1936, E. Negelein (Biochem. Z., 287, 329 (1936)), published a method for the preparation of highly active and stable yeast PFK.

PURIFICATION AND PROPERTIES OF RABBIT SKELETAL MUSCLE PHOSPHOFRUCTOKINASE

E. G. Krebs and A. Parmeggiani

Department of Biochemistry, University of Washington
School of Medicine
Seattle, Washington

In view of Professor Lowry's review of the background and current interest in PFK as a regulatory enzyme, I will present no introduction other than to say that it appeared desirable to have this protein available in the pure form in order to have a better understanding of its physico-chemical and kinetic properties. Our efforts have been directed to that end. Recently it was observed that a fractionation procedure developed for the purification of rabbit muscle phosphorylase b kinase (1) could also be applied to PFK (2,3). Further steps have now led to the isolation of the latter enzyme in a stable, crystalline form.

The purification procedure (Table I) involves a mild acid precipitation at pH 6.1, two differential centrifugation steps, a heat step, and finally an ammonium sulfate precipitation followed by crystallization in the presence of ammonium sulfate and ATP. I will not give details of the method, since these have already been published (3,5), but I would like to draw attention to the use of ATP in the last step. Addition of this regulatory cofactor was prompted by analogy to the use of AMP in the crystallization of phosphorylase b (6). Another feature of the preparation that deserves comment is the fact that several of the steps make use of the high sedimentation coefficient (see below) of PFK, a property which this enzyme has in common with phosphorylase b kinase.

On electrophoresis, crystalline PFK migrates as a single symmetrical boundary in the presence of ATP. In the absence of the nucleotide, turbidity often develops in the cell and noticeable asymmetry of the peak is present. In the ultracentrifuge the enzyme shows an asymmetric peak with a trailing edge. The $S_{20,w}$ for the main component is about 40S. In the presence of ATP the sedimentation coefficient is reduced to around 25S, and there is still a pronounced asymmetry of

TABLE I

Purification of PFK from 1 Kg of Rabbit Skeletal Muscle

PFK activity was assayed by determining the amount of fructose-1,6-di-P formed in a reaction mixture at pH 8.2 and 26°, containing 50 mM glycylglycine - 1 mM EDTA buffer, 1 mM fructose-6-P, 1 mM ATP, 6 mM $MgCl_2$, 4 mM NH_4^+, 10 mM cystein, 0.5 mM DPNH, and 0.01 per cent albumin. The auxiliary enzymes, aldolase, α-glycero-P dehydrogenase, and triose-P isomerase (all from Boehringer) were present in excess. The rate of fructose diphosphate formation was followed spectrophotometrically at 340 mμ as DPNH disappearance (4). Activity is expressed as μmoles fructose diphosphate formed per minute.

Fraction	Total Activity	Specific Activity	Purification
	Units	Units/mg	X
Extract	35,000	0.9	
Acid Precipitate*	21,300	6.3	7
30,000 rpm Supernatant	13,200	18.6	21
40,000 rpm Pellet	7,000	36.8	41
Heated 40,000 rpm Pellet	6,715	96.2	104
$(NH_4)_2SO_4$ Precipitate	5,300	121	134
First Crystals	4,600	139	154
Second Crystals	4,400	145	161

* In the preparation illustrated here the acid precipitation was carried out at pH 6.15; a somewhat greater yield is achieved at pH 6.0.

the peak. We have also observed that the sedimentation properties of crystalline PFK are markedly affected by dilution. Table II gives values for the sedimentation constants in the presence and absence of ATP determined at protein concentrations from 0.05 to 24 mg/ml. Further dissociation of the enzyme can be achieved by 8 M urea in which PFK shows a single symmetrical peak with a $S_{20,w}$ of about 2.5S.

TABLE II

Effect of the Protein Concentration on the $S_{20,w}$ of 3X Crystallized Rabbit Muscle Phosphofructokinase in the Absence or in the Presence of ATP*

Protein Concentration mg. ml.$^{-1}$	Technique	$S_{20,x}$	
		no ATP	with ATP*
24.1	schlieren optics		29S
17.0	"	36S	
10.0	"	37S	26S
5.0	"	37S	24S
2.0	schlieren optics absorption optics sucrose gradient	35S	22S
0.5	"	27S	17S
0.2	sucrose gradient	19S	11S
0.05	"	14S	8S

* 10 mM

It was not surprising to find that PFK is a protein which exhibits unusual physico-chemical properties and appears to be involved in a complicated associating-dissociating system. We have all become accustomed to thinking of regulatory enzymes as having properties which allow for a high degree of variability in their native structures. How the various structural features of PFK are related to its activity and regulation is not yet known; however, with purification of the enzyme this aspect of the study can now be readily pursued.

REFERENCES

1. Krebs, E. G., Love, D. S., Bratvold, G. E., Trayser, K. A., Meyer, W. L., and Fischer, E. H., Biochemistry, 3, 1022 (1964).

2. Parmeggiani, A., Love, D. S., and Krebs, E. G., Fed. Proc., 23, 533 (1964).

3. Parmeggiani, A. and Krebs, E. G., Biochem. Biophys. Res. Commun., 19, 89 (1965).

4. Racker, E., J. Biol. Chem., 167, 843 (1947).

5. Parmeggiani, A. and Krebs, E. G., Fed. Proc., 24, 284 (1965).

6. Fischer, E. H. and Krebs, E. G., J. Biol. Chem., 231, 65 (1958).

PHOSPHOFRUCTOKINASE FROM RABBIT MUSCLE

Henry A. Lardy

Institute for Enzyme Research and Department of Biochemistry
University of Wisconsin, Madison

The procedure elaborated by Dr. Ling for isolating phosphofructokinase was described in the May issue of the Journal of Biological Chemistry. It involves only three fractionation steps. The extract of rabbit muscle is brought to a 10 percent concentration of isopropanol at 40°. The soluble fraction from the treatment is brought to 20 percent isopropanol at low temperature and the precipitated enzyme is purified on DEAE cellulose. The muscle from one rabbit (650 grams) gives about 350 mg of the purified enzyme in a yield of 60 percent. Figure 1 shows the three components that are observed in the ultracentrifuge. A is the sedimentation diagram in the presence of 0.1 M phosphate buffer. With the same conditions, but with 2 M urea present the three components are merged into one, very nearly homogenous component. When urea is removed by dialysis the preparation reverts to the three component system in C, or if the enzyme is precipitated from the 2 M urea with ammonium sulfate, the monomer, dimer and tetramer forms are regained.

Mr. Verner Paetkau has found that dithiothreitol (Cleland's reagent) very effectively stabilizes the enzyme. Dilution and dialysis lead to inactivation because of dissociation of the enzyme and several compounds will prevent this inactivation or even restore activity to the inactive protein.

This interconversion of active and inactive forms is extremely interesting, and is exploited in the isolation procedure.

Dr. Ling found that extraction with dilute KOH by the old procedure of Taylor gives a stable extract but a much lower yield of enzyme than can be obtained by extraction with phosphate buffer. The activity in the phosphate extract drops off during storage at 4° (Fig. 2, open circles) but can be completely regained by incubating in 4 mM ATP for 10 minutes at 28° (solid dots). In agreement with what Dr. Krebs just said, there is no evidence for the enzyme being phosphorylated during the reactivation process. It will be interesting to learn the physiological significance of these interconversions.

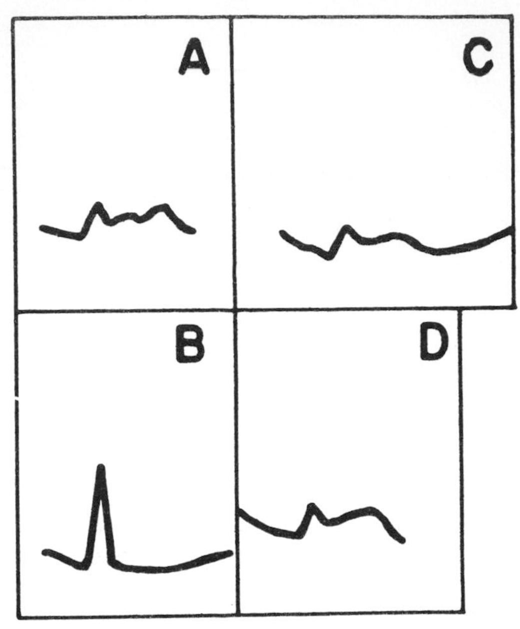

Figure 1. Sedimentation patterns of purified PFK. Direction of sedimentation is from left to right. 24 min. at 59,780 rpm. Spinco Model E centrifuge. **Courtesy, J. Biol. Chem., 240, 1896 (1965)**

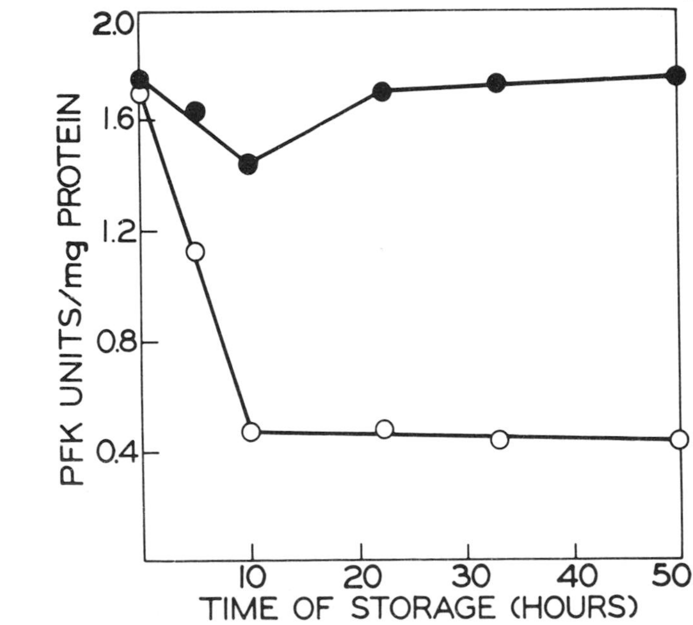

Figure 2. Loss of PFK activity during storage and recovery in the presence of Mg ATP. **Courtesy, J. Biol. Chem., 240, 1894 (1965).**

SOME PROPERTIES OF FRUCTOSE-6-PHOSPHATE-KINASE FROM RABBIT SKELETAL MUSCLE

Dirk Pette and Hans Werner Hofer

Physiologisch-Chemisches Institut der Universität München, Germany

In all tissues so far investigated, fructose-6-phosphate kinase (phosphofructokinase [PFK]) has been proved to be located exclusively within the extramitochondrial compartment of the cell. In spite of this fact, two fractions of PFK can be extracted separately from skeletal muscle as well as from heart. In Figure 1, conditions and results of the fractionated extraction of PFK from white rabbit skeletal muscle have been

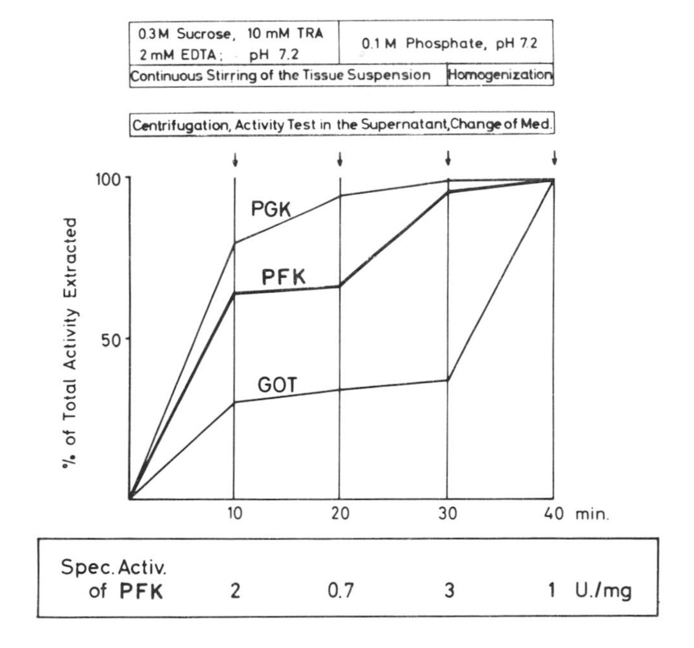

Figure 1. Schematical representation of a fractionated extraction of rabbit skeletal muscle. Enzyme activities as extracted under various conditions (arrows) have been plotted as percentage of their total extractable activity against the time course of the extraction. Specific activities of PFK as determined in the different supernatants, are given in the bottom line.

summarized schematically. For comparison, the extraction procedure of two other enzymes, phosphoglycerate kinase (PGK) and glutamate-oxaloacetate-transaminase (GOT), has been included in this demonstration. The principle of the method illustrated in Figure 1 consists of a stepwise extraction of extra- and intramitochondrial enzyme activities (1,2,3). For this reason, the tissue is passed carefully through a special meat grinder and is then suspended and stirred in the 20-fold volume of an isotonic extracting medium of physiological pH. Successive incubations of the tissue in media of rising ionic strength lead to a complete extraction of extramitochondrial enzymes before the extraction of intramitochondrial enzymes is initiated by the mechanical disintegration of the tissue. As is clearly shown in the case of GOT, extra- and intramitochondrial activities are thus eluted separately from the tissue. A biphasic extraction also occurs in the case of PFK. However, the two fractions of this enzyme which can be eluted separately are both derived from the extramitochondrial space. A first fraction of PFK is set free when the pre-extracted tissue is then transferred into a phosphate buffer of relatively high ionic strength (μ - 0.25). This observation is of interest for several reasons. For instance, it may be suggested that the fraction of PFK which can only be extracted by high ionic strength media is present within the cell in an aggregate condition different from that of more easily extracted fractions. Binding to structural proteins of the muscle, as has been shown in the case of aldolase (4), may explain the special conditions which are necessary in order to extract the enzyme completely. In consequence it cannot be excluded that the two fractions of PFK which can be extracted under different conditions indicate two different types of location within the extramitochondrial compartment. Whether such a difference is related only to the presence of a soluble and of a bound fraction of PFK at the site of the contractile filaments, or also extends to multiple location remains an open question at present.

In this connection, a parallel may be drawn between the extractibility of PFK and creatine kinase (CK) in muscle. As a matter of fact, in skeletal muscle and heart the extractibility of CK resembles that of PFK. Furthermore, it could be shown that the fraction of CK which, as in the case of PFK can only be extracted by high ionic strength media, is related to the external mitochondrial membrane (3). Nevertheless, the suggestion of a corresponding type of location in the case of the less easily extracted fraction of PFK would be speculative at present, although it might be indicated by the findings described for creatine kinase.

Another point which should be considered is the question of whether the fraction of PFK which is extractable at high ionic strength represents an inactive form of the enzyme. A definite answer to this question is complicated by the fact that the conditions of the extraction procedure are certainly non-physiological. Therefore, inactivation of the enzyme might occur during the extractions, for example by lowering the ionic strength below a critical value. That this is not the case is shown in Figure 2.

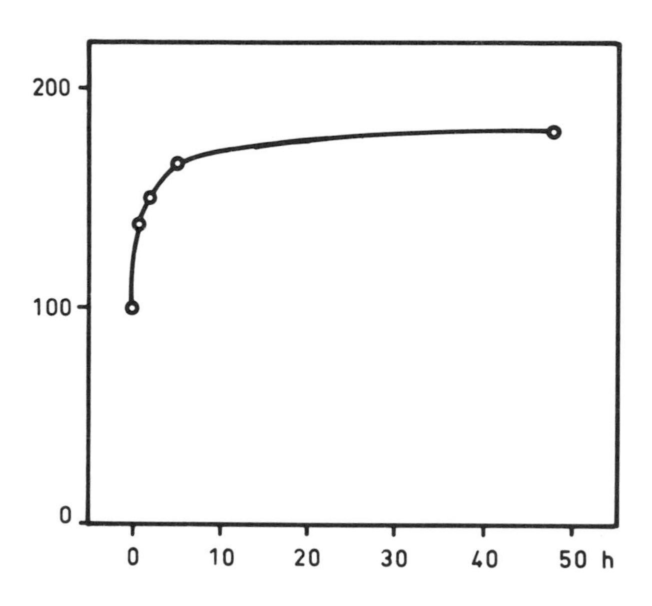

Figure 2. Time dependent increase of PFK activity in the clear supernatant of a pigeon breast muscle homogenate prepared in a 0.1 M phosphate buffer, pH 7.2.

Here a typical experiment is shown which demonstrates the activation of the enzyme even when extracted at high ionic strength. The time-dependent increase of PFK activity in a crude extract from pigeon breast muscle is evident. The extract had been prepared by homogenization of the muscle in a 0.1 M phosphate buffer, pH 7.2. Immediately after homogenization, the activity of the PFK was measured in the homogenate and the value obtained was made equal to 100 per cent (first point in the curve of Figure 2). The homogenate was then centrifuged at 10^5 g and further activity tests were performed at various times in the clear supernatant. As can be seen, an increase to about 180 per cent of the initial activity does occur during the first hours after extraction. The fact that similar increases in the activity of PFK are also observed after the enzyme has been purified by $(NH_4)_2SO_4$ precipitation and the precipitated enzyme redissolved in a phosphate buffer, suggests that this type of activation is due to changes of conformation, probably the dissociation of an inactive complex.

We have taken advantage of the special extractibility of PFK in purifying the enzyme by different methods. Three methods of purification have been applied:

1) A chromatographic purification on a DEAE-Sephadex anion exchange column, providing enzyme preparations with a specific activity of about 110 units/mg of protein (2);

2) A purification by means of acetone fractionation and $(NH_4)_2SO_4$ precipitation providing enzyme preparations with a specific activity of about 100 units/mg of protein;

3) A purification by means of heat fractionation and subsequent $(NH_4)_2SO_4$ precipitation. This method leads to PFK preparations with a specific activity of about 80 to 90 units/mg of protein (5).

Interestingly enough, all the three methods of purification lead to enzyme preparations which differ with respect to structural and catalytic properties (5). In Figure 3 ultraviolet absorption spectra of two different preparations of PFK from rabbit skeletal muscle are compared. The preparation with the absorption maximum at 278 mμ has been purified by method 3. While the enzyme prepared by acetone fractionation and subsequent $(NH_4)_2SO_4$ precipitation shows an absorption spectrum which resembles more or less that of a nucleic acid, as a matter of fact, it could be proven that the low absorbancy quotient, A_{280}/A_{260} of 0.68, of this enzyme preparation is due to the presence of a bound nucleic acid (5). Thus it has been possible to split off a compound from the enzyme with the absorption maximum at 261 mμ which reveals the typical ultraviolet absorption spectrum of a nucleic acid (See Figure 4). So far, the splitting off of this compound could only be achieved by heating the preparation for 80 minutes to 75°. In addition, the absorption spectrum of the heat precipitated protein redissolved in a 1 per cent aqueous solution of dodecylsulfate is demonstrated in the same illustration (dotted line). A distinct shoulder in this absorption spectrum clearly indicates that the separation of the nucleic acid protein complex has not yet been completed.

The shape of the absorption spectrum which characterizes the compound split off from the enzyme, the position of absorption minima and maxima, as well as pH-dependent shifts of the latter, reveal the complex nature of this compound. The

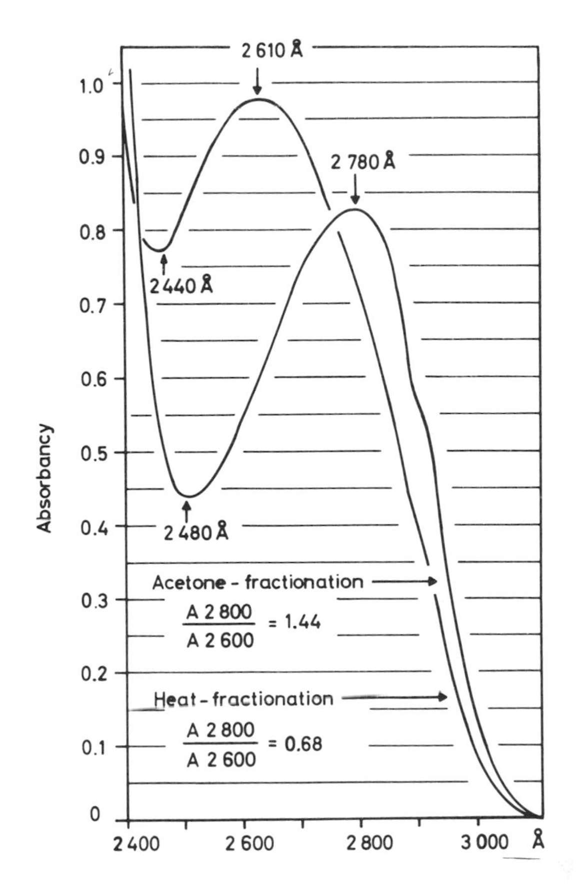

Figure 3. Absorption spectra of two differently prepared samples of PFK. In the case of the acetone-treated enzyme the protein concentration is 0.56 mg/ml. It is 0.42 mg/ml in the case of the enzyme which has been purified by heat fractionation.

extremely low absorbancy quotient A_{280}/A_{260} of the intact enzyme (See Figure 3) suggests that the high absorption of 261 mμ is due rather to the presence of a nucleic acid than to the presence of a mononucleotide. From the quantitative evaluation of the 261 mμ absorption of the compound split off from the enzyme, an approximate calculation of the chain length of the nucleic acid can be performed. Thus, a ratio of at least 20 moles of mononucleotide per 100,000 grams of protein has been calculated (5). A preliminary analysis of the nucleic acid has been undertaken by ion exchange chromatography of the alkaline hydrolysate on a Dowex-1 x 8 column. As a first result, several mononucleotides have been separated. The identity of these compounds, however, has still to be elucidated.

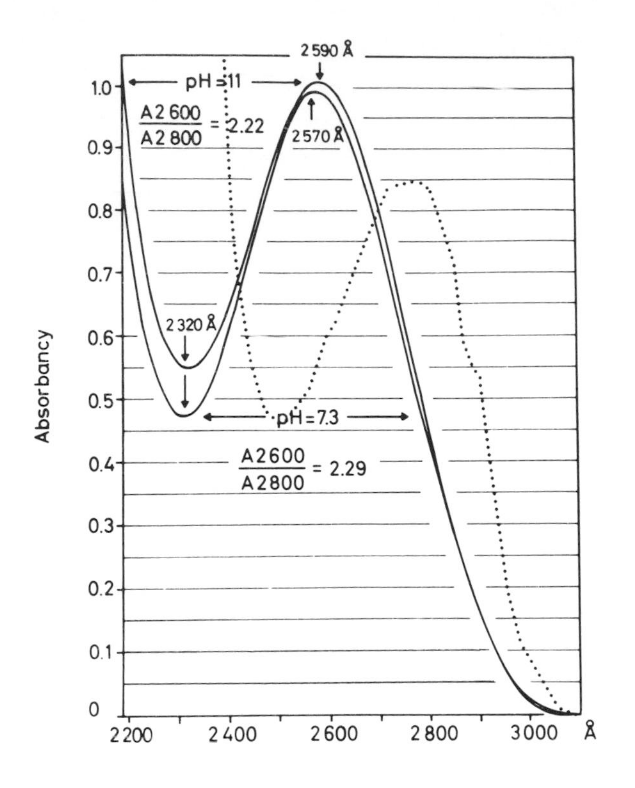

Figure 4. Absorption spectra at pH 7.3 and 11 of the nucleic acid component of PFK as separated from the protein by heat denaturation (full lines). The absorption spectrum of the heat denaturated protein which has been redissolved in 1 per cent dodecylsulfate, is illustrated by the dotted line.

In summary, it can be stated that depending on the method chosen for purification, two types of PFK have been prepared at high and comparable purity from rabbit skeletal muscle: an enzyme which has been characterized as a nucleic acid protein complex or nucleoprotein, and an enzyme which by its absorption spectrum is characterized as a pure protein. These findings pose the question of whether the two different PFK preparations obtained by different methods represent two forms of the enzyme which coexist under physiological conditions in the muscle cell, or whether one of the two has to be envisaged as an artificial product due to changes which are caused by the procedure of purification. As a matter of fact the two preparations of PFK which are compared in Figure 3 represent extremes. In a series of experiments, preparations of highly purified PFK have also been obtained which show absorption quotients, A_{280}/A_{260}, the values of which lie between 0.68 and 1.44 as shown in Figure 5.

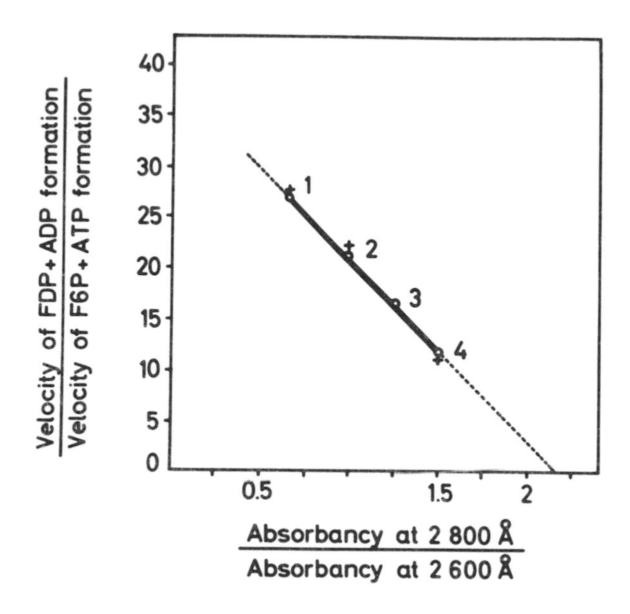

Figure 5. Activity ratio of forward to backward reaction of PFK plotted against the absorbancy quotient A_{280}/A_{260} for different preparations of the enzyme. Points and crosses mark measurements which have been performed at different times.

These observations indicate that the nucleic acid can be split off partially or completely depending upon the method of purification. Thus, prolonged treatment of the enzyme with acetone in the course of the acetone fractionation leads to enzyme preparations with a higher absorbancy quotient A_{280}/A_{260}. On the other hand, the nucleic acid rich preparation of PFK which is obtained by heat fractionation and subsequent $(NH_4)_2SO_4$ precipitation in the alkaline, is rather resistant to procedures which usually are known to separate complexes of nucleotides or nucleic acid and protein, for example, treatment with charcoal or chromatography on a DEAE-Sephadex exchange column. Therefore, we can exclude neither the suggestion that PFK is present in the cell in an original state as a nucleoprotein nor the hypothesis that the enzyme exists in two forms which are probably transformed into each other. With respect to the biphasic extractibility of the enzyme, as described above, this latter possibility might be of interest.

So far, only the structural differences between the two preparations of PFK have been discussed. Naturally, the question arises of whether functional differences exist between the enzyme free of nucleic acid and the enzyme which has been characterized as a nucleoprotein. This question is justified, since it has been reported that the two forms of PFK which have been highly purified are comparable with respect to their specific activities. On the other hand, a very distinct difference between these two forms of the enzyme is found when the catalytic properties are compared. This difference, however, is related to the quality of PFK which in itself already appears to be of special interest. It is concerned with the catalysis of the reverse reaction.

It has been found (5) that PFK not only catalyses the reaction:

fructose-6-phosphate + ATP ⟶ fructose-1,6-diphosphate + ADP (1)

but also catalyses the reaction:

fructose-1,6-diphosphate + ADP ⟶ fructose-6-phosphate + ATP (2)

The catalytic activity of PFK in the "backward reaction" (Eq. 2) could be proven by measuring the amounts of F-6-P as well as that of ATP which are formed under appropriate conditions in the presence of PFK (5). Thus, the stoichiometric formation of F-6-P and ATP, as well as the fact that the rate of formation of these two products is proportional to the quantity of the enzyme present, could be shown (5).

The two forms of PFK which have been prepared from rabbit skeletal muscle, as described above, have been compared with respect to their activity in catalyzing the backward reaction. (Eq. 2). Although the enzyme free of nucleic acid and the enzyme present as nucleoprotein are comparable with respect to their activity in the forward reaction, as shown by their nearly identical values of specific activity in the forward reaction (Eq. 1), marked differences are found when the two enzymes are compared with regard to their activity in catalyzing the backward reaction (Eq. 2). Thus, the specific activity of the enzyme prepared as pure protein is significantly higher in the backward reaction (Eq. 2) than that of the enzyme present as nucleoprotein. This difference is more impressive if the ratios between the catalytic activity in the forward and the catalytic activity in the backward reaction are calculated for the different enzyme preparations. Interestingly enough, there is a linear relation between the "forward to backward ratio" and the absorbancy quotient A_{280}/A_{260} for the different enzyme preparations which have been compared so far. This linear relation is presented graphically in Figure 5, where the "forward to backward ratio" has been plotted against the absorbancy quotient A_{280}/A_{260}. It is clear that the initial reaction velocities measured under constant conditions are not true maximum velocities of forward and backward reactions. Shifts in the forward to backward ratio as observed under the experimental conditions do therefore, not affect the thermodynamics of the reaction. This is evident from values of V_{max} in the backward reaction, which have been extrapolated in the case of the different PFK preparations from Lineweaver-Burk plots. Preliminary studies indicate that the differences which are found in the apparent reaction velocities of the backward reaction are due to the varied sensitivity of the different PFK preparations against inhibition by ADP.

A further difference of free nucleic acid and nucleic acid containing preparations of PFK is related to the phenomenon of AMP stimulation on the ATP-inhibited enzyme in the forward reaction at low concentrations of F-6-P (6,7,8). Comparing the inhibitory effect of ATP in different preparations, only slight variations are found. However, marked differences of the preparations consist, in regard to the stimulatory effect of 5'-AMP, of the ATP-inhibited enzyme. Thus, maximum activation of the ATP-inhibited enzyme is produced by 5'-AMP in the case of the nucleic acid containing enzyme, whereas no or scarcely any activation is observed in the preparation free of nucleic acid. This finding may be envisaged as a further proof of the functional significance of the nucleic acid component of PFK.

References

1. Pette, D., Vogell, W., and Brandau, H., Vth Internat. Congress of Electron Microscopy, Philadelphia, 1962.

2. Guerritore, A., Pette, D., and Bücher, Th., Boll. Soc. Ital. Biol. Sper., 38, 1763 (1962).

3. Pette, D., in Symposium on the Regulation of Metabolic Processes in Mitochondria, Bari, 1965, Elsevier Publishing Co., Amsterdam, in the press.

4. Bauer, A. C., Pette, D., Roisen, F., and Amberson, W. R., Fed. Proc., 23, 1254 (1964).

5. Hofer, H. W., and Pette, D., Life Sciences, in the press.

6. Passonneau, J. V., and Lowry, O. H., Biochem. Biophys. Res. Commun., 7, 10 (1962).

7. Mansour, T. E., J. Biol. Chem., 238, 2285 (1963).

8. Ramaiah, A., Hathaway, J. A., and Atkinson, D. E., J. Biol. Chem., 239, 3619 (1964).

MULTIPLE FORMS OF HEART PHOSPHOFRUCTOKINASE*

Tag E. Mansour

From the Department of Pharmacology, Stanford University
School of Medicine, Palo Alto, California

In our previous investigations (1) on phosphofructokinase from the liver fluke, *Fasciola hepatica*, it was reported that the enzyme can be activated by cyclic 3',5'-AMP in two different ways: 1) activation of assay levels of phosphofructokinase inhibited by ATP which I will call "kinetic activation"; 2) activation through a direct effect on a concentrated inactive form of the enzyme which I will call "structural activation." Under the latter conditions, this kinetic effect of cyclic 3',5'-AMP during enzyme assay was excluded because of the dilution of the nucleotide to a subeffective concentration.

Experiments reported later from our laboratory and others indicated that kinetic activation can be demonstrated with phosphofructokinase from the guinea pig heart (2), rat brain (3), yeast (4,5) and *E. coli* (6). Kinetic data suggested the presence of regulatory sites on the enzyme. Attempts to determine enzyme activation of phosphofructokinase isolated soon after the animal was sacrificed failed because the enzyme was fully active. In the time given to me, I will review briefly some of our recent efforts to study different forms of phosphofructokinase from the mammalian heart.

Active and Inactive Forms of Phosphofructokinase

Effect of adenylic nucleotides and of hexose phosphate esters. Partially purified preparations of guinea pig heart phosphofructokinase (2) when incubated at pH values which ranged from 5.8 to 6.5 lost 90-95 per cent of their activity almost instantaneously. When the inactive enzyme was incubated at pH 7.5 to pH 8.2 at 37° for 10 min, only a small fraction of the activity lost could be recovered (approximately 2-10 per cent). Adenylic nucleotides which included ATP, ADP, AMP and cyclic 3',5'-AMP caused a marked increase in the

*Supported by USPHS AI 04214 and GM-K3-3848 and a grant from the Santa Clara County Heart Association.

amount of enzyme activity recovered. In addition to the adenylic nucleotides, the hexose phosphate, fructose-1,6-di-P and fructose-6-P, also accelerated enzyme reactivation. A combination of a hexose phosphate and an adenylic nucleotide was found to be much more effective in reactivation of the enzyme than either nucleotide or hexose or hexose phosphate alone (7) (Table I).

Effect of Hexose Phosphate and Adenylic Nucleotides on Reactivation of Phosphofructokinase

Enzyme assay, enzyme inactivation and reactivation, and other experimental methods were carried out as described before (7). Enzyme activity before inactivation was 170 units per ml. Enzyme inactivation was carried out at pH 5.9 to an activity of 5.4 units per ml. Enzyme reactivation was at pH 7.5 and resulted with "no additions" to reactivation of approximately 2 per cent of the original activity. Phosphofructokinase-reactivated values were calculated after subtraction of the "no additions" values.

Expt. No.	Additions	Phosphofructokinase reactivated in 10 min (units/ml)
1	10^{-3} M ADP	21.4
	10^{-4} M FDP	22.6
	10^{-5} M FDP	7.2
	10^{-3} M ADP + 10^{-4} M FDP	97.0
	10^{-3} M ADP + 10^{-5} M FDP	56.0
2	10^{-3} M ATP	24.0
	10^{-3} M F-6-P	14.0
	10^{-4} M F-6-P	4.5
	10^{-3} M ATP + 10^{-3} M F-6-P	73.0
	10^{-3} M ATP + 10^{-4} M F-6-P	72.0
3	10^{-3} M cyclic 3',5'-AMP	12.5
	10^{-3} M F-6-P	14.0
	10^{-3} M cyclic 3',5'-AMP + 10^{-3} M F-6-P	43.0

The optimum mixture for enzyme reactivation was the two products of the phosphofructokinase reaction, fructose-1,6-di-P and ADP. The substrates fructose-6-P and ATP could also re-activate the enzyme but at a lesser degree than the products of the reaction. Glucose-6-P, glucose-1-P and dextrose had no significant effect on enzyme reactivation. These results indicate (7) that a multivalent system for enzyme regulation is present in phosphofructokinase. This is analogous to what has been demonstrated already with glutamic dehydrogenase (8,9).

Effect of heart extracts on enzyme reactivation. Fresh heart extracts, when added with ATP and Mg^{++}, caused a marked increase in enzyme reactivation (Table II). ATP could be replaced by ADP, AMP and cyclic 3',5'-AMP. Furthermore, Mg^{++} was not required for enzyme reactivation. Precipitation of the proteins in the heart extract by perchloric acid reduced the effect of the fresh heart extract by 70 per cent while boiling reduced the effect by 40 per cent. Thus, the effect of fresh heart extracts on reactivation of the enzyme could be at least partly due to a thermostable fraction in the heart. This was further suggested by the fact that dialysis of heart extracts reduced its ability to reactivate the enzyme. It is therefore possible that the effect of the fresh heart extract in accelerating phosphofructokinase reactivation might be due, at least in part, to the presence of a hexose phosphate or another tissue component which might enhance the effect of the adenylic nucleotides.

TABLE II

Effect of Heart Extracts on Reactivation of Phosphofructokinase

Enzyme assay, enzyme inactivation and reactivation, and preparation of heart extracts were carried out as described before (7). Enzyme activity before inactivation was 170 units/ml. Enzyme inactivation was carried out at pH 5.9. Enzyme reactivation was at pH 7.5. ATP (2.5×10^{-4} M) and $MgCl_2$ (5×10^{-4} M) were added where indicated.

Additions	Phosphofructokinase reactivated in 10 min (units/ml)
None	0
ATP/Mg^{++}	2.3
Fresh heart extract	5.2
Fresh heart extract + ATP/Mg^{++}	47.5

Activation of phosphofructokinase activity in ethanol precipitate of sheep heart extracts. Activated phosphofructokinase extracts from the sheep heart were precipitated with ethanol between 8 and 13 per cent. Phosphofructokinase in this fraction was not fully active. Addition of 10^{-4} M ATP to this fraction always resulted in 50-100 per cent increase in enzyme activation (Table III). This process occurred at 0° immediately.

TABLE III

Activation of Sheep Heart Phosphofructokinase

Expt. No.	No ATP (units/mg protein)	With 10^{-4} M ATP (units/mg protein)
1	4.3	9.3
2	4.0	8.7
3	4.8	9.4
4	4.5	7.8
5	5.8	7.9

Properties of Purified Phosphofructokinase

Activated phosphofructokinase has been purified and crystallized from heart extracts prepared as described above. It was shown that purified heart phosphofructokinase is present in the form of aggregates. The following evidence suggests the presence of a monomer-polymer system in equilibrium.

(A) The enzyme in the presence of glycylglycine buffer (pH 6.9) showed a Schlieren pattern with one asymmetric peak with an S_{20w} value of 53.6. This pattern could be replaced by Schlieren patterns with multiple peaks in the presence of 2 x 10^{-3} M ATP and 4 x 10^{-3} M fructose-1,6-di-P. The Schlieren pattern had three peaks with S_{20w} values of 7, 38.7 and 44.4.

(B) The presence of sodium chloride 2 M in a solvent which favors a two peak pattern resulted in a Schlieren pattern with a single peak of 16.6 S. This was accompanied by a decrease in enzyme activity by 50 per cent. A direct effect of NaCl on the assay mixture was ruled out. Thus, NaCl causes a change in the structure and the activity of the enzyme. Removal of NaCl by dialysis resulted in restoration of the original Schlieren pattern and enzyme activity.

Sedimentation behavior of active and inactive forms of phosphofructokinase. The distribution of inactivated and fully active phosphofructokinase on sucrose gradient was analyzed by the method of Martin and Ames (10). Aldolase was used as a marker. The S_{20w} determined for active phosphofructokinase at pH 6.9 was 16.7 or more, depending on the enzyme concentration. The enzyme collected from the gradient in tris maleate buffer at pH 5.8 was inactive and had to be reactivated for assay. The peak for the active enzyme at pH 5.8 coincided with that of aldolase which gives it an S_{20w} value of 8.79. These results strongly suggest that phosphofructokinase can undergo reversible change from active to inactive form (7).

Solubilization and Activation of Phosphofructokinase

Homogenates of sheep heart received in the laboratory from the slaughter house were found to contain low phosphofructokinase activity. No significant activity was demonstrated in the soluble fraction or the residue of these homogenates. When the residue was incubated at 37° for 20 min with ATP and $MgSO_4$, high phosphofructokinase activity was observed in the supernatant fluid of the incubate. This indicates that the enzyme in the sheep heart, when received in the laboratory, was present in the inactive form and that it can be extracted from the residue as the active enzyme. The supernatant fluid of this incubate had a reasonably high specific activity and was used as a starting material for further enzyme purification and crystallization (11). Experiments on the conditions necessary for enzyme activation and solubilization showed that AMP, ADP or cyclic 3',5'-AMP can replace ATP in the activating solubilizing mixture. $MgSO_4$ in high concentration (0.1 M) in the absence of ATP was also effective in solubilizing and activating the enzyme.

(C) The sedimentation coefficient of phosphofructokinase was found to be concentration dependent. This was demonstrated at concentrations below 1 mg/ml in sucrose gradients. The lowest sedimentation coefficient obtained was 15.2 for an amount of protein of 6 μg or less placed on a 4.8 ml sucrose gradient.

The results so far obtained on crude, partially purified and purified enzyme preparations indicate that phosphofructokinase is endowed with many properties which make it well adapted for regulation in the cell. Three possible mechanisms for regulation can be recognized here: first, kinetic properties of the enzyme; second, reversible dissociation of the active enzyme to an inactive enzyme; third, aggregation of the enzyme in a monomer-polymer system in equilibrium. The fact that a common effector on these three effects are the adenylic nucleotides and the hexose phosphates would argue for a primary change in the molecular configuration of phosphofructokinase induced by these agents.

REFERENCES

1. Mansour, T.E., and Mansour, J.M., J. Biol. Chem., 237, 629 (1962).
2. Mansour, T.E., J. Biol. Chem., 238, 2285 (1963).
3. Passoneau, J.V., and Lowry, O.H., Biochem. Biophys. Res. Comm., 7, 10 (1962).
4. Vinuela, E., Salas, M.L. and Sols, A., Biochem. Biophys. Res. Comm., 12, 140 (1963).
5. Ramaiah, A., Hathaway, J.A., and Atkinson, D.E., J. Biol. Chem., 239, 3619 (1964).
6. Atkinson, D.E., and Walton, G.M., J. Biol. Chem., 240, 757 (1965).
7. Mansour, T.E., J. Biol. Chem., 240, 2165 (1965).
8. Frieden, C., J. Biol. Chem., 238, 3286 (1963).
9. Tomkins, G.M., Yielding, K.L., Talal, N., and Curran, J., Cold Springs Harbor Symposia on Quantitative Biology, XXVIII, 461 (1963).
10. Martin, R.G., and Ames, B.N., J. Biol. Chem., 236, 1372 (1961).
11. Mansour, T.E., Wakid, N., and Sprouse, H.M., Biochem. Biophys. Res. Comm., 19, 728 (1965).

ON THE MECHANISMS OF INHIBITION AND ACTIVATION OF PHOSPHOFRUCTOKINASE IN NOVIKOFF ASCITES TUMOR CELLS*

Ray Wu

Department of Biochemistry, The Public Health Research Institute of the City of New York, Inc., New York 9, N. Y.

The phosphofructokinase (PFK) of Novikoff ascites tumor homogenates showed several unique properties which permitted an examination of the mechanism of inhibition and activation of this enzyme in greater detail.

It has been reported that PFK from several mammalian tissues is subject to inhibition by ATP (1) as well as stimulation by P_i, AMP, cyclic 3,5-AMP, fructose-6-P (F-6-P) and fructose-1, 6-di-P (2-5). On examining the ATP inhibition of Novikoff ascites tumor PFK, a lag in the onset of inhibition by ATP was observed. The results given in Table I demonstrate that the initial activity of PFK differed by 3-fold at low and high levels of ATP, but later on a 25-fold difference was observed. At 0.5 mM ATP, the rate of PFK reaction was constant with time and therefore considered uninhibited. Starting from 1 mM ATP, the rate decreased with time during the assay. The higher the ATP concentration the sharper the decrease in rate.

In the experiments of Figure 1, PFK was assayed in the presence of 3 mM ATP and 0.06 mM F-6-P. The lower curve of the figure shows that the rate of the reaction fell off gradually with time. The rate was lowered to about 20 per cent of the initial rate by 3 minutes, and to less than 5 per cent after another 5 minutes. The addition of P_i (6 mM) and AMP (0.3 mM), at the time indicated by the arrow, restored the activity to the initial rate, indicating that no irreversible inactivation of PFK had occurred. Although either P_i (curve 2) or AMP (curve 3) when added at the beginning of the assay, partially prevented the drop in the activity, the combination of both (curve 4) gave the highest rate. These observations again demonstrated that the PFK in this tumor is not immediately inhibited by ATP in contrast to the immediate onset of inhibition observed in extracts of Ehrlich ascites tumor and rat kidney.

* This investigation was supported by Public Heatlh Service Research Grant No. CA-05706 from the National Cancer Institute.

TABLE I

Activity of PFK at different levels of ATP and $MgCl_2$

Assay mixture		PFK activity*		
ATP conc.	$MgCl_2$ conc.	0.5-1.5 min	1.5-2.5 min	2.5-3.5 min
mM	mM			
0.5	0.75	200	220	222
1.0	1.5	164	145	120
1.5	2.25	146	119	65
2.0	3.0	122	75	34
3.0	4.5	93	41	17
4.5	6.75	71	19	8

PFK activity was assayed as in the control experiment described in Figure 1, except that the levels of ATP and $MgCl_2$ varied as indicated.

* Expressed as mμmole DPNH oxidation per min per mg protein.

The concentrations of P_i or AMP required for maximal stimulation of PFK were examined in order to determine whether P_i and AMP act at the same or different sites on PFK. As illustrated in Table II, 6 mM P_i or 0.3 mM AMP gave maximal stimulation. However, the addition of saturating levels of both P_i and AMP resulted in almost additive stimulation. These data suggest, therefore, that P_i and AMP act at different sites of the enzyme.

It was of interest to determine whether ATP or the ATP-Mg^{++} complex was the true inhibitor of PFK. Since both ATP and Mg^{++} were required for the assay of PFK activity, advantage was taken of the lag period observed in the inhibition of PFK by ATP. The PFK preparation (dialyzed supernatant solution of Novikoff ascites tumor) was preincubated at 26° for 2 minutes with ATP (3 mM) alone, Mg^{++} (4.5 mM) alone, or ATP (3 mM) plus Mg^{++} (4.5 mM). Following this preincubation, an aliquot of the mixture (0.03 ml) was diluted with 1 ml of the assay medium and the PFK activity assayed in two ways, (A) in the presence of a high level of ATP (3 mM ATP and 4.5 mM $MgCl_2$), and (B) in the presence of a low (non-inhibitory) level of ATP (0.5 mM ATP and 0.75 mM $MgCl_2$).

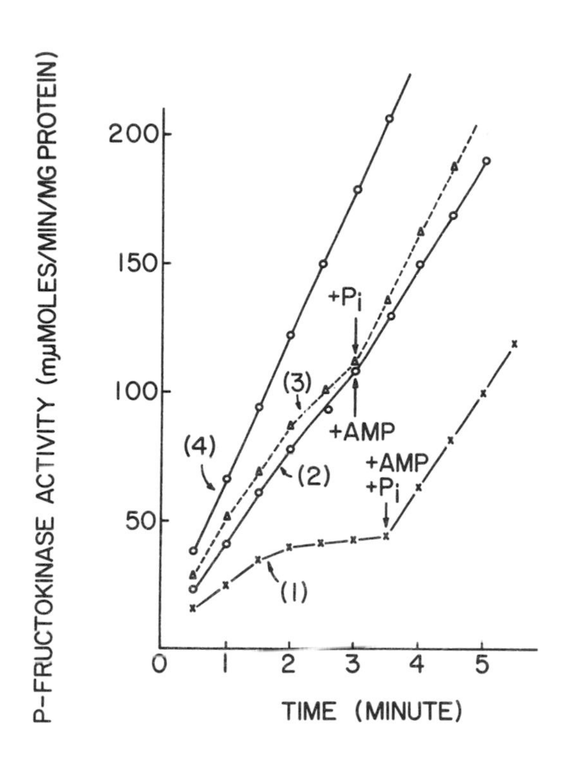

Figure 1. Time course for the assay of PFK in Novikoff ascites tumor. PFK activity was assayed spectrophotometrically (in 1 ml final volume) at 26° C in a system which contained ATP, 3 mM; $MgCl_2$, 4.5 mM; glucose-6-P and fructose-6-P (kept near equilibrium with P-glucoisomerase), 0.24 mM; triethanolamine buffer, pH 7.4, 25 mM; DPNH, 0.14 mM; α-glycero-P dehydrogenase, 0.5 unit; glyceraldehyde-3-P isomerase, 1.0 unit; aldolase, 0.2 unit. Dialyzed Novikoff ascites tumor homogenates (10,000 x g supernatant solution), 50 μg of protein, was added to initiate the reaction (control experiment, lower curve). The two curves in the middle represent experiments to which P_i (6 mM) or AMP (0.3 mM) were added at zero time. After the reactions have proceeded for 3 or 4 min, a second addition of P_i or AMP, or a combination of both, was made as indicated by the arrows. PFK activity is expressed as mμmoles of DPNH oxidation per mg protein.

TABLE II

PFK activity in the presence and absence of P_i and AMP

P_i	AMP	PFK activity*	o/o Stimulation of PFK activity
(mM)	(mM)		
0	0	50	0
3		140	180
6		210	320
9		214	324
	0.1	160	220
	0.3	240	380
	0.4	240	380
6	0.3	345	590
9	0.4	340	580

Novikoff ascites tumor homogenate (10,000 x g supernatant solution was fractionated with ammonium sulfate, and the fraction precipitated between 25-50 per cent saturation was resuspended in 50 mM triethanolamine buffer containing 5 mM EDTA. PFK activity was assayed as in the control experiment described in Figure 1. The rates of PFK activity were fairly constant within the first 3 minutes.

* Expressed as mμmole DPNH oxidation per minute per mg protein.

(A) The results shown in Figure 2 represent the measurement of PFK activity at a high level of ATP. Curve 1 represents a control experiment, in which the PFK preparation was preincubated for 2 minutes in the absence of inhibitor, and as expected (cf. Figure 1), the rate of the reaction fell off gradually with time, reaching a state of severe inhibition at 3 minutes. Incubation of the enzyme preparation with either ATP alone (curve 2) or with ATP plus $MgCl_2$ (curve 4) resulted in an immediate and severe inhibition of PFK activity. Frequently, preincubation with ATP plus $MgCl_2$ was found to give a more marked inhibition than with ATP alone. Unexpectedly, preincubation of the PFK preparation with $MgCl_2$ alone also resulted in considerable inhibition of PFK activity, although the inhibition was not as severe as in the case of preincubation with ATP or ATP plus $MgCl_2$

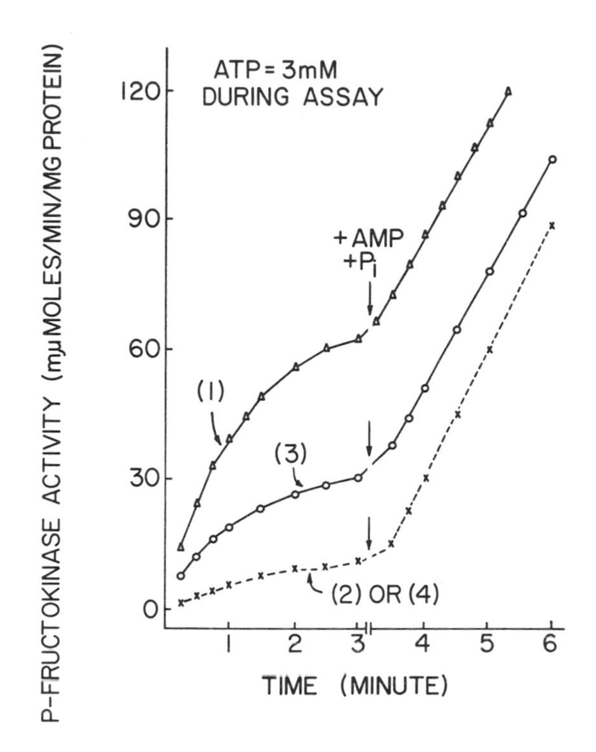

Figure 2. Effects of preincubation of PFK preparation with ATP, $MgCl_2$ or ATP-$MgCl_2$ on the enzyme activity. PFK preparation (0.3 ml with 1.5 mg protein/ml as in Figure 1) was preincubated at 26° for 2 min with no addition (curve 1), 3 mM ATP (curve 2), 4.5 mM $MgCl_2$ (curve 3), or 3 mM ATP plus 4.5 mM $MgCl_2$ (curve 4). After preincubation, 0.03 ml was assayed in 1 ml of the assay medium as described in Figure 2.

(B) Figure 3 summarizes the results obtained by measuring the PFK activity at a low level of ATP (0.5 mM) which did not inhibit PFK activity (curve 1). In experiment 2 the PFK preparation was preincubated with ATP alone. This experiment shows that after preincubation with 3 mM ATP, the enzyme remained severely inhibited, in spite of the fact that the assay system now contained a non-inhibitory level of ATP. After approximately a minute, the activity of PFK was accelerated, due to the gradual reversal of the inhibitory effect of ATP. A more effective reversal of this inhibition was achieved after the addition of P_i and AMP. Since the binding of ATP by PFK is likely to be a very fast process, the observed lag of approximately a minute for the onset of inhibition (Figure 1, curve 1), as well as the reversal of inhibition (Figure 3, curve 2), prior to the addition

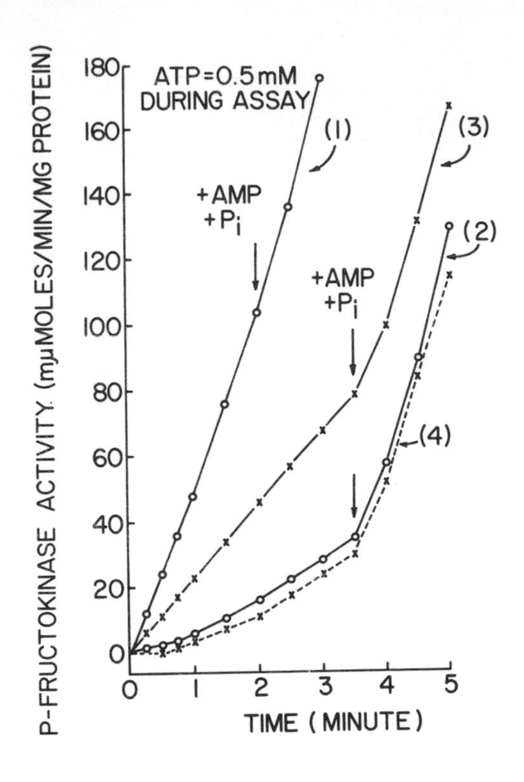

Figure 3. Effects of preincubation of PFK preparation with ATP, $MgCl_2$ or ATP-$MgCl_2$ on the enzyme activity. PFK preparation was preincubated as in Figure 2, and then assayed in a system as described in Figure 2, except that the ATP concentration was lowered to 0.5 mM and the $MgCl_2$ concentration lowered to 0.75 mM.

of AMP and P_i, may represent an ATP-induced conformational change of PFK, which follows the binding or dissociation of ATP. Curve 3 represents an experiment in which the PFK preparation was preincubated with $MgCl_2$. Since the preincubation medium contained 5 mM EDTA to protect PFK from irreversible inactivation, the observed inhibition of PFK following the preincubation with $MgCl_2$ may be due to either the EDTA-Mg^{++} complex or Mg^{++} itself. The former appeared to be the true inhibitor, since at 1 mM EDTA, little or no inhibition by Mg^{++} was observed. EDTA alone up to 5 mM had no effect on the activity. It should be emphasized that the degree of inhibition obtained by preincubating the enzyme preparation with ATP and $MgCl_2$ was identical with either 1 or 5 mM EDTA.

It is clear that no irreversible inactivation of PFK occurred during the preincubation and the assay period, since the subsequent addition of P_i and AMP restored the enzyme activity to the level found prior to the preincubation.

Most of the experiments just presented here have been repeated with a partially purified preparation of PFK. The purification was achieved by passing 4 ml of the high speed supernatant solution of Novikoff ascites tumor through a sephadex G-200 column (6), 1.8 x 20 cm, which had been equilibrated with triethanolamine buffer (50 mM, pH 7.4) and EDTA (5 mM). The enzyme was eluted with the same buffer and 2 ml fractions were collected. Most of the PFK was collected in a volume of 6 ml after a void volume of 14 ml. Using this partially purified PFK, similar results were obtained, except that the lag period in the onset of inhibition by ATP was shorter and the concentration of ATP required for 50 per cent inhibition was somewhat lower, as compared to the unpurified PFK.

Proposed mechanism

Finally, an attempt is made to represent schematically the sequence of events involved in the inhibition and reactivation of Novikoff ascites tumor PFK, which incorporates some of the proposals originally made by Passonneau and Lowry (2,5) and by Mansour (4) in assuming that there are two ATP sites, a substrate site and an inhibitor site (or sites), and that P_i, F-6-P and other stimulators all can compete with ATP for the inhibitor site. In the hypothetical scheme presented in Figure 4, the active molecular species of PFK is depicted with adjacent but separate substrate sites for F-6-P and ATP. Two inhibitor sites are arbitrarily placed at opposite ends of the molecule. At low concentrations of ATP, only one of the inhibitor sites is occupied and the enzyme is only partially inhibited. In the presence of high concentrations of ATP, both inhibitor sites are occupied and the enzyme becomes severely inhibited. According to this scheme, attachment of ATP occurs at allosteric sites on the enzyme and results in a conformational change in the molecule of PFK such that the catalytic sites for F-6-P and ATP are now far apart, and the interaction of these two substrates becomes less likely. The lag observed before the onset of maximal inhibition may be a reflection of the time required for these conformational changes to occur.

P_i and AMP did not appreciably stimulate the activity of PFK unless the enzyme was already inhibited by ATP. Therefore, P_i and AMP are not considered as activators but rather as agents which displace ATP from the inhibitor sites and thus restore the enzyme to its original configuration. In the presence of

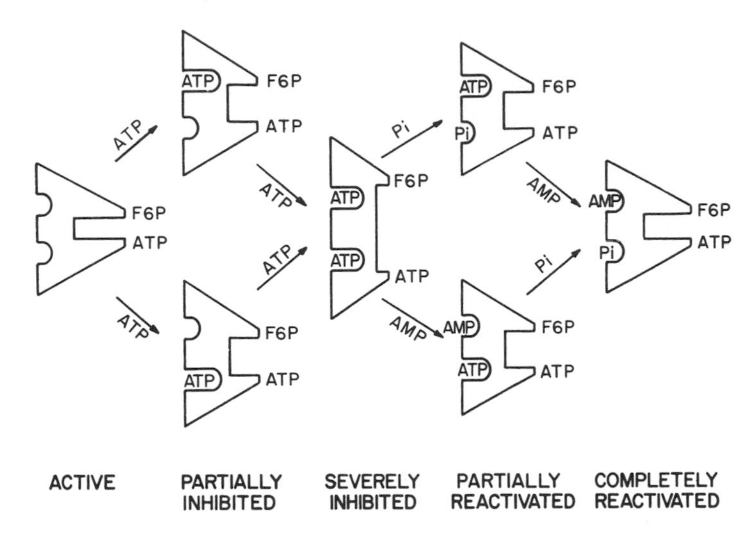

Figure 4. A model to represent the inhibition of PFK by ATP and the reversal of inhibition by P_i and AMP.

P_i, one ATP may be displaced from the inhibitor site resulting in partial reactivation of the enzyme. The displacement of the second ATP by AMP results in a completely reactivated enzyme. Similarly, a high level of F-6-P may exert its stimulatory effect by displacing both ATP from the inhibitor sites. In this scheme, ATP was placed in the inhibitor sites, though the ATP-Mg^{++} or EDTA-Mg^{++} complexes could also fit into these sites.

A modification of this scheme arises if it is assumed that P_i and/or AMP occupy sites different from the inhibitor sites for ATP, and that they function without actually displacing ATP from the enzyme. In fact, Passonneau and Lowry (5) have already postulated that AMP (but not P_i) occupies an enhancing site which is different from the ATP inhibitor site. It may be possible to differentiate these possibilities by the use of highly purified PFK, to test if radioactive ATP will be bound to the enzyme and if the subsequent addition of P_i and/or AMP actually displaces ATP from the enzyme.

Alternative mechanism

An ATP-dependent cleavage of the enzyme into inactive subunits, rather than or following the conformational changes proposed above, could also explain many of the observations, including the time lag. The proposed inactive subunits presumably can be formed under physiological conditions and are readily reactivated. Other experiments (to be presented elsewhere), carried out by preincubating ATP with different concentrations of the PFK preparations, have shown that the rate as well as the maximal degree of inhibition was considerably less with higher concentrations of PFK. These results may be interpreted in favor of an ATP-dependent cleavage of PFK into inactive subunits. Recently, subunit formation under somewhat more drastic conditions have been shown by incubating PFK at pH 5.8 (7) or with 2 M urea (8).

These studies have been limited to the mechanism of action of the ATP inhibition on the one hand and the release of this inhibition by AMP and P_i on the other. Experiments now under way are designed to examine other inhibitors (citrate) and activators (cyclic AMP) in relation to the proposed schemes.

REFERENCES

1. Lardy, H. A., and Parks, R. E., Jr., in Enzymes: Units of Biological Structure and Function (O. Gaebler, ed.), Academic Press, New York, 1956, p. 584.

2. Passonneau, J. V., and Lowry, O. H., Biochem. Biophys. Res. Commun., 7, 10 (1962).

3. Mansour, T. E., and Mansour, J. M., J. Biol. Chem., 237, 629 (1962).

4. Mansour, T. E., J. Biol. Chem., 238, 2285 (1963).

5. Passonneau, J. V., and Lowry, O. H., Biochem. Biophys. Res. Commun., 13, 372 (1963).

6. Uyeda, K., and Racker, E., in preparation.

7. Mansour, T. E., J. Biol. Chem., 240, 2165 (1965).

8. Ling, K. H., Marcus, F., and Lardy, H. A., J. Biol. Chem., 240, 1893 (1965).

CONTROL PROPERTIES OF PHOSPHOFRUCTOKINASE FROM SACCHAROMYCES CEREVISIA

Cyril L. Moore, Augustin Betz and Britton Chance

Johnson Research Foundation, University of Pennsylvania
Philadelphia, Pennsylvania

Data are presented here on the kinetic behavior of PFK relevant to the relationship of enzyme activity to the availability in the cell of substrates, activators and inhibitors of this enzyme. From the data of Betz and Chance (1) as well as from Cassuto and Chance (2), the evaluated concentrations of adenine nucleotides and glycolytic intermediates in the whole yeast cell as well as in extracts of sonicated cells are known. This enables an estimation of the effect which extremes in concentration of metabolites may have upon the enzyme *in vitro* and possibly relate to the activity *in situ*.

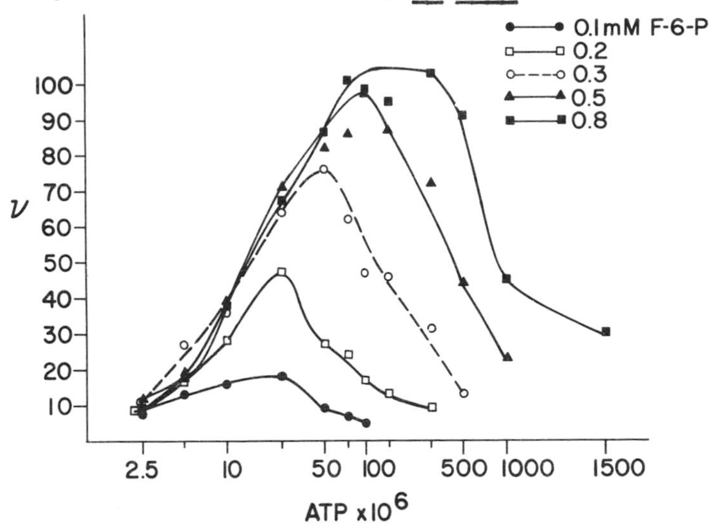

Figure 1. The inhibition of the PFK reaction by high concentrations of ATP, at various F-6-P concentrations. ATP concentrations are represented on a logarithmic scale. The enzyme activity was measured in a coupled system of excess aldolase, triose phosphate isomerase, and α-glycerophosphate dehydrogenase. The decrease in DPNH concentration was followed fluorometrically at 23° C. The system was maintained at pH 7.4.

Figure 1 shows the influence of ATP concentration on the PFK activity at several fixed F-6-P concentrations and in the absence of AMP. The inhibitory effect of ATP seen here is in agreement with the findings of Viñuela, et al. (3), using PFK from brewers yeast, of Ramaiah et al. (4) using the enzyme from Baker's yeast, and of Mansour and Mansour (5) using the enzyme from the liver fluke. The estimated concentration of ATP in the yeast cell fluctuates between 1.4 and 1.9 mM. In the yeast extract, the same maximal level is observed, but the minimum value can be as low as 0.3 mM as reported by Cassuto and Chance (2).

The inhibitory effect of ATP at concentrations above 0.025 mM can control PFK activity especially in systems where the F-6-P concentration is below 0.3 mM the maximal concentration in both the cell and the extract. This may be an oversimplification since the problem of compartmentation of ATP must be seriously considered as well as the stimulatory effect of AMP in such systems where the inhibition by ATP at concentrations dependent on the F-6-P concentration is evident as demonstrated in Figure 1. That F-6-P, localized at the enzyme site, may be of higher concentration that the overall value obtained for the whole cell is important and could therefore act (as shown in Figure 1) to release the inhibition of ATP, need not be further emphasized.

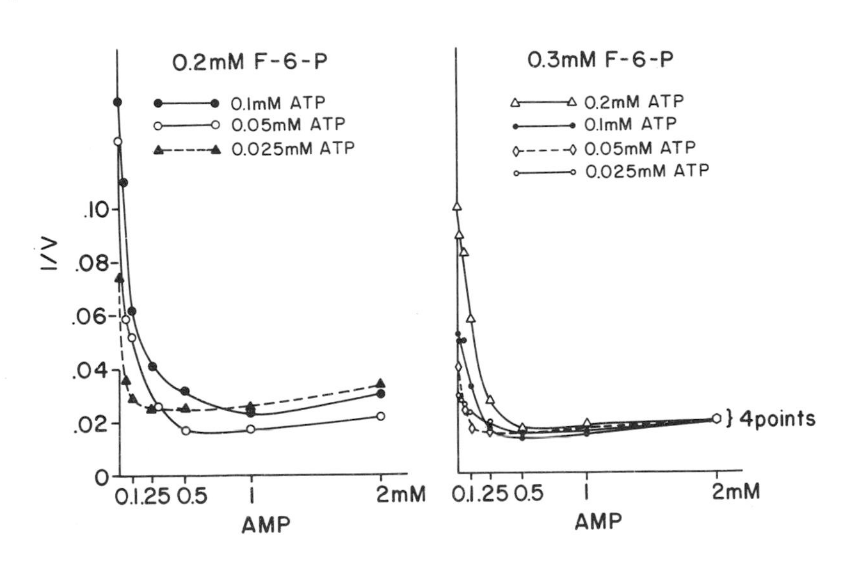

Figure 2. The release of ATP inhibition by AMP at two different concentrations of F-6-P. Enzyme activity was measured as described in Figure 1.

The effect of AMP is shown in Figure 2. Here, the release of ATP inhibition of the PFK activity by AMP is exemplified. From the extremes of ATP concentrations shown in the two sections of this figure representing two F-6-P concentrations, it can be concluded that the high ATP concentration is not severely critical as long as the AMP concentration is in the vicinity of 0.2 to 0.5 mM. These findings are contrary to the findings of Viñuela et al. (3) who noted a lack of effect by AMP on PFK. The concentration of AMP in the yeast cell is in the vicinity of 0.2 mM at its maximum concentration, but at this point, a nearly maximal stimulation of the enzyme is to be expected. While these data would indicate that the relative concentrations of AMP to ATP is a controlling mechanism of the PFK activity, nevertheless, the possibility that decreased AMP concentration leading to a decrease in enzymic activity is manifested as a

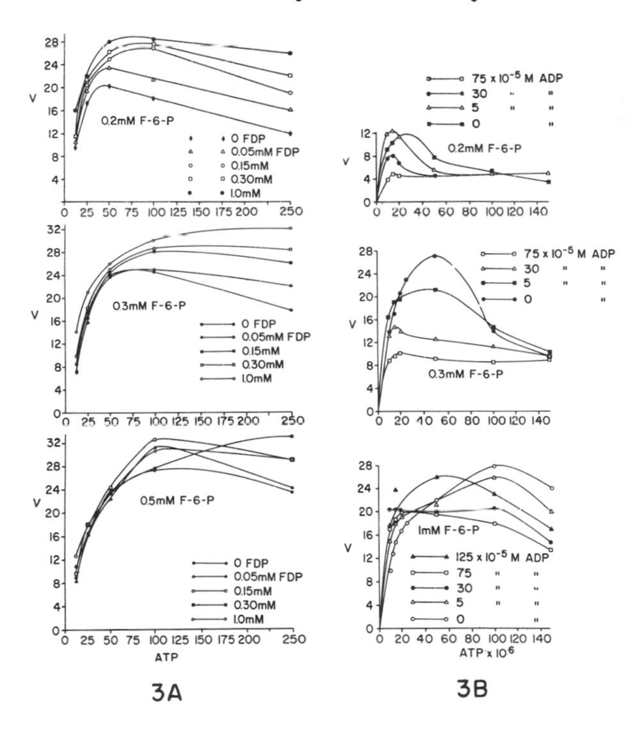

Figure 3A. The effect of FDP on the inhibition of PFK by high ATP concentrations. The enzyme activity was followed by coupling the ADP production to the pyruvic kinase-pyruvate kinase-lactic dehydrogenase system, and the oxidation of DPNH followed fluorometrically at 23° C and pH 7.4. Figure 3B. The inhibition of PFK by ADP, and the release of this inhibition by elevated F-6-P concentrations. The assay system was the same as described in Figure 1.

glycolytic control is important. The effect of FDP on the activity must also be considered since it also has a stimulatory effect on the enzymatic rate.

Figure 3A illustrates the effect of FDP on PFK activity. At concentrations far below the estimated intracellular minimum of 0.6 mM FDP is seen to decrease the inhibitory effect of ATP. Stimulation of activity at an initial concentration of 0.05 mM FDP is observed.

The inhibitory effect of ATP at concentrations above the estimated maximum value of 0.06 mM is shown in the uppermost plot of Figure 3B. The release of this inhibition by high F-6-P is shown in the bottom tracing.

It can be concluded therefore, that a delicate substrate-inhibitor-activator balance or control is very possible for this enzyme in the intact cell, and as such the controlled activity of this enzyme could contribute substantially to the control of anaerobic glycolysis.

REFERENCES

1. Betz, A., and Chance, B., Arch. Biochem. Biophys., 109, 585 (1965).

2. Cassuto, Y., and Chance, B., 1965, in preparation.

3. Viñuela, E., Salas, M. L., and Sols, A., Biochem. Biophys. Res. Commun., 12, 140 (1963).

4. Ramaiah, A., Hathaway, J. A., and Atkinson, D. E., J. Biol. Chem., 239, 3619 (1964).

5. Mansour, T. E., and Mansour, J. M., J. Biol. Chem., 238, 2875 (1963).

A COMPUTER SIMULATION STUDY OF THE METABOLIC CONTROL BEHAVIOR OF PHOSPHOFRUCTOKINASE*

D. Garfinkel

The Johnson Foundation for Medical Research
University of Pennsylvania, Philadelphia, Pennsylvania

I would like to describe a computer simulation of the kinetic results which were obtained by Drs. Passonneau and Lowry, mostly with rabbit muscle (1,2). The methodology of this simulation has been described elsewhere (3,4). Fig. 1 shows the mechanism which we adopted for this simulation. I do not believe it is critical that it is random order in the

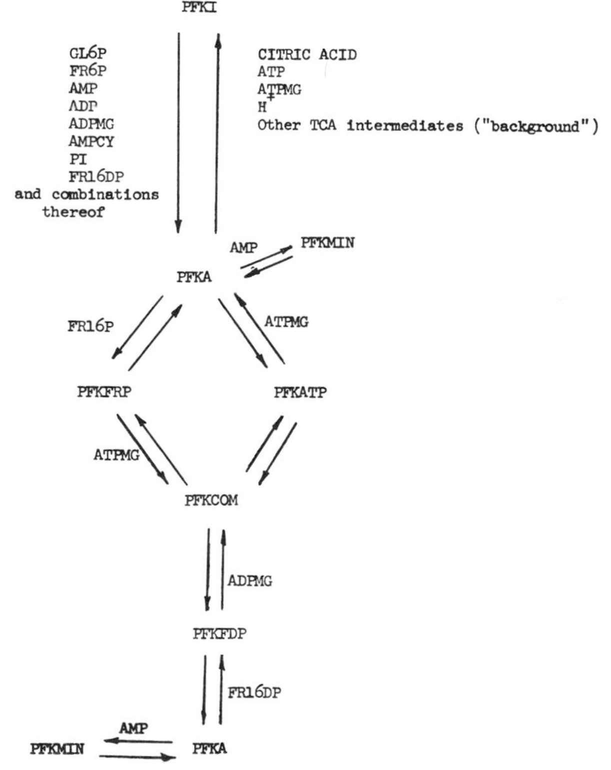

Figure 1. Overall scheme for the model of phosphofructokinase.

*Supported by USPHS FR-15 and GM 5469.

forward direction and compulsory order the other way; this was adopted mostly to imitate other kinases.

We have a long list of activators and a number of inhibitors which take this system from the inactive to the active form and vice versa. To add to the confusion, AMP appears to be both an activator and an inhibitor of the enzyme it has activated, i.e. it competes with ATP for the activated enzyme. The number of activator molecules that are involved is of great importance. This is still subject to revision, but in order to obtain a good fit of the computer model with the experimental data, I had to postulate that 2 F-6-P molecules, and presumably 2 of G-6-P also, were involved in activation; that the adenine nucleotides AMP and cyclic AMP all required 3 molecules each to be activating (the effect of ADP is not determined). P_i required 4 molecules, and there is insufficient data on FDP, although it probably acts like F-6-P.

Among the inactivators, citric acid required one molecule only. It was synergistic with ATP, and gave fairly good results on the assumption that only one molecule of ATP was involved in this synergism. But by itself, ATP requires 3 molecules with or without Mg^{++} bound to it. The ATP without Mg^{++} is about 35 times as strong an inhibitor as ATP with magnesium; H^+ seems to belong in the same group although there is little data for it.

The importance of these results in metabolic control is shown in Figures 2a and 2b. When the metabolite pattern of the aerobic state changes to that of the anaerobic state, PFK activation follows the "velocity" curve. The addition of 0.1 mM of each of the substances shown produces the following results: FDP activates very strongly in an aerobic pattern and then falls off, indicating that once the enzyme is fully activated by other compounds, additional activator will have less effect. F-6-P increases the activity fairly uniformly throughout, perhaps in part because the conditions selected did not yield complete Michaelis saturation with respect to F-6-P. ATP decreases activity slightly under aerobic conditions and has much less effect under anaerobic conditions.

Figure 2b shows the rather unusual curve of AMP. It is strongest as an activator about halfway between the aerobic and anaerobic patterns and then falls off again. In this region, the strongly synergistic reaction between AMP and phosphate accounts for the majority of the activation exerted on the enzyme. ADP is a relatively weak activator in the aerobic situation; citrate is important throughout, and apparently strongest halfway between.

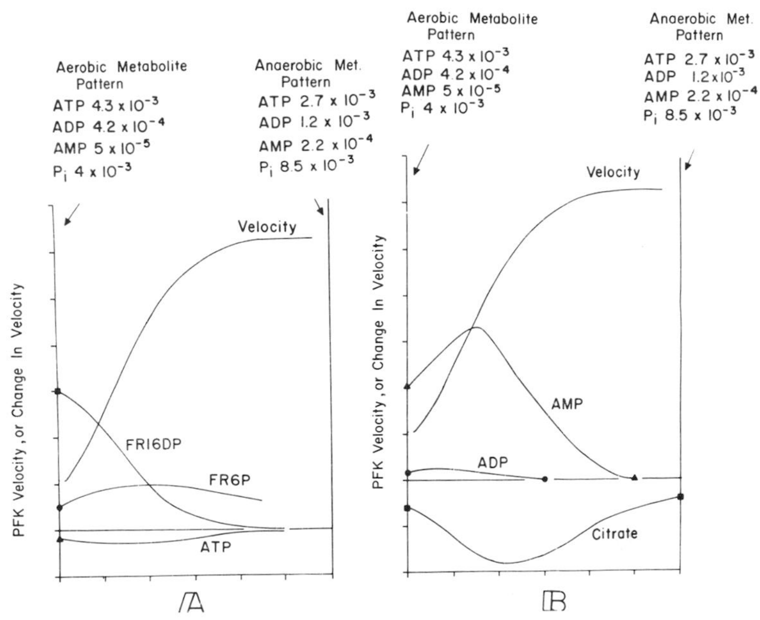

Figure 2a and 2b. Effect on the velocity of phosphofructokinase (curve marked "velocity") as conditions are changed from aerobic to anaerobic metabolite patterns (from the left to the right edge of each figure). The other curves are the change in the velocity curve when 0.1 mM of the substance indicated is added (these changes are negative for ATP and citrate).

It cannot be stated with certainty to what extent these different activators and inhibitors occupy different sites. I think it is possible to suggest some complicated experiments to find out. Thus far, it is conceivable that they can overlap with each other on the same sites and thus strengthen their respective activities; there may be of the order of half a dozen such sites. On the other hand, we may have to have 3 sites for each, which would lead to quite a complicated system for so many substances.

REFERENCES

1. J.V. Passonneau and Lowry, O. H., Biochem. Biophys. Res. Comm., 7, 10 (1962).

2. J.V. Passonneau and Lowry, O. H., Biochem. Biophys. Res. Comm., 13, 372 (1963).

3. D. Garfinkel, Rutledge, J.D. and Higgins, J.J., Comm. Assoc. Comput. Mach., 4, 559 (1961).

4. D. Garfinkel and Hess, B., J. Biol. Chem., 239, 971 (1964).

SUMMARY

Oliver H. Lowry

The preceding presentations make it clear that this difficult enzyme PFK, which offers so many kinds of problems, is giving way before the attack. More rapid progress now seems possible due to the fact that several different groups have succeeded in isolating PFK, and have learned how to stabilize it and even reactivate it when necessary.

As Mansour points out PFK exhibits three well established phenomena, all of which may have significance for the control process. First there is the aggregation and disaggregation phenomenom reported by all the groups that have isolated PFK. This appears to take place without change in activity as measured subsequently at high dilution. It is quite possible, however, that aggregation and disaggregation might cause changes in activity in the concentrated states existing within cells. (Skeletal muscle fibers contain PFK at concentrations greater than 1 mg per ml.) The second phenomenon is the rapid inactivation process observed at least 20 years ago by Colowick (1) and by Utter (2), which 3 of our speakers have recently found to be reversible, and which Mansour has discovered to be a monomer-polymer transformation. This resembles the disaggregation phenomenon except that the monomeric form is inactive. This transformation has definite control possibilities, although the monomeric, inactive, form has yet to be demonstrated *in vivo*. The third phenomenon consists of the bizarre kinetic behavior of the active form (s) of PFK. One would suppose that this behavior is complicated enough to provide all the control needed, but nature does not avoid any amount of complexity if it has the slightest survival value. There is a fourth phenomenon, reported by Viñuela *et al.* (3) for yeast, which resembles the *b* to *a* transformation of glycogen phosphorylase. Both forms are active, but the *a* form has lost the susceptibility to ATP inhibition. Dr. Pette has presented us with yet a fifth control possibility, i.e., that nucleic acid may be associated with PFK to a greater or lesser degree and thereby influence the kinetic behavior. One is tempted to say that the number of control possibilities is out of control.

It is not difficult to foresee some of the things that must be done next. As Dr. Garfinkel points out, the kinetic behavior of PFK demands many binding sites, certainly no less than 7 or 8. With pure enzyme now available, attempts to blockade and to identify the responsible groupings must be made. This promises to be more interesting and conceivably no more difficult than with enzymes having only 1 or 2 functional groups, since more of the molecule may be involved in one way or another. Another kind of problem has to do with the relationship between PFK properties and cell composition. PFK activity is influenced not just by one final end product, but by no less than 8 metabolites, 7 of which (ATP, ADP, AMP, fructose-6-P, fructose diphosphate, P_i, and citrate) are all affected, or capable of being affected, by PFK activity. Many of these in turn determine through equilibria the level of other metabolites. Consequently cell composition may to a considerable extent be determined by the kinetic parameters of the particular brand of PFK present. One foresees many studies in this area. This is feed-back control not only of flux but of cell pattern.

REFERENCES

1. Colowick, S. P., Proc. Amer. Chem. Soc., 112th Meeting, 56C (1947).

2. Utter, M. F., Federation Proc., 6, 299 (1947).

3. Viñuela, E., Salas, M. L., Salas, M., and Sols, A., Biochem. Biophys. Res. Commun., 15, 243 (1964).

ENZYME CONTENT, SUBSTRATE AND COFACTOR AVAILABILITY, AND CATION TRANSPORT AS FACTORS IN METABOLIC REGULATION

IV

Enzyme Profile Patterns and Reconstituted Systems

ENZYME AND METABOLITE PROFILES*

Benno Hess and Karl Brand

Max-Planck-Institute für Ernährungsphysiologie, Dortmund

For a number of years, the study of enzyme and metabolite profiles under steady state and transient conditions in living cells or in model systems has directed our attention to newer systems of metabolic control which have greatly clarified our concepts of the operation of metabolic pathways (see Table I).

1. The activity of enzymes is not only controlled by the level of substrates and products, but also by "allosteric" activation or inhibition through control metabolites.

2. The concentrations of enzymes is controlled by induction, repression, and de-repression devices which involve the operation of genetically controlled protein synthesis.

Here we generally understand that the control elements in such systems are the metabolite intermediates, whereas the enzymes and their reaction velocities are the controlled unit. The controlled enzymes may be present in a number of states: (1) in a state of free solution within the cell, (2) embedded in membranes, or (3) acting as a carrier in the membrane. Furthermore, we realize that the network of controlled biochemical reaction sequences follows the structure commonly known in engineering terms as "feedback". Finally there is multi-site control by control metabolites, leading to a rigid coordination of biochemical processes in time.

Furthermore, we must distinguish between the two ways in which a control chemical may be coupled in terms of energetic coupling by stoichiometric reactions, and also serving as an information signal by cybernetic coupling. The action of the control chemical at the control site can be either positive or negative in its influence upon the rate of an enzyme reaction.

* Supported by a grant from the U. S. Public Health Service and the Deutsche Forschungsgemeinschaft Bad Godesberg, Bonn.

TABLE I

Mechanism of control of glycolytic enzymes

Type	Mechanism*		Examples
A. Control of enzyme activity			
1. Energetic control by mass action			
Autocontrol	Substrate activation	$S + E \longrightarrow SE$	ENO,GAPDH,a.o.
	Substrate inhibition	$S + E \longrightarrow SE'$	GAPDH
	Product activation	$P + E \longrightarrow PE$	PFK
	Product inhibition	$P + E \longrightarrow PE'$	GAPDH
Competitive control	Activation and inhibition of various enzymes by common substrates and/or products $S_1 + E_1 + E_2 \longrightarrow SE_1 + SE_2$		PGK, PK, GAPDH, LDH, ADH, a.o.
2. "Allosteric" control	Activation	$A + E \longrightarrow AE$ $2\,A + E \longrightarrow A_2E$ etc.	PFK, PK
	Inhibition	$I + E \longrightarrow IE$ $2\,I + E \longrightarrow I_2E$ etc.	PFK
B. Control of enzyme concentration			
Induction of enzyme synthesis	$S_A \longrightarrow$ "GEN" $\longrightarrow E_A$		PDC
Repression of enzyme synthesis	$P_P \longrightarrow$ "GEN" $\longrightarrow E_A$		?
Catabolic repression	$S_A \longrightarrow$ "GEN" $\longrightarrow E_X$		MDH/LDH

* S = substrate, E = enzyme, SE = enzyme substrate complex, SE' = modified enzyme substrate complex, P = product, PE = product enzyme complex, PE' = modified product enzyme complex, A = activator, AE = activator enzyme complex, I = inhibitor, IE = inhibitor enzyme complex, S_A = specific substrate for enzyme E_A, P_P = specific product of enzyme E_A, E_X = any enzyme along a pathway to which S_A is prior substrate in the chain, "GEN" = active gene element concerned with the control of the synthesis of the enzyme specified.

The time differences between the two general mechanisms of metabolic control are important: when the reaction velocity is controlled by a variation in the enzyme activity, the control is effective in a matter of seconds, while control by variation of the enzyme concentration takes considerably more time -- minutes, or hours.

Whereas the mechanism of control of enzyme concentration is only known to a rather superficial extent, the operation of activity control is far better established, and can be reasonably approached by means of computer models (1). Activity control, or control of active sites of enzymes, especially by allosteric mechanisms, has far-reaching functional consequences. It has been shown that activity control can produce all-or-none functioning of enzymes, in contrast to the suggestion of Professor Krebs at the CIBA meeting (2) in 1958, thereby behaving like a biochemical "switch". Furthermore, such systems can display, under suitable conditions, biochemical clock functions.

In view of this rather general concept, we would like to discuss the functional significance of the enzyme and metabolite profile, especially in order to elucidate control mechanisms operating in the living cell, and ask which of the various mechanisms which have been detected in single enzyme systems are actually operating in the complete cellular system.

Enzyme profiles. Whereas enzyme activities in tissues and cells have been measured by numerous authors, systematic studies of functionally related groups of enzymes of metabolic pathways were originally performed by Bücher and his coworkers (3). Their results are presented as enzyme distribution patterns or enzyme profiles. These are based on enzyme assays in tissue extracts under standardized and so-called "optimal" conditions. Figure 1 summarizes the enzyme activity pattern of a yeast extract which demonstrates an oscillating glycolysis. The enzyme activities were measured at pH 7.6 and 6.5 under the same conditions as used by Bücher and his group. Indeed, the extract contains the same so-called constant proportion group of five glycolytic enzymes (TIM, PGM, PGK, ENO, GAPDH) in the proportions described by Bücher and co-workers for a great number of tissues. The level of the quintet group with respect to the biuret value of protein concentration can be read from the figures for enolase activity, which was found to be in the same order of magnitude for S. carlsbergensis (3.0 I.U.), Baker's yeast of Marburg (1.2), Baker's yeast of Heidelberg (12.0)(4). But the activities in absolute terms per tissue or cell can vary.

The activity levels for PK, PFK, PGI, ALD, MK, and PC are appreciably lower and different when compared with the figures given, for instance, for muscle. Of special interest is the activity of PFK, which shows the mean value given in the Table; however, it was found to vary in some of the preparations to a level as high as 1.5 and as low as 0.03.

We present this enzyme profile with respect to the functional significance of the pH 6.5 pattern, which gives the

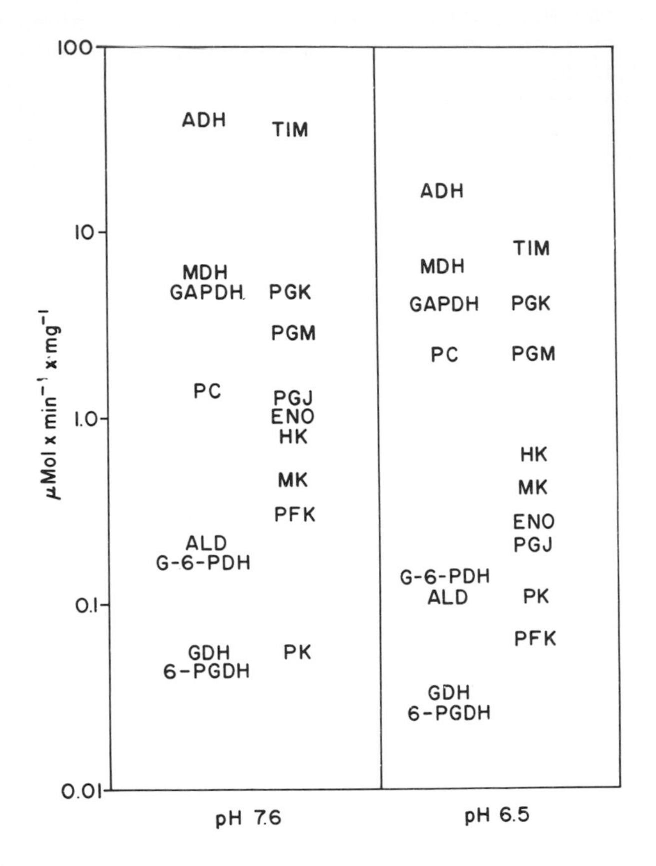

Figure 1. Enzyme profiles of an extract of S. carlsbergensis (from Refs. 4 and 6). Only the pH 6.5 profile displays oscillation.

descriptive status of the system displaying an oscillatory glycolysis, which does not occur at pH 7.6.

However, it is obvious that the functional significance of such a pattern can scarcely be qualified for a number of reasons. The conditions used for the enzyme assay do not hold for the steady state flux of glycolysis, where a steady (and not optimal) level of substrate is maintained, and also the operation of the enzyme is influenced by the back reaction. Thus, it is the difference between the forward and the backward flux which sets the overall flux through the system. This overall, or net flux is the same throughout glycolysis if no branching of the pathway occurs, and is equal to the activity of all enzymes (7).

In cases in which, because of a quasi-unidirectional flux in the intact system, the backward reaction may be neglected, as for instance, in the PFK reaction, the assayed enzyme activity might be comparable to the flux in the intact system. However, such a comparison does not yield reasonable results. A metabolite "loadline" drawn through the figures given in Fig. 1 runs at the level of 7 nM/min/mg protein for such an extract, and accounts for only 11 per cent of the maximum capacity of PFK, as measured under standardized conditions.

Finally, as we have stated, the PFK activity varies with varying preparations over a large range, so that no direct relationship can be established between the assayed activity and the activity operating in the intact tissue. The large number of factors influencing the activity of this enzyme provides another reason for discarding the relationship between the activity pattern and its function. Similar considerations apply to the relatively low activity of PK, as shown in Fig. 1, which can be increased 20-50 fold in the presence of FDP, as we have recently found (8) (see Table I, p. 58).

Such considerations become even more difficult if one takes into account the oscillatory performance, where activities vary over a large range of patterns, indirectly demonstrating control features which are imposed upon the pattern at multiple sites along the pathway.

Only for some of the more simple enzymes given on the pattern can relationships between the steady state activity of the intact system and the "V_{max}" represented in Fig. 1 be established, as will be seen later, if one relates these figures to the net flux of the system. Thus, we would suggest that enzyme profiles generally do not have a functional significance, and should only be considered valuable for descriptive purposes, as relative figures which must necessarily be used for problems of comparative biochemistry.

Metabolite and flux profiles. Metabolite profiles and the overall (net) flux of the system under steady state conditions can be used for the computation of flux profiles which thoroughly define a metabolic steady state with respect to the overall operation and direction of each enzymic step along a pathway, as has been demonstrated for the glycolytic system in ascites tumor cells (7,9,10,11). The steady state concentration of all intermediates can be used to calculate the mass action ratio (Γ) and to relate this figure to the apparent equilibrium constant and the fluxes (see Table II) (10).

TABLE II

Equations for forward and reverse fluxes

For the reaction: $A + B \underset{k_2}{\overset{k_1}{\rightleftharpoons}} C + D$ (1)

in equilibrium:

$$v_1 = v_{-1} \quad \text{and} \quad K_{app} = \frac{[C]\ [D]}{[A]\ [B]} \qquad (2,3)$$

in the steady state:

$$v_{net} = v_1 - v_{-1} \quad \text{and} \quad \Gamma = \frac{[C]\ [D]}{[A]\ [B]} \qquad (4,5)$$

Since, in the steady state, $K_{app} \frac{v_{-1}}{v_1} = \Gamma$ (6)

then, in this case,

$$v_1 = \frac{v_{net}}{1 - \Gamma/K_{app}} \quad \text{and} \quad v_{-1} = \frac{v_{net}}{K_{app}/\Gamma - 1} \qquad (7,8)$$

The calculation of the flux pattern for the glycolytic pathway is presented in Fig. 2. It is obvious from such a computation that under the steady state conditions of a fully activated glycolysis many reactions run in a state of quasi-equilibrium, where the mass action ratio is nearly equal to the apparent equilibrium constant, while other reactions are far displaced from equilibrium. The following reactions are greatly displaced from equilibrium: phosphofructokinase (PFK), phosphoglycerate kinase (PGK), pyruvate kinase (PK). In addition the presence of a high concentration of glucose requires hexokinase (HK) to be included in this last group. All other reactions are rather near equilibrium.

The general meaning of the deviation can be easily understood in the following terms: if there is a small deviation from the apparent equilibrium constant, one can conclude that the enzyme is able to keep up with the supply of substrate from the activity of the predecessor enzyme in the sequence and the enzyme is adjusting itself to the overall glycolytic rate. The activity of such enzymes is controlled through an energy control by mass action. At least, other controlling factors cannot be evaluated under steady state conditions. It is interesting to note that usually a series of such reactions are coupled directly in sequence to each other. Such a group of enzymes would thus connect pools of intermediates reversibly and with almost no energy dissipation. There is no doubt that such pools of metabolic intermediates have a buffering with respect to rapid changes of metabolic flux patterns, according to changes of the physiological demand of the system.

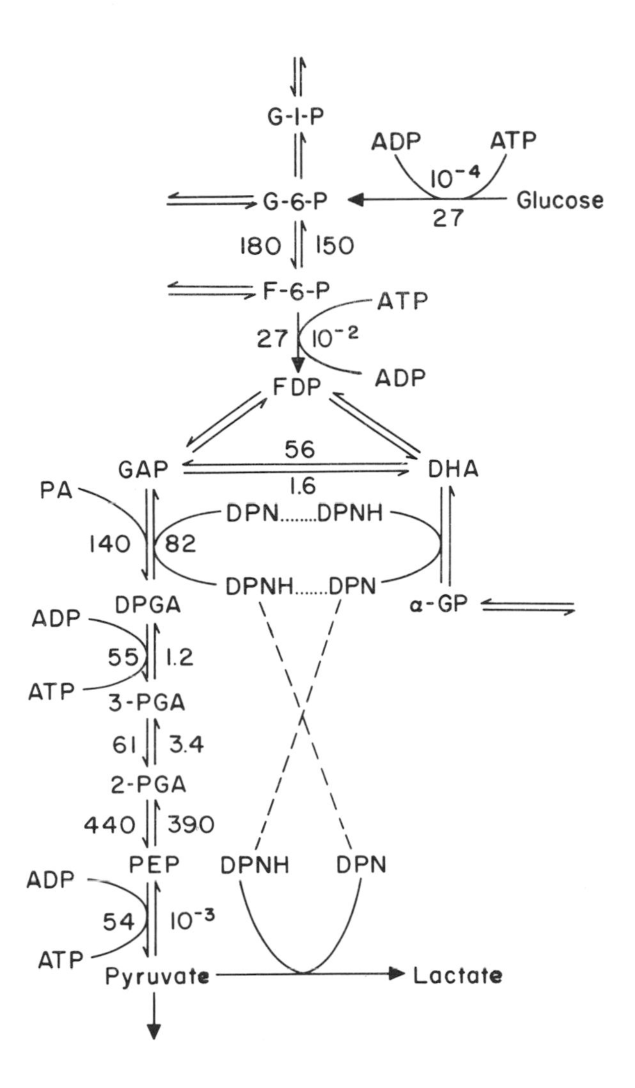

Figure 2. Flux patterns of glycolysis in Ehrlich Ascites tumor cells (from Ref. 11)(numbers are given in $\mu M \times sec^{-1}$).

In such cases, a relationship between the forward flux, the Michaelis constant, the steady state concentration of the substrates and the maximal activity (V_{max}) can approximately be established by use of the steady state Michaelis kinetics:

$$v_1 = \frac{V_{max} \cdot [S]}{K_m + [S]} \tag{9}$$

assuming that the initial reaction velocity of an enzyme is nearly equal to the forward flux (v_1) as computed on this basis (10). In Table III such a calculation is carried out for the enzymes phosphoglycerate mutase (PGM) and enolase (ENO), one finds that the maximal activity as well as the activity ratios of both enzymes computed from the mass action ratio, the net flux and the Michaelis constant, are in accord with the total activity as well as the activity ratios of both enzymes after extraction. An extract shows a maximal activity of enolase of 1.9×10^3 µmoles/h/gm wet weight and an activity ratio for both PGM and ENO of 10. The computed values agree with the activity being extracted from the cells. The ratios and the absolute values are also of the order of magnitude compared with the data given by Pette and co-workers for the constant-enzyme-proportion group (3). Thus, in this simple case a certain relationship between the enzyme pattern and the steady state metabolite and flux profiles can be found. Such relationships can only be easily applied to the so-called "two-partner" reactions where the overall kinetics are clearly controlled by a single step over a large range of substrate concentrations. Such properties are related to the steady state relaxation time (10).

TABLE III

Maximal activities of PGM and ENO in ascites tumor cells*

Enzyme	v_1 (µM/gm/sec)	K_m (µM/ml)	Substrate (µM/gm)	V_{max} (µM/gm/sec)
PGM	0.061	5×10^{-5}	5.7×10^{-7}	5.3*
ENO	0.44	1.5×10^{-5}	2.5×10^{-7}	0.53

* 1.9×10^4 µmole/gm/h; $V_{max} \longleftrightarrow \frac{PGM}{ENO} = 10$

(Data taken from Hess, B. (10).

Turning now to reactions which are greatly displaced from equilibrium, we suggest that the displacement occurs because either kinetically the enzyme activity is not high enough to keep up with the flux, or else the supply of one reaction partner is limited. Also, a functional compartmentation must be taken into account. Recent developments clearly favor the first consideration, i.e., that the enzyme activities are governed by control metabolites, probably by way of allosteric interaction. The large displacement is a consequence of control interaction with the controlled unit.

The two most significant enzymes of this group are PFK and PK. The variety of activities at which PFK can operate has been studied for some time and discussed in detail in this colloquium (p. 63). We have recently investigated the properties of PK, and found that its activity increases strongly upon addition of FDP, as shown in Table I, p. 58. Since FDP is acting in this case not only eventually to supply substrate to PK, but also to activate PK by an enzymatic control mechanism, we choose to distinguish the latter function by the term forward control or to accept the engineering jargon "feed-forward" control. In this case, the activity of PK increases with the FDP concentration so the effect of the control upon the rate is positive, rather than negative and thus a full description of the control is afforded by the term "positive feed-forward". Work on the detailed mechanism of this activation is in progress. We also think that a similar feedback control mechanism acts upon HK. Re-investigation of the properties of PGK has not revealed an active control metabolite so far.

In the scheme (Figure 2) the flux ratio for pyruvate decarboxylase has not been inserted since this enzyme does not exist in ascites cells. However, for yeast, it must be taken into account because of the great displacement of this reaction from equilibrium. Also, in this case we have studied the sensitivity of the activity of isolated pyruvate decarboxylase to a variety of metabolic intermediates, and found that the enzyme is influenced by DPNH (18).

In this short presentation we cannot discuss the control features responsible for the adjustment of the dehydrogenase activity to the overall activity of the pathway. However, indirect evidence seems to show that at least GAPDH is controlled by mass action and by product inhibition through 1,3-DPG (see p. 196).

In summary, the steady state metabolite and flux profiles are significant for an evaluation of the overall operation of enzymic steps in glycolysis, and no doubt in metabolism in general. They are valuable for the identification of control mechanisms, and can serve as a basis for computer models, as we have shown (1). In some cases, the figures can readily be converted into maximal activity for the cell, and serve for the establishment of a functional enzymic activity pattern. The detection of unidirectional steps in metabolic pathways is of great heuristic value, since they point to control units operating by various control mechanisms. The kinetic structure of such steps is particularly appropriate for activity control mechanisms.

Transient metabolite and flux profiles are based on far more complex control interactions. However, qualitatively, they have also been found most useful for the identification of important control sites on the basis of the crossover theorem (p. 12) (12). It should be mentioned that transient metabolite profiles have been established in the form of phase plane plots with great efficiency for the identification of control points of oscillating glycolysis in yeast cells (13) and extracts (14). These studies may substitute for the steady state analyses and may generally lead more directly to the same type of result with respect to the identification of control sites.

In metabolic systems with oscillating properties, such as the cell-free extract of S. carlsbergensis, the functional significance of enzyme and metabolite profiles under transient conditions can be studied by titration experiments. In displaying an oscillating performance, the cooperative function of the glycolytic enzyme sequence is revealed over a wide range of enzyme activity, as well as of substrate co-enzyme concentrations. Here the system runs repetitively through all possible states of metabolic control, as revealed by such parameters as the amplitude of the changes of metabolite levels, their frequency and damping factor, as well as their overall rate of turnover. And here (see Figure 3), not only the concentrations of the glycolytic intermediates are oscillating, but also the enzyme activities vary in an oscillatory fashion in response to the operation of the control circuitry.

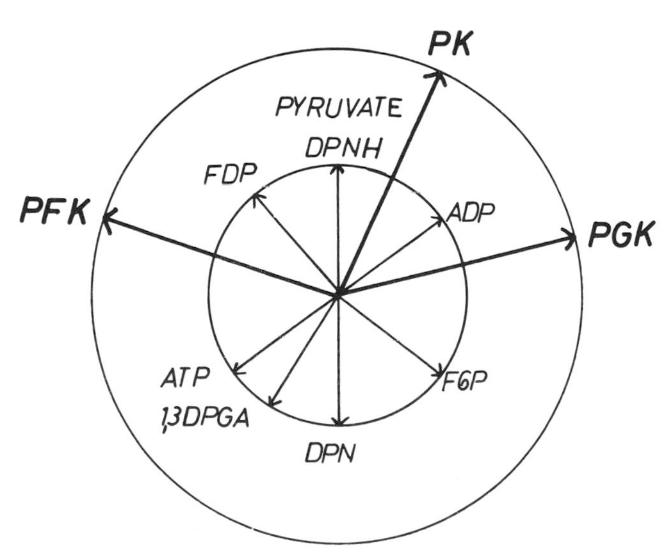

Figure 3. Clock diagram of kinase activities.

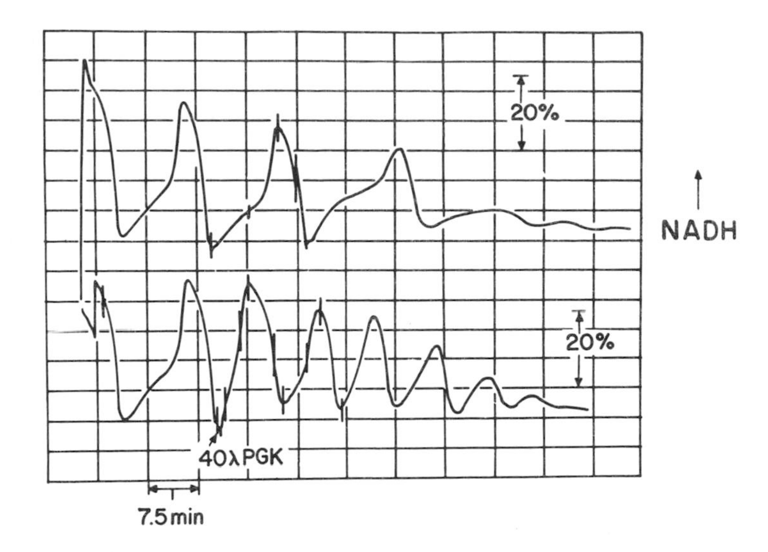

Figure 4. Spectrophotometric traces of two filter double beam spectrophotometers recorded at 340 mμ minus 400 mμ. Upward deflection corresponds to a reduction of pyridine nucleotide d = 1 mm. The upper and lower traces were recorded simultaneously with two samples of yeast extract (vol. 40 λ) (15).

In Figure 3 the positions of the kinase activities with respect to the intermediates, their phase differences, etc., have been computed in approximation from the results of titration experiments. Indeed, such titrations may demonstrate the response of the system on addition of only small amounts of critical enzymes, as demonstrated in the case of PGK presented in Figure 4. Here 40 λ crystallized PGK has been added during the oxidized phase of a period of an oscillating yeast extract as recorded on the lower trace, in comparison to the upper trace, which was run simultaneously as a control. Whereas the oxidation of pyridine nucleotide does not seem to be greatly changed, the rate of reduction is sharply increased and the reduction time has been very much shortened. The relative sensitivity of the enzyme pattern to PGK demonstrates directly the controlling function of PGK on the glycolytic pathway. In such titration studies, it has been found that the glycolytic system is highly sensitive to a change of the kinase activity, and rather insensitive to an increase of the activity of GAPDH. Interestingly, the system responds also, although to a lesser degree, to additions of PGM and ENO. The latter experiments show that enzymes cannot be in excess in such systems, but that their activity will always be established in response to the control network of the system (6,15).

In summary, enzyme profiles may not be used for a functional definition of the metabolic state. Enzyme activities are governed by a variety of control mechanisms which can best be recognized by steady state and transient state analyses of metabolites, and by analysis of the system's response in titration experiments with pure enzymes under conditions under which the system displays an oscillatory behavior of its overall flux. The important parameter for the definition of a metabolic state is the net flux through the system, since this parameter, along with the steady state levels of the metabolites, gives the steady state flux pattern and reveals the kinetic state of enzymic reactions and also points to control points of metabolism.

References

1. Garfinkel, D., and Hess, B., J. Biol. Chem., 239, 971 (1964).
2. Krebs, H., in G. E. W. Wolstenholme (ed.), Regulation of Cell Metabolism, Little, Brown and Company, Boston, 1959, p. 1.
3. Pette, D., Luh, W., and Bücher, Th., Biochem. Biophys. Res. Commun., 7, 419 (1962).
4. Hess, B., Chance, B., and Betz, A., Berichte der Bunsenges. f. physikalische Chemie, 68, 8/9 (1964).
5. Hess, B., Brand, K., and Cassuto, Y., unpublished experiments.
6. Hess, B., Brand, K., and Cassuto, Y., Fed. Proc., 24, 537 (1965
7. Hess, B., Clin. Chem., 11, 223 (1965).
8. Hess, B., and Brand, K., unpublished experiments.
9. Hess, B., in B. Wright (ed.), Control of Metabolic Rates: Regulation of Metabolism, Ronald Press, New York, 1963, p. 333.
10. Hess, B., in V. P. Karlson (ed.), Funktionelle und morphologische Organisation der Zelle, Springer, Göttingen, 1963, p. 1
11. Hess, B., in Proceedings of the VIth International Congress of Biochemistry, New York, VI-41, 1964.
12. Chance, B., and Williams, G. R., Adv. Enzymol. 17, 65 (1956).
13. Betz, A., and Chance, B., Arch. Biochem. Biophys., 109, 585 (1965).
14. Cassuto, Y., unpublished experiments.
15. Hess, B., Cassuto, Y., and Brand, K., unpublished experiments.

ENZYME PROFILE OF BEEF HEART SUPERNATANT FRACTION

René Frenkel

Johnson Research Foundation, University of Pennsylvania
Philadelphia, Pennsylvania

I would like to show a figure which indicates the enzyme profile that we have obtained in a soluble fraction prepared from beef heart. In this figure, the different enzymatic activities are indicated in mμmoles per minute and per mg of protein, as measured by standard enzyme assay procedures. These units are somewhat different from those used by Dr. Hess, but we can also observe the constant proportion group proposed originally by Dr. Bücher (1). The highest enzymatic activity of this particular type of extract is that of the triosephosphate isomerase and the lowest by far that of hexokinase. This low activity is possibly due, at least in part, to the extraction procedure.

Using these enzymatic activities, as well as the metabolite pattern, we have started the construction of a computer model in conjunction with Dr. Garfinkel. At this time we have a fairly good agreement between the results given by the computer simulation and the measured intermediates. However, there is one discrepancy, and this brings us to the point mentioned by Dr. Hess regarding the difficulty of equating a measured enzymatic activity with its proper biological one. This discrepancy concerns the triosephosphate isomerase. Even if the measured enzymatic activity is extremely high, when the triose phosphates are measured, they never appear to be in equilibrium; instead of the equilibrium of 20:1 in favor of dihydroxyacetone phosphate over phosphoglyceraldehyde, a ratio of 4 or 5:1 is found. The triose phosphates have been measured fluorometrically as described by Maitra and Estabrook (3). Appropriate controls have shown that the relatively high values of G-3-P are not due to contamination of the extracts with aldolase. This has led us to include in the model, the proposal made several years ago by Dr. Garfinkel (2) which assumes the existence of a bound aldolase-triphosphate isomerase complex which should prevent the attainment of equilibrium by the triose phosphates.

REFERENCES

1. Pette, D., Luh, W., and Bücher, Th., Biochem. Biophys. Res. Commun., 7, 419 (1962).

2. Garfinkel, D., Ann. N. Y. Acad. Sci., 108, 293 (1963).

3. Maitra, P. K., and Estabrook, R. W., Anal. Biochem., 1, 472 (1964).

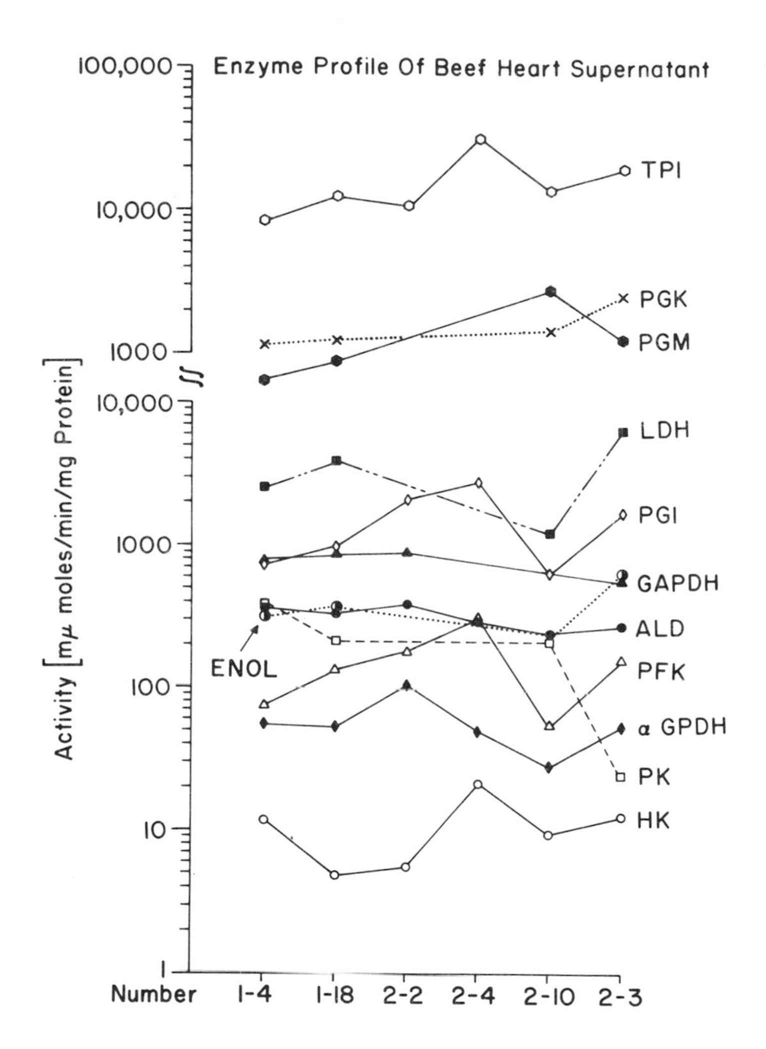

Figure 1. Enzyme profile of beef heart soluble fraction. The soluble fraction was prepared by homogenization of beef heart in a Waring Blendor, using 150 mM KCl, 10 mM phosphate, pH 7.4, 10 mM $MgCl_2$ and 1 mM EDTA as extracting medium and high speed centrifugation (100,00 g for 90 minutes). The enzymatic activities are expressed as millimicromoles of the appropriate substrate being converted per minute, per milligram of protein at 30° C. The numbers on the abscissa indicate the particular preparation studied.

COMMENT

Estabrook: I just want to take two minutes to play the devil's advocate here and state what I consider to be the obvious but the unmentionable, by indicating some of the limitations or boundaries on the interpretation of metabolite and enzyme patterns. I do this because I believe that we would be remiss if we did not indicate our awareness of some of these limitations.

The first limitation concerns the meaning of the enzyme assays, and how these can be then extrapolated to the cell. We must be aware of the nonphysiological state of the enzymes as they are concerned in the assays. I immediately think of the instance of yeast hexokinase which has about an 8 to 10-fold greater activity when bound on a membrane system than when assayed as a purified enzyme, yet these factors are very rarely considered.

Another limitation, which was pointed to in part today, is the nonphysiological nature of the Tris method of assay; I heard Dr. Pette and perhaps he would say more about the use of the reversal for the PFK assay and also about FDP activation of pyruvate kinase.

Very briefly, the third is the meaning of the metabolite assay itself. The nature of the problem requires that in general we assume the cell to be homogeneous, yet we have heard Dr. Garfinkel raise the question of compartmentation. This is apparent in such instances as ascites cells, where phosphate is invoked as a limiting factor, yet there is a very high basal level upon the assay of phosphate in such inhibited systems.

I think that, although we are all required to work within the framework of our knowledge, we should not forget the restrictions imposed by our own ignorance.

COORDINATED STIMULATION OF HEXOKINASE AND PHOSPHOFRUCTOKINASE BY PHOSPHATE IN A RECONSTITUTED SYSTEM OF GLYCOLYSIS*

Kosaku Uyeda+ and Ephraim Racker

Department of Biochemistry, The Public Health Research Institute of the City of New York, Inc., New York 9, New York

The discovery that uncoupling agents of oxidative phosphorylation eliminate the Pasteur effect (1) suggested two alternative theories as an explanation of the control of glucose metabolism (2): a) Competition between oxidative phosphorylation and glycolysis for the common cofactors ADP and P_i (3-5); b) Production of an inhibitor of glucose utilization, which is diminished in the presence of uncouplers (6).

The first theory was supported by experiments in reconstructed systems (7) demonstrating a marked inhibition of glycolysis, as measured by lactate formation, when either ADP or P_i was rate-limiting in a competing system between glycolysis and oxidative phosphorylation. However, glucose utilization was not supressed in this system as long as ATP was available. It became apparent from these studies that any study of the Pasteur effect must include an evaluation not only of the rate of lactate or CO_2 and ethanol formation, but also of the rate of glucose and the formation of hexose phosphates. This concept of the need to analyze glucose utilization is not quite as old as the University of Pennsylvania, but has already passed its 25th anniversary (8); yet, it is frequently ignored.

The initial steps of glucose phosphorylation require ATP, but neither P_i nor ADP, and a sufficient supply of ATP should be made available by oxidative phosphorylation. Therefore, the first theory required amplification. One possibility was that there was compartmentation and ATP was not available for

* Aided by Grant No. CA-03463 from the National Institutes of Health, United States Public Health Service.

+ Present address: Department of Biochemistry, University of California, Berkeley, California.

glucose phosphorylation by hexokinase. This theory was favored for a while by Hess and Chance (9) as well as by ourselves, and we have obtained some evidence for compartmentation of ATP (10). A second possibility was that an inhibitor of glucose phosphorylation was produced under aerobic conditions which brings us back to the second theory.

The second theory states that glucose utilization is impaired under aerobic conditions because inhibitors are produced which interfere with either glucose transport or glucose phosphorylation. Since G-6-P was known to inhibit hexokinase (11), this intermediate was proposed to participate in the regulation of the Pasteur effect (6). But it was already then obvious that this explanation was insufficient and it was proposed that "several different compounds might function as Pasteur inhibitors."

During the past years, significant developments have taken place in our understanding of the regulation of glycolytic enzymes. Pertinent to our discussion here is the discovery that ATP inhibits P-fructokinase (12), that AMP, F-6-P, P_i and other intracellular constituents counteract this inhibition (13) and that P_i stimulates hexokinase (14) by counteracting the inhibition due to G-6-P (15).

These findings prompted a re-investigation of reconstructed systems in our laboratory. Since yeast hexokinase which was used in the previous experiments is not inhibited by G-6-P, a soluble hexokinase was purified from ascites tumor cells (16). This purified enzyme was inhibited by G-6-P and the inhibition was reversed by P_i as shown in Table I. P-fructokinase was purified from rabbit muscle and was examined for its inhibition by ATP (16). In addition to a marked pH dependency, considerable specificity of reactivity with different nucleotides was noted. As shown in Figure 1, ATP and UTP at 5 mM concentrations inhibited strongly whereas ITP did not. Since ITP serves as a glucose phosphorylating agent with either partially purified ascites tumor hexokinase or yeast hexokinase, the following comparative study of a reconstructed system of glycolysis became feasible. With tumor hexokinase substituting for yeast hexokinase the role of G-6-P inhibition was evaluated with ITP instead of ATP; the role of P-fructokinase activity was also examined.

In order to explore the effect of P_i in the initial steps of glycolysis in a reconstructed system, it was decided to examine a segment of glycolysis which did not involve direct participation of P_i and which could be measured continuously by a spectrophotometric procedure.

TABLE I

Effect of P_i on the Inhibition of Purified Ascites Tumor Hexokinase by Glucose-6-Phosphate

Glucose-6-P (mM)	P_i (mM)	Δ A/min.	% Inhibition
0	0	0.066	0
0	5	0.068	0
0.05	0	0.034	50
0.05	5	0.050	24
0.07	0	0.027	60
0.07	5	0.041	38
0.09	0	0.013	80
0.09	5	0.027	60

The reaction mixture contained in a final volume of 1 ml, Tris-HCl, pH 7.4, 100 mM; $MgCl_2$, 5 mM; P-enolpyruvate, 1 mM; glucose, 1 mM; ATP, 1 mM; DPNH, 0.15 mM; pyruvate kinase, 1.2 units; and lactate dehydrogenase, 1.5 units. Glucose-6-P and P_i were added as indicated. The reaction was initiated by the addition of hexokinase (0.013 unit), and the decrease in absorbance at 340 mμ was recorded.

The formation of triose-P from glucose was chosen as a suitable partial pathway linked to the oxidation of DPNH in the presence of excess α-glycero-P dehydrogenase and triose-P isomerase.

As shown in Figure 2, this system is markedly stimulated by P_i especially at low concentrations of P-fructokinase.

It can be seen from Table II that strikingly different results were obtained with yeast and tumor hexokinase, although the same number of units of hexokinase activity were used. With yeast hexokinase the G-6-P levels as well as the F-6-P levels were very high in the presence of P_i, and gradually decreased with increasing concentrations of P_i. These findings indicated that the observed increases in the rate of

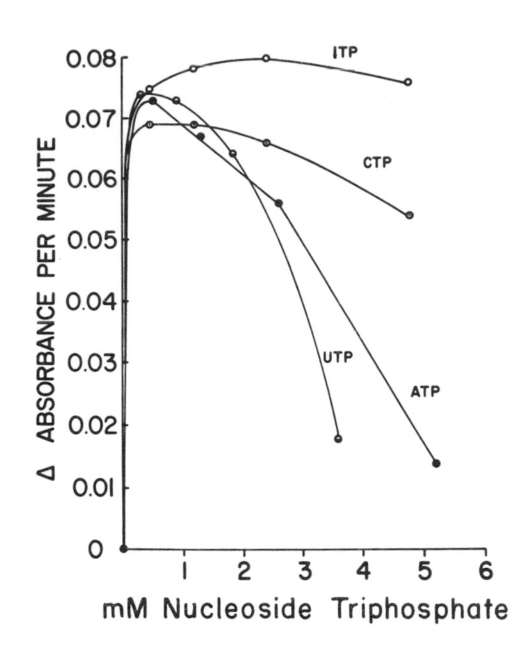

Figure 1. Inhibition of P-fructokinase by nucleoside triphosphates. The reaction mixture contained in a final volume of 1 ml; imidazole HCl, pH 7.1, 50 mM; $MgCl_2$, 5 mM; fructose-6-P, 60 μM; DPNH, 0.2 mM; 2-mercaptoethanol, 100 mM; aldolase, 0.8 unit; triose-P isomerase, 1.5 units; and α-glycero-P, 0.5 unit. Variable concentrations of UTP, ATP, ITP or CTP were added to the reaction mixture. P-fructokinase (0.013 unit) was added to initiate the reaction.

the reaction in the presence of P_i were primarily due to the stimulation of P-fructokinase. This explanation was supported by the experiment with the higher concentration of P-fructokinase. It can be seen that a doubling of this enzyme resulted in a 7-fold stimulation of the rate of the reaction in the absence of P_i, whereas only a 2-fold stimulation was observed in its presence.

With tumor hexokinase, on the other hand, there was virtually no triose-P formation in the absence of P_i at either concentration of P-fructokinase. The levels of G-6-P formed were considerably lower than with yeast hexokinase. Moreover, with tumor hexokinase, increasing the P_i concentration resulted in only minor changes in G-6-P levels, indicating that P_i stimulated both G-6-P formation and its removal. This stimulation of hexokinase and P-fructokinase was so well coordinated that the hexose monophosphate levels remained constant.

TABLE II

Comparison of P_i Effect on Reconstructed Systems with Tumor and Yeast Hexokinase

	PFK (unit/ml)	P_i (mM)	Δ A/min	G-6-P (mM)	F-6-P (mM)
Ascites hexokinase (0.013 u/ml)	0.02	0	0	0.069	0.019
	0.02	3	0.015	0.086	0.024
	0.02	10	0.036	0.080	0.021
	0.04	0	0.003	0.058	0.020
	0.04	3	0.044	0.055	0.019
	0.04	10	0.079	0.040	0.014
Yeast hexokinase (0.014 u/ml)	0.02	0	0.005	0.49	0.14
	0.02	1	0.028	0.47	0.15
	0.02	3	0.054	0.33	0.10
	0.02	5	0.075	0.28	0.049
	0.02	10	0.084	0.16	0.046
	0.04	0	0.037	0.26	0.072
	0.04	1	0.080	0.22	0.065
	0.04	3	0.114	0.18	0.049
	0.04	5	0.140	0.14	0.041
	0.04	10	0.160	0.09	0.034

The reactions were carried out as described in Figure 2 and stopped by addition of 0.05 ml of 10 N $HClO_4$. The reaction was terminated when the rate of the reaction reached a linear portion of the graph and varied from 10 to 15 minutes. The acidified reaction mixture was allowed to stand for 10 minutes at 0° and then neutralized with 5 N KOH. The precipitate was removed by centrifugation. Aliquots of the supernatant solutions (0.1 to 0.2 ml) were assayed enzymatically for G-6-P and F-6-P according to the methods of Wu (21).

Even at 10 mM P_i the rate of the overall reaction was controlled by the G-6-P inhibition of the tumor hexokinase, since the overall rate was about 50 per cent of the rate with yeast hexokinase.

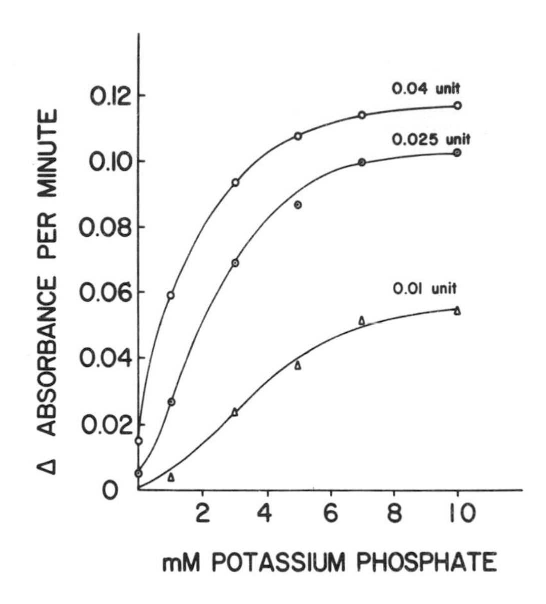

Figure 2. Effect of phosphate concentration on a reconstructed system of partial glycolysis. The following reagents were added to a final volume of 1 ml; tris-HCl, pH 7.4, 50 mM; $MgCl_2$, 5 mM; DPNH, 0.2 mM; glucose, 5 mM; ATP, 1.1 mM; 2-mercaptoethanol 20 mM; NH_4Cl, 1 mM; phosphoglucose isomerase, 0.6 unit; aldolase, 0.2 unit; triose-P isomerase, 0.3 unit; α-glycero-P dehydrogenase, 0.4 unit; P-fructokinase, 0.04, 0.025, 0.01 unit and variable concentrations of potassium phosphate. The reaction was initiated by addition of 0.013 unit of ascites tumor cell hexokinase. The reaction was carried out at 25° in a Beckman D-U spectrophotometer equipped with a Gilford multiple sample changer and recorder. The rate of the reaction was calculated from the linear portion of the graph.

Since ITP served as a substrate for P-fructokinase without exerting an inhibitory effect, a comparison of the two phosphorylating agents in the reconstructed system was performed as shown in Figure 3. With ATP as phosphorylating agent a pronounced stimulation by P_i on triose-P formation from glucose was observed in the presence of either tumor or yeast hexokinase. With ITP a marked stimulation by P_i was observed only with tumor hexokinase, not with yeast hexokinase. Since ITP did not significantly inhibit P-fructokinase and since P_i did not stimulate the system containing yeast hexokinase, the marked stimulation of the overall activity by P_i with tumor hexokinase was most likely due to a counteraction of the G-6-P inhibition of this enzyme.

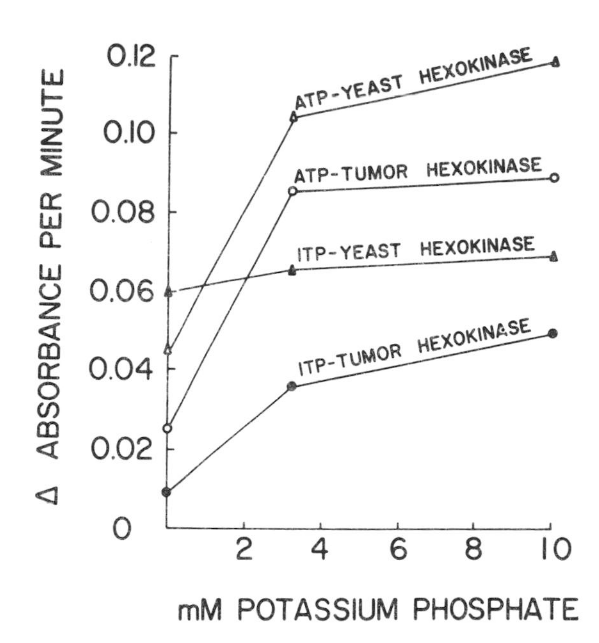

Figure 3. Comparison of ITP and ATP as phosphorylating agents in a reconstructed system of partial glycolysis. Experimental conditions were as described in Figure 2 except that either 1 mM ATP or 5 mM ITP were added. P-fructokinase (0.02 unit) was present in all experiments. In the experiments with yeast hexokinase, 0.024 unit was used with ATP and 0.048 unit with ITP; with tumor hexokinase, 0.013 unit was used with ATP and 0.026 unit with ITP.

It was shown by Passonneau and Lowry (13) that AMP as well as P_i releases the inhibition of P-fructokinase by ATP. In order to evaluate the relative contribution of AMP as a regulatory factor, its effect in the presence and absence of P_i was examined in the reconstructed system. The results are summarized in Table III. There was little triose-P formation with tumor hexokinase in the absence of P_i with or without AMP. In the presence of P_i a slight stimulation by AMP was observed. With yeast hexokinase, however, there was considerable triose-P formation in the absence of P_i which was stimulated over 100 per cent by AMP. In agreement with the conclusions reached above, the latter system was controlled mainly by P-fructokinase and responded to AMP, whereas with tumor hexokinase P_i was required to release the G-6-P inhibition, a function which AMP could not perform.

In order to investigate the effect of P_i on a complete system of glycolysis, two concentrations of P_i were chosen,

TABLE III

The Effect of AMP on the Reconstructed System of Partial Glycolysis

	AMP (mM)	P_i (mM)	Δ A/min.	Glucose-6-P (mM)	Fructose-6-P (mM)
Ascites hexokinase (0.026 u/ml)	0	0	0.005	0.087	0.018
	0.05	0	0.008	0.062	0.016
	0.2	0	0.007	0.080	0.015
	1.0	0	0.011	0.082	0.020
	0	3	0.064	0.086	0.017
	0.05	3	0.075	0.083	0.016
	0.2	3	0.077	0.084	0.015
Yeast hexokinase (0.013 u/ml)	0	0	0.035	0.152	0.044
	0.05	0	0.071	0.114	0.030
	0.2	0	0.089	0.112	0.029
	1.0	0	0.080	0.179	0.018

Experimental conditions were as described in Figure 2, except that AMP and P_i were added as indicated. P-fructokinase (0.02 unit/ml) was added.

3 and 10 mM, which correspond to variations in the intracellular P_i levels found in ascites tumor cells (2).

Enzyme concentrations were also chosen to correspond to the levels found in crude homogenates of ascites tumor cells (2). In a reconstructed system with glycolytic enzymes, as can be seen from Table IV, the rate of lactate production was increased by raising P_i concentration from 3 to 10 mM. Although a stimulation of lactate production by P_i was observed with either yeast or tumor hexokinase, there was no effect on glucose uptake with yeast hexokinase. With tumor hexokinase, on the other hand, a significant stimulation of glucose uptake by P_i was observed.

These experiments clearly demonstrate in a reconstructed system of glycolysis a regulation of glucose utilization as well as lactate formation by the concentration of P_i. This is in contrast to previous experiments (7) in which a control of only lactate formation could be shown. The critical difference between the current and the earlier experiments is the use of

TABLE IV
Reconstructed Glycolytic Systems with Variable Phosphofructokinase and Phosphate Concentrations

P-fructo-kinase unit/ml	P_i mM	Glucose uptake	Lactate formation	Glucose-6-P	Fructose-1,6-P_2
		ASCITES HEXOKINASE (0.13 unit ml)			
0.1	3	1.2	0.26	0.71	0.0
	10	1.5	0.86	0.62	0.0
0.21	3	1.4	0.96	0.44	0.0
	10	2.0	1.45	0.49	0.19
0.31	3	1.7	1.3	0.33	0.48
	10	2.7	1.7	0.35	0.48
		YEAST HEXOKINASE (0.12 unit/ml)			
0.1	3	2.1	0.8	1.2	0.24
	10	2.1	0.8	1.3	0.16
0.21	3	2.0	1.2	0.73	0.71
	10	2.1	2.0	0.86	0.32
0.31	3	2.2	1.7	0.49	1.1
	10	2.2	2.5	0.41	0.71

The reaction mixture contained in a final volume of 1 ml; histidine (pH 7.4), 50 mM; glucose, 8 mM; $MgCl_2$, 5 mM; ATP, 5 mM; DPN, 0.2 mM;P-glucose isomerase, 3.8 units; aldolase, 1.6 units; triose-P isomerase, 3.2 units; glyceraldehyde-3-P dehydrogenase, 2.4 units; 3-P-glycerate kinase, 6 units; P-glycerate mutase, 2.3 units; enolase, 4.1 units; pyruvate kinase, 2.2 units; lactate dehydrogenase, 4.6 units. P-fructokinase, and hexokinase as indicated. The reaction was initiated by the addition of hexokinase and the mixture was shaken at about 140 times per minute in a Dubnoff shaker at 30°.

At 10 minute intervals two 0.1 ml aliquots were removed, and 0.1 ml was transferred into 0.4 ml 6.5 °/o trichloroacetic acid for lactate determination and the 0.1 ml aliquot into 0.4 ml of 0.6 N perchloric acid for the determination of glucose and other intermediates. The results obtained after 20 min of the reaction are shown.

tumor hexokinase which is controlled by product inhibition, instead of yeast hexokinase which is not inhibited by G-6-P. This difference in the properties of the two enzymes brings up the problem of how glucose utilization might be controlled in yeast. Several possibilities should be considered. Hexokinase in yeast may become sensitive to G-6-P when the enzyme is attached to a membrane. Numerous examples for such alterations in the properties of the enzymes are known. To mention one example, the conferral of oligomycin sensitivity to ATPase by a mitochondrial membrane (17). A second possibility is that a metabolic side-product of G-6-P acts as a feedback inhibitor. The observation that mannose-6-P inhibits yeast hexokinase (18) is of considerable interest in this connection, since this compound is a known side-product in yeast metabolism. A third possibility is that glucose transport may be the site of the control mechanism. An exploration of the effect of P_i, ADP or ATP on this process may be rewarding. Either a stimulation by ADP or P_i or an inhibition by ATP or by any other product associated with oxidative phosphorylation could account for the control of glucose utilization in yeast under aerobic conditions.

Finally we should like to re-emphasize two points. One is that studies of reconstructed systems do not tell us what happens in intact cells (7). They serve, however, as important model systems under conditions that allow variation of the catalytic components and thus permit us to evaluate the potential contributions of individual enzymes and cofactors to metabolic regulations. The second point was also stressed many years ago (6). It is quite probable that nature has not confined itself to a single mechanism of controlling carbohydrate metabolism. Dr. Wu in our laboratory (6) as well as other investigators has obtained evidence (19-22) that different rate-limiting factors control glucose utilization in different cells. There are probably multiple mechanisms for the Pasteur effect in various cells and there is no need to search for an all-encompassing theory. Although we have claimed (2) and still claim that in a particular ascites tumor cell P_i is the major rate-limiting factor, we are happy to concede that there do exist other cells. We have become increasingly convinced of the truth of the statement once made by Oliver Wendell Holmes: "All generalizations are worth a damn, including this one."

In conclusion, with the use of reconstructed systems of glycolysis, the possible sites of regulation of carbohydrate metabolism by P_i were investigated. A comparison of hexokinase from yeast and tumor which differ in their susceptibility to G-6-P inhibition, and a comparison of ATP and ITP which differ in their ability to inhibit P-fructokinase permitted an evaluation of the stimulation by P_i. A rather remarkable coordinated stimulation of hexokinase and P-fructokinase by P_i was observed with the system containing tumor hexokinase. With yeast hexokinase, on the other hand, the system lacked this coordinated stimulation. In a reconstructed system of complete glycolysis an increased glucose utilization and lactate production was observed when P_i concentration was increased from 3 to 10 mM. A role in a coordinated regulation at three sites can now be assigned to P_i; a counteraction of the inhibition of hexokinase and P-fructokinase by G-6-P and ATP, respectively, and a stimulation of oxidation of glyceraldehyde-3-P.

REFERENCES

1. Judah, J. D., and Williams-Ashman, H. G., Biochem. J., 48, 33 (1951).
2. Wu, R., and Racker, E., J. Biol. Chem., 234, 1029, 1036 (1959).
3. Belitzer, W. A., Biochem. Zeit., 283, 339 (1936).
4. Lynen, F., Ann. Chem. Liebig, 546, 120 (1941).
5. Johnson, M. J., Science, 94, 200 (1941).
6. Racker, E., in F. F. Nord (ed.), Advances in Enzymology, Vol. 15, Interscience Publishers, New York, 1954, p. 141.
7. Gatt, S., and Racker, E., J. Biol. Chem., 234, 1015, 1024 (1959).
8. Dixon, K. C., Biological Reviews, 12, 431 (1937).
9. Hess, B., and Chance, B., J. Biol. Chem., 236, 239 (1961).
10. Wu. R., and Racker, E., in B. Wright (ed.), Control Mechanisms in Respiration and Fermentation, Ronald Press, Co., New York, 1963, p. 265.
11. Weil-Malherbe, H., and Bone, A. D., Biochem. J., 49, 339 (1951).
12. Lardy, H. A., and Parks, R. E., Jr., in O. Gaebler (ed.), Enzymes: Units of Biological Structure and Function, Academic Press, Inc., New York, 1956, p. 584.
13. Passonneau, J. V., and Lowry, O. H., Biochem. Biophys. Res. Commun., 7, 10 (1962).
14. Tiedemann, H., and Born, J., Z. Naturforsch., Pt. 6, 14, 477 (1959).
15. Rose. I. A., Warms, J. V. B., and O'Connell, E. L., Biochem. Biophys. Res. Commun., 15, 33 (1964).
16. Uyeda, K., and Racker, E., J. Biol. Chem., submitted.
17. Kagawa, Y., and Racker, E., Fed. Proc., 24, 1297 (1965).
18. Fromm, H. J., and Zewe, V., J. Biol. Chem., 237, 3027 (1962).
19. Park, C. R., Morgan, H. E., Henderson, M. J., Regan, D. M., Cadenas, E., and Post, R. L., Recent Progress in Hormone Res., 17, 493 (1961).
20. Newsholme, E. A., and Randle, P. J., Biochem. J., 80, 655 (1961).
21. Wu. R., Biochem. Biophys. Res. Commun., 14, 79 (1964).
22. Regan, D. M., Davies, W. W., Morgan, H. E., and Park, C. R., J. Biol. Chem., 239, 43 (1964).

A RECONSTITUTED ENZYME SYSTEM*

A. Betz

Botanisches Institut der Technischen Hochschule,
Braunschweig, Germany

We attempted to reconstitute the oscillating glycolytic system we had studied previously in yeast cells and extracts (1-4). It is very easy to observe DPNH-oscillations in a system going from F-6-P through the glycolytic pathway to lactate, when the enzyme activities and the substrate concentrations are somewhat balanced. Figure 1 gives an example. The reaction is started by PFK. DPNH rises with the oxidation of GAP; the LDH reaction terminates this rise, and after going through a very small overshoot cycle, production and consumption of DPNH are very nearly balanced. Additions of ATP and DPNH bring an inhibition of PFK and GAPDH, in this way limiting the further production of DPNH. In this transition to a new steady state there occur some cycles of alternating oxidation and reduction. This system is, however, not very satisfactory, since our PFK preparation was contaminated with other enzymes, i.e., with 2-3 per cent α-GPDH.

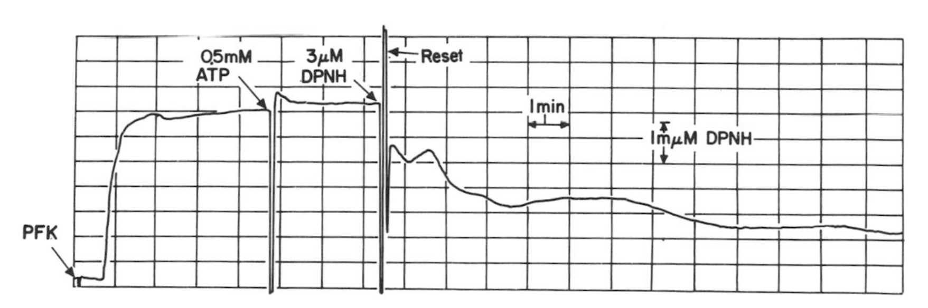

Figure 1. Cyclic changes in the level of DPNH as followed by fluorescence measurement in a system containing the substrates, cofactors and enzymes to convert F-6-P to lactate. The activity of GAPDH was some 40 times higher than PFK and slightly higher than LDH.

* Supported by PHS GM 12202-02 and a NATO Fellowship.

We therefore, tried to find a somewhat simpler system by combining all the substrates, cofactors and enzymes which are necessary to convert 1,6-FDP in lactate, omitting only GAPDH and LDH. As shown in Figure 2, the addition of GAPDH is followed by the reduction of DPN to DPNH in a slowly declining rate. During this time the system accumulates pyruvate as well as DPNH.

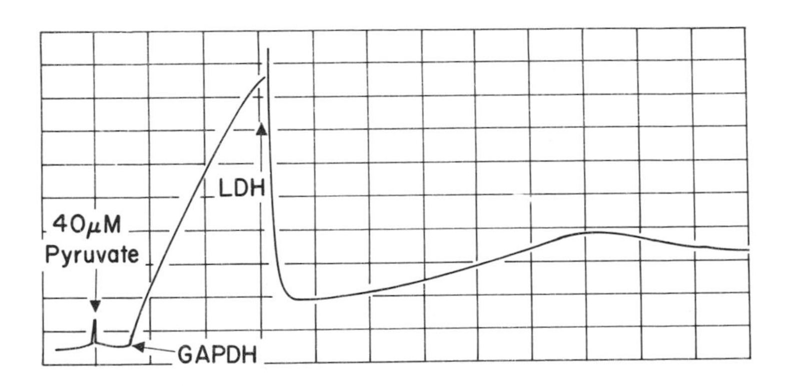

Figure 2. Production and consumption of DPNH, measured by double beam spectrophotometry, following the addition of GAPDH and LDH respectively, to a system capable of converting FDP to lactate. In the experiment shown in the lower trace, DPNH and pyruvate had been added previous to the addition of GAPDH and LDH. 1 division = 80 sec.; 1 vertical division = 5 mμmoles DPNH.

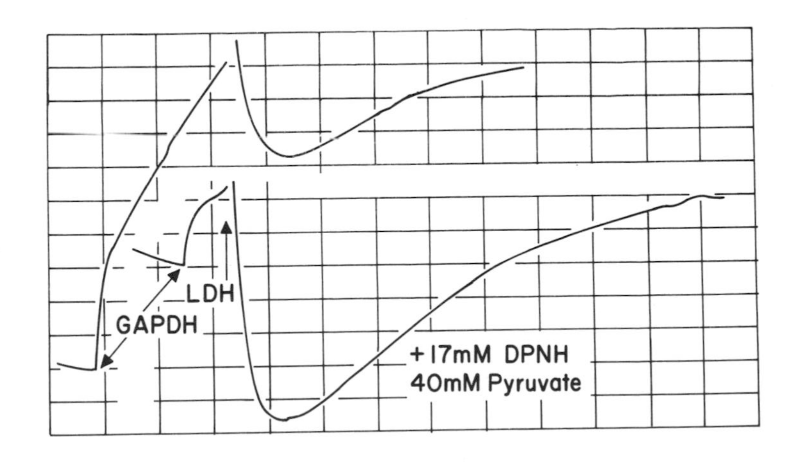

Figure 3. Conditions as in Figure 2, but with previously added pyruvate.

The addition of LDH causes DPNH to become oxidized in the reduction of pyruvate to lactate. This abrupt oxidation of DPNH becomes slower within a few seconds and after a minute or so production and consumption of DPNH come to an equilibrium, but instead of staying at a steady state level, DPNH begins to rise again, indicating a prevalent reduction. We have here a clear overshoot cycle, the amplitude of which can be enhanced by adding pyruvate and DPNH previous to the start of enzymatic reactions (lower trace in Figure 2).

If pyruvate had been added alone, the DPNH oxidation is even more pronounced, but the overshoot cycle is very poor (Figure 3). The second fall in the DPNH trace is due to ADP depletion and is therefore, not to be considered as a real oscillation.

The LDH reaction removes DPNH and pyruvate, which are both inhibitory to GAPDH, the first directly by product inhibition, the second indirectly since 1,3-PGA is accumulated in the presence of ATP. These facts could perhaps explain the observed overshoot cycle, with the assumption that the coupling between GAPDH and LDH reactions would bring some time delay or retardation. But as shown in Figure 4, the amplitude of these cycles depends on the concentration of FDP rather than of pyruvate or

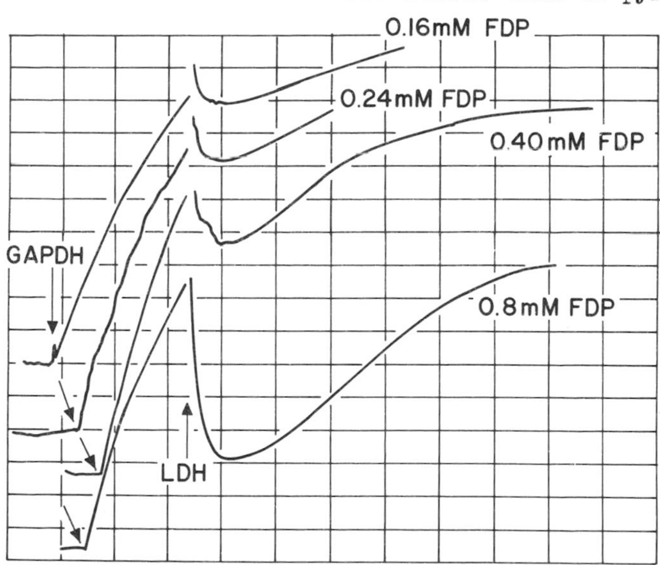

Figure 4. DPNH level in 4 experiments in which the same amount of DPNH and pyruvate has been accumulated by the GAPDH reaction previous to the addition of LDH. The balance between the production and consumption of DPNH is dependent on the concentration of FDP.

DPNH. In all of the experiments of Figure 4 the same amount of DPNH and of pyruvate had been accumulated before the addition of LDH; there is therefore, no apparent reason why LDH should be more active in one case than in the other. The LDH reaction is obviously enhanced by FDP or some of its derivatives. Thus it makes no difference whether yeast or rabbit muscle GAPDH is used in this system. FDP can be replaced by GAP in suitably high concentrations.

When some earlier step in a sequence of reactions controls one of the later steps, we are dealing with some "feed forward" similar to that mentioned for PK this morning by Dr. Hess. It is obvious that such an interaction would fit nicely in Higgins' scheme of mechanisms generating oscillations in enzymatic systems. As we are working here with a completely defined system, future experiments may be directed towards identifying the control site.

REFERENCES

1. Chance, B., Hess, B. and Betz, A., Biochem. Biophys. Res. Comm., 16, 182 (1964).

2. Betz, A. and Chance, B., Arch. Biochem. Biophys., 109, 579 (1965).

3. Betz, A. and Chance, B., Arch. Biochem. Biophys., 109, 585 (1965).

4. Betz, A. and Chance, B., Naturwissenschaften, 1965, in the press.

DISCUSSION

Hess: To start this discussion, I should like to present a scheme which represents the control pathway of oscillating glycolysis in *Saccharomyces carlsbergensis*. Such a system has general significance since it is reasonable and fruitful to assume that the mechanism producing the oscillations is in principle also responsible for the control of the non-oscillating and stabilized glycolytic system. The scheme is based on control interactions of a stoichiometric as well as a catalytic nature and contains the same logical elements as presented recently by Higgins (Proc. Nat. Acad. Sci., 51, 989 (1964)) in his analog computer model of the oscillating metabolic system. The Higgins system exhibits oscillatory behavior because (1) one of the chemicals produced by one pathway activates its own production while the corresponding product of the other pathway inhibits its own production, and (2) there is a cross coupling of opposite character when one of the chemicals causes the activation of the net production of the other one. Under these conditions the accumulation of the other product must lead to an inhibition of the net production of the first product or vice versa. The scheme on Fig. 1 represents the interactions of the two types of inhibitory or activating pathways of the glycolytic enzyme sequence.

The control network is based on the following facts. (1) The PFK activity of yeast is inhibited by high levels of ATP and it is activated also by high levels of its own product (FDP). (2) The pyruvate kinase as well as phosphoglycerate kinase activities are inhibited by high, yet different levels of ATP, where the latter enzyme (PGK) has a lower affinity. Most important, however, is the recent observation that yeast pyruvate kinase is activated with high levels of FDP. (3) The amplitude of the changes of the ATP concentrations and its mean levels are high enough and within the range which should be expected for such a control function. (4) The amplitude of the changes of the FDP concentration during oscillations and its mean level are high enough and within the range which should be expected for such a control function. (5) The glycolytic intermediates between the PGK and PK levels do not oscillate.

As more ATP is synthesized in the lower pathway of glycolysis the enzymes PGK and PK as well as PFK are inhibited.

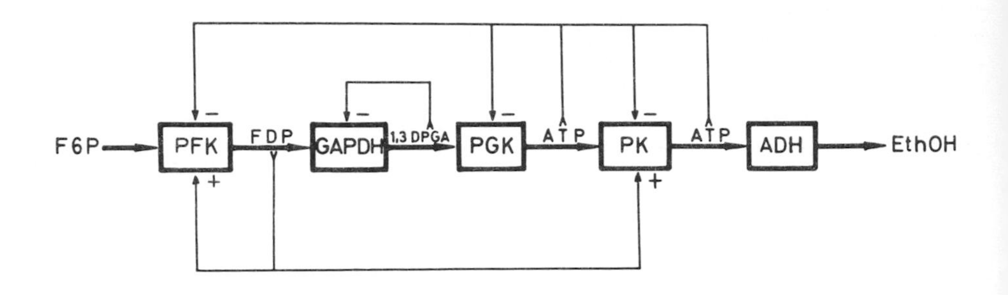

Fig. 1. Control pathway of oscillating glycolysis.

In addition GAPDH is inhibited by its own product, 1,3-diphosphoglycerate. Since F-6-P and DPN are the substrates of the inhibited enzymes and enzyme sequences, they will accumulate. Furthermore, the activating effect of FDP which proceeds roughly 90° ahead of ATP in the phase plot approaches the minimum of its concentration cycle, thereby losing its controlling properties to regenerate ADP at the site of PFK and also its activating function pyruvate kinase. When the maximum of the ATP level is passed, FDP takes over and activates the lower pathway of glycolysis and at the same time, its own production at the site of PFK!

The operation characteristics of pyruvate decarboxylase need special consideration. It has been found that pyruvate accumulates in spite of the availability of DPNH. Both compounds are cycling without any phase difference. This behavior points to a modulation of the pyruvate decarboxylase activity in synchrony with the changes of pyruvate and DPNH, since the rates of ethanol production during the oscillations is steady. Indeed, we have recently found that purified yeast pyruvate decarboxylase is influenced by DPNH (Hess, B. and Hampel, B., unpublished experiments (1965)).

This control network of oscillating glycolysis is further supported by titration studies in which the functional enzyme pattern is titrated with pure enzyme preparations in order to influence the frequency, amplitude, the waveform and the damping factor as displayed by the system. This study shows the relative insensitivity of the oscillatory behavior toward GAPDH and its great sensitivity toward the three phosphokinases (Hess, B., Brand, K. and Cassuto, Y., Fed Proc., 23, 537 (1965)).

Bücher: My question concerns the oscillating system within a suspension of intact cells. There must be some primary factor operative which couples the oscillation of all the cells in order to keep then synchronous?

Hess: It is glucose. After addition of glucose, the system becomes saturated with all the intermediates of glycolysis; then the aerobic-anaerobic transition is initiated, and the system runs into the oscillatory state. I believe it is the input of the metabolite, glucose, which couples the cells together.

Bücher: That is sufficient to start it. But I cannot imagine that the one million cells have the same rhythm from day to day as the system continues to oscillate. There must be some factor which couples the cells together continuously, or at least once in every cycle.

Hess: I believe we have two different phenomena here. One is the oscillation of the metabolic pathways, and the other is the controlled synchrony of the cell population operating at quite different frequency levels. However, since the classic rates of metabolism in non-synchronous cells and tissues are steady over a long period, I do not think that it is necessary to postulate a coupling between individual cells in such a cell population. Certainly such couplings may exist, for instance by exchanging diffusable metabolites such as pyruvate or even citrate.

Chance: In reply to Dr. Bücher's question, we have attempted to determine whether the cessation of oscillations in a suspension of yeast cells was due to asynchrony of a continuous oscillation or to a cessation of all oscillations. Observation of a single cell in *S. carlsbergensis* by sensitive microfluorometry (Chance, B., unpublished observations) showed no detectable fluctuations of DPNH and, i.e., continuous oscillations are unlikely *in vivo*. Therefore, the oscillation is a phenomenon which occurs when the ADP level rises abruptly in the aerobic-anaerobic transition and sets the glycolysis off in a synchronized transient which will then oscillate for about ten minutes. Our finding of oscillations of about the same number of cycles in a cell-free extract suggests that synchrony *in vivo* has not limited the number of observable oscillations. It is a remarkable fact, however, that the individual cells are sufficiently alike to allow observation of the oscillations *in vivo* for such a long period.

V

Control in Single-Cellular Systems Due to P_i or ADP Availability

CONTROL CHARACTERISTICS OF THE ADENINE NUCLEOTIDE SYSTEM+

Martin Klingenberg

Physiologisch-Chemisches Institut
der Universität Marburg

The frequent participation of the adenine nucleotide system in phosphate transfer reactions makes this system admirably suited for multi-site control. Being a common substrate for widely separated reactions, the adenine nucleotides are an efficient instrument for the coordination of metabolic steps. In this function, the adenine nucleotide system encompasses other types of controls discussed below (cf. Figure 1).

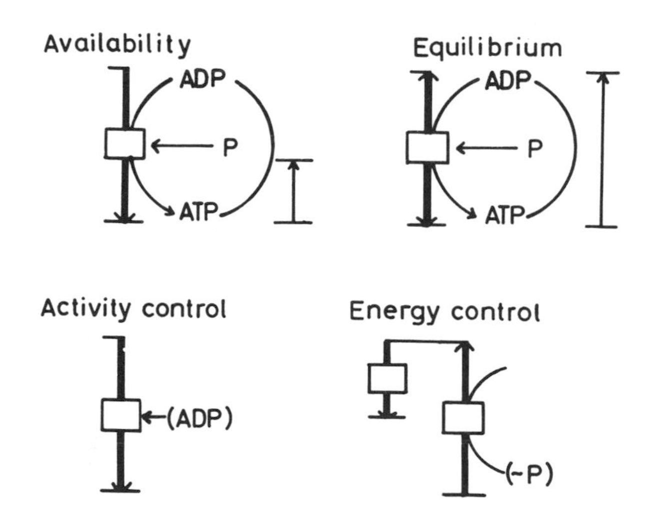

Figure 1. Control types of the adenine nucleotide system.

+This research was supported by a grant from the United States Public Health Service.

Control in which adenine nucleotides are the substrate leads to a primitive self-regulation. This control may be either kinetic ("availability control") or thermodynamic ("equilibrium control"). In the availability control, the reaction rate is limited by the concentration of ADP or ATP, whereas in the equilibrium control, the ATP/ADP ratio, as it approaches equilibrium, is the controlling factor. Intermediate cases between availability and equilibrium control are to be expected.

A more sophisticated control by the adenine nucleotide system may be termed "activity control". In this case, the adenine nucleotides activate or inhibit specific enzymes without being a substrate of the enzyme in question. This type of control appears to have developed in only a comparatively few special cases. Activity control is a regulation in the narrower sense, since the regulator--the adenine nucleotide--does not participate in the reaction.

Another type of control linked to adenine nucleotide, the "energy control" is still poorly understood. It appears that the adenine nucleotides do not catalyze these reactions in the stoichiometric relation P/2H = 1 which holds for the succinate → DPN hydrogen transfer. This type of control occurs in hydrogen transfer from the DPN to the TPN system. The energy control of ion translocation and distribution in the mitochondria also belongs to this category.

Examples for the Various Types of Adenine-Nucleotide-Linked Control. The best known example of availability control is found in oxidative phosphorylation in the mitochondria (1, 2). Recently, however, this respiratory control has been reinterpreted more in terms of an equilibrium control in which, through the reversibility of oxidative phosphorylation, the ATP/ADP ratio can control respiration and oxidative phosphorylation in mitochondria (3). Control of respiration *in vivo* must depend largely upon this equilibrium control, since a high amount of ATP prevails always in living organs. Therefore the ratio ATP/ADP remains 1 even when the ADP level increases as the tissue goes from the resting to the active state.

The kinetic as well as the equilibrium control by the adenine nucleotide system appears to be particularly important for the coordination of the intra- and extra-mitochondrial metabolism. A simple case is the utilization of ATP for cellular function, and the ensuing availability of ADP for oxidative phosphorylation in mitochondria. More complex is the competition for ADP between the extramitochondrial glycolytic system and the intramitochondrial respiratory system, for example, in the Pasteur effect.

The intra- and extra-mitochondrial coordination by equilibrium control has a remarkable effect on the intra- and extra-mitochondrial DPN system, as shown in Figure 2. With an increasing [ATP] / [ADP][P_i] ratio, the redox potential of the extra-mitochondrial DPN system should become more positive as a consequence of an equilibrium at the GAPDH (6). In contrast, all available spectrophotometric observations (4) and chemical analyses of the mitochondrial pyridine nucleotides (5) point to an increase in the DPNH/DPN ratio with increasing phosphorylation potential, as does the function of the DPN-linked substrate couples in the mitochondria. The parallel shift of the ATP/ADP and DPNH/DPN ratios in the same direction within the mitochondria is linked to the energy transfer system of oxidative phosphorylation. Therefore, this mechanism is unexplained, in contrast to the opposite relation in the glycolytic system.

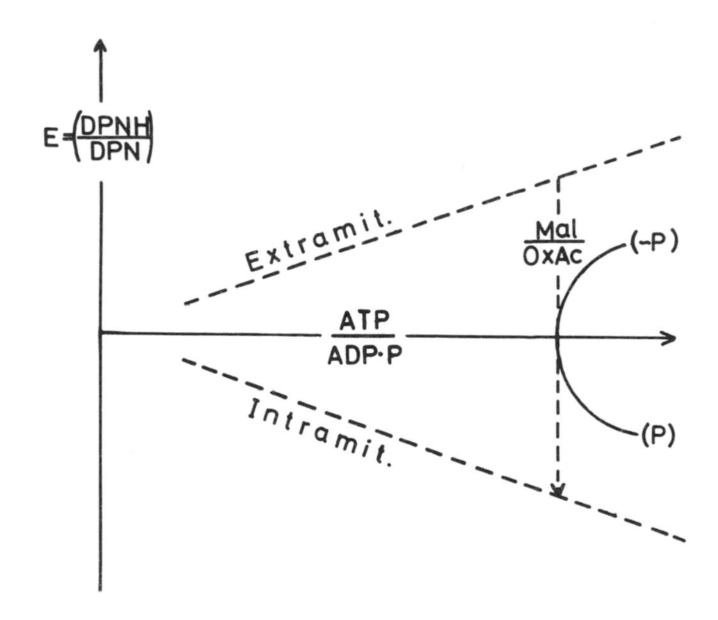

Figure 2. The opposite shifts of the redox potential of the intra- and extra-mitochondrial DPN system in dependence upon the phosphorylation potential of the adenine nucleotide system. Scheme depicting the influence of the adenine nucleotide system upon the DPN system, as exerted by equilibrium control.

Thus, with increasing phosphorylation potential, an increasing discrepancy of the redox potentials between the glycolytic and intramitochondrial DPN systems evolves (cf. Figure 2). This poses great problems in understanding the function of a substrate redox couple common to both the intra- and extra-mitochondrial system, such as the malate/oxaloacetate couple. In various tissues, such as liver and skeletal muscle, the malate/oxaloacetate couple appears to follow the comparatively positive extra-mitochondrial redox potential of the DPN system (6,7). How then, can malate be oxidized in mitochondria, where the DPN system appears to have a considerably more negative redox potential, particularly at high ATP/ADP ratios.

A possible answer is provided by the discovery that, in mitochondria, hydrogen from the malate/oxaloacetate couple can be transferred to systems of more negative redox potential under the influence of internal high energy intermediates of the mitochondria (X ~ I) or indirectly by ATP (8,9).

An hypothesis for the mechanism of malate oxidation in mitochondria is an ATP-linked removal of oxaloacetate from the malate dehydrogenase (9), similar to the postulated removal of oxaloacetate from succinate dehydrogenase (10). Related to this would be a differential permeability of malate and oxaloacetate through the mitochondrial membranes. Another hypothesis is the existence of at least two functional compartments in the DPN system in mitochondria (11,12), as shown in Figure 3.

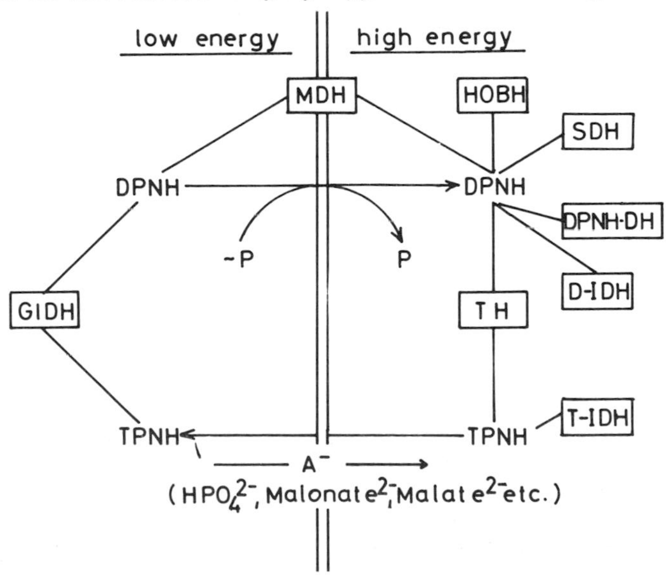

Figure 3. Two functional compartments of the intra- and extramitochondrial DPN system.

One compartment with a more positive redox potential is primarily linked to the malate/oxaloacetate system (lower energy system) and the one with a more negative redox potential is linked to various other mitochondrial dehydrogenases, such as the DPNH dehydrogenase, hydroxybutyrate and isocitrate dehydrogenase (higher energy system)(cf. Figure 3). According to this hypothesis, hydrogen is pumped from one pool to the other by an ATP-linked translocation of DPNH.

Intra-extramitochondrial coordination presupposes a permeation of the adenine nucleotides through the mitochondrial membranes. Recent studies have shown that both ADP and ATP can enter as intact molecules into the intramitochondrial space in a highly specific exchange reaction (13). This exchange reaction excludes largely the entrance of AMP and nearly completely the exchange by other nucleotides such as guanosine, cytidine, inosine, and pyridine nucleotide systems. The entrance of ATP is partially inhibited in the presence of excess Mg^{++} (14). It is therefore to be assumed that in the cell with a high content of Mg^{++} the control effect of ATP on the respiratory chain is somewhat restrained in comparison to that of ADP.

The specificity of the intra- and extramitochondrial adenine nucleotide exchange reaction establishes that only the adenine nucleotide system can participate in the nucleotide-linked coordination of intra- and extramitochondrial metabolism. Other systems, such as the pyridine, guanosine, and cytidine nucleotide systems, exist in separate intra- and extramitochondrial pools. The coordination between intra- and extramitochondrial pools of these systems is accomplished indirectly, via the adenine nucleotide system catalyzed by nucleotide phosphate transferases. In fact a double location of adenylate kinase in liver mitochondria on both sides of the ATP, ADP specific exchange barrier was observed (15). This double location may be related to the finding that AMP itself cannot readily permeate the mitochondria.

Activity control by the adenine nucleotide system appears to occupy a strategic position in the regulation of substrate degradation. The activity control of phosphofructokinase has been extensively discussed at this colloquium. Phosphofructokinase is activated by AMP or ADP, and inhibited by ATP. Another ADP-activated enzyme, the DPN-linked isocitrate dehydrogenase, is located at an early part of the tricarboxylic acid cycle. The control characteristics of this enzyme and its mode of action have been investigated in detail, particularly on the basis of its pronounced pH dependence (16). On this basis, we have elaborated a mechanism of the activity control for an enzyme.

This mechanism appears to be of general significance, and may apply to other regulatory enzymes, such as phosphofructokinase, as well. Here, the activation or, in a reciprocal sense, the inhibition is the result of changes in the interaction of various substrate sites on this enzyme. We must assume that each single substrate and modifier site is located in a single subunit. The activation and inhibition, therefore, are the results of the varying strengths of interaction between the subunits. These may be changed according to the modifier site, or without modifier, according to the substrate site alone, especially at lower pH. The substrate itself has a modifier function acting from the substrate site.

In the case of isocitrate dehydrogenase, only the DPN has the modifier property, whereas isocitrate modifies the enzyme only indirectly by tightening the binding of DPN. It appears that, generally, nucleotides are primary modifiers of enzymes and that the modifier effects of other substrates are secondary. Substrates and DPN exert their modifying influence from the substrate site and not from a different modifier site, which, in the case of isocitrate dehydrogenase, is highly specific for ADP.

The function of activity control of isocitrate dehydrogenas in the hydrogen transfer from isocitrate to the TPN or DPN has been discussed (17). With increasing levels of ADP, more hydrogen will be directed into the DPN system in accordance with its role in the oxidative degradation. Thus, this control coordinates the activity of DPN-linked isocitrate dehydrogenase with the availability of ADP to the respiratory chain. When oxidation in the respiratory chain is inhibited due to a lack of ADP, activity control of the isocitrate dehydrogenase may prevent an accumulation of citric acid cycle substrates, because of its position at the entrance of the cycle. Thus, as a result of the inhibition of this enzyme, a rather high level of isocitrate or citrate would be maintained which may exert other controls, such as that on phosphofructokinase discussed in this colloquium.

(Part of this paper was presented orally at the VIth International Congress of Biochemistry, in the Symposium on "Metabolism and its Control". cf. Abstract IX - S15).

REFERENCES

1. Lardy, H. A., and Wellman, H., J. Biol. Chem., 195, 25 (1952).
2. Chance, B., and Williams, G. R., Adv. Enzymol., 17, 65 (1956).
3. Klingenberg, M., Angew. Chem., 75, 900 (1963).
4. Chance, B., and Williams, G. R., J. Biol. Chem., 217, 409 (1955).
5. Klingenberg, M., Slenczka, W., and Ritt, E., Biochem. Z., 332, 47 (1959).
6. Bücher, Th., and Klingenberg, M., Angew. Chem., 70, 552 (1958).
7. Hohorst, H., Kreutz, F., and Bücher, Th., Biochem. Z., 332, 18 (1959).
8. Klingenberg, M., Tagung in Wein, Sept. 1962. Symposium über "Redoxfunktionen cytoplasmatischer Struckturen", p. 163.
9. Tager, J. M., and Slater, B., Biochim. Biophys. Acta, 77, 258 (1963).
10. Klingenberg, M., Vortrag auf dem 11. Mosbacher Kolloquium über: "Zur Bedeutung der freien Nukleotide", Springer Verlag, Heidelberg, 1961, p. 82.
11. Klingenberg, M., Fed. Proc., 22, 527 (1963).
12. Klingenberg, M., in Energy-Linked Functions of Mitochondria, (B. Chance, ed.), Academic Press, New York, 1963, p. 121.
13. Pfaff, E., and Klingenberg, M., Biochim. Biophys. Acta, in the press.
14. Klingenberg, M., and Pfaff, E., in Proceedings of the Symposium on Regulation of Metabolic Processes in Mitochondria, Elsevier Publishing Company, in the press.
15. Schwalbach, personal communication.
16. Klingenberg, M., Goebell, H., and Wenske, G., Biochem. Z., 341, 199 (1965).
17. Goeball, H., and Klingeberg, M., Biochem. Z., 340, 441 (1964).

ADP AND P_i CONTROL IN ASCITES TUMOR CELLS

P. K. Maitra and B. Chance

Johnson Research Foundation, University of Pennsylvania
Philadelphia, Pennsylvania

The discovery of the oxidation of reduced pyridine nucleotides upon addition of ADP to isolated mitochondria and on the stimulation of excised sartorius muscle (1,2) has made available a direct non-destructive assay for metabolite transitions which involve changes in the concentration of this critical control substance. The addition of glucose to ascites tumor cells or to suspensions of Baker's yeast cells provides another example of a transition in the steady state of respiratory enzymes which could be attributed to increases in intracellular ADP concentration (3) in ascites or yeast cells which are in the controlled state (State 4)(4). The preliminary observations have now been documented in detail (5-14). When hormonal responses are not of primary interest, cell suspensions have particular advantages for the study of rapid transients of glycolytic intermediates, since the cells can be more easily depleted of glucose and the mixing time in the cell suspension is shorter than in the tissue.

Stimulation of cell respiration is a general phenomenon caused by adding substances which are phosphorylated by ATP. The rapid penetration of glucose and the high hexokinase activity afford a fast rise of intracellular ADP. This results in a rapid transition from the resting to the active state of respiratory metabolism (State 4-3) and is accompanied by a rise of ADP and a fall of phosphate within the cell, a reaction which can be employed to determine the energy status of the cell -- whether it is in the resting State 4, the active State 3, or at an intermediate state.

The initial energy demand due to phosphorylation of glucose serves to stimulate respiratory metabolism only momentarily; ascites tumor cells and yeast cells exhibit stimulated respiration for about a minute. There has been a great deal of discussion as to whether the slowing of respiration was due to a lowering of the ADP level (15), a lowering of the phosphate level (16,17,18), a change of adenylate kinase control (19), or a change of intracellular pH (20). The phenomenon is further studied here.

Control phenomena in sequential enzymes are of general interest, and control mechanisms in ascites tumor cells afford unusual experimental material for the demonstration of metabolic control principles (21). Mechanisms which control the initial phases of glucose metabolism are generally of interest but in particular because they stimulate metabolic controls in the *in vivo* environment of the mouse peritoneum (22). The development of rapid kinetic methods for the continuous read-out of the intracellular concentrations has been essential for a formulation of metabolic control principles (23). Optical methods are limited to read-out of single components in the mitochondrial and cytoplasmic spaces, for example, cytochrome b and DPNH (23). These methods indicate the response times of intracellular events to be inthe range of simple sampling methods (24) and verified their applicability to measurements of the principle kinetic intermediates of the glycolytic system. This information is essential for a detailed understanding of the metabolic control phenomena involved, and a number of attempts along these lines have already been made (19,25), where the enzymatic methods for metabolite assay (24,26,27) give practically continuous information on possible control intermediates under appropriate metabolic conditions. Two phenomena in particular are studied: the activation of respiratory metabolism by glucose addition (3) and feedback control of glucose utilization under aerobic and anaerobic conditions (3).

The various hypotheses invoked to explain these phenomena, ATP compartmentation (3,15) or feedback control of the glycolytic system, are examined in detail and may be compared with similar results on metabolic control phenomena in yeast cells under non-oscillatory (13) or oscillatory conditions (28,29,30).

Experimental Methods

The Ehrlich-Lettré hyperdiploid ascites tumor strain was obtained from Dr. C. E. Wenner at the Roswell Park Institute and from Dr. Revesz at the Karolinska Institute. The tumors were grown in Hauschka/ICR mice by weekly transfer of 0.2 ml of a 7 day growth. The cells were harvested on the 7th day and were found to be essentially blood-free. The reaction medium contained 20 mM triethanolamine, 154 mM NaCl and 6 mM KCl at pH 7.2. The cells were washed twice in the medium by centrifugation at room temperature and were kept aerated by occasional gentle shaking. The temperature of the experiment was 22-26°. Cell concentrations were obtained by using the factor that 1 mg wet weight contained 10^6 cells (8). Determinations of oxygen consumption were made by a Clark oxygen electrode or rotating electrode. Samples were withdrawn every few seconds. Fluorometric methods were employed for the assay of DPNH directly in the cells or for the analysis of metabolites (27,31), and phosphate was determined by the method of Fiske and Subba Row (32).

Experimental Results

ADP control of respiratory activation. A detailed kinetic analysis of the changes of nucleotides that accompany the activation of respiration on adding glucose to an aerobic suspension of ascites tumor cells is indicated in Figure 1A. On adding glucose, the top trace shows respiratory activation from 0.48 to 0.97 µM O_2/ min x g cells for an interval of 40 seconds. The initial value of the ATP/ADP ratio is about 1. On addition of glucose the bottom traces indicate an abrupt rise of ADP to a maximum accompanied by an abrupt fall of ATP and phosphate and a slight rise of AMP, the State 4-3 transition due to increased ADP. At the end of the 40 second interval ADP drops rapidly to a value lower than it had prior to the addition of glucose, as does the respiratory rate which falls to 0.21 µmole/ g cells x min. ATP falls slightly and AMP rises slowly. Of considerable interest is the fall of phosphate to 6 µmoles/g of cells and its slight rise in the inhibited stage of respiration while ATP is still falling. These data lead us to conclude that under these conditions the State 3-4 transition was caused by a fall of the ADP concentration, in confirmation of our previous conclusions (31). Evidence favoring this is the rise of phosphate in the inhibited phase. Also the abrupt diminution of respiratory activity corresponds to a sufficiently small change of oxygen concentration that ADP control at a K_m value of 30 µM was indicated (10)*.

ADP and phosphate control. It is found empirically that pre-treatment of the cells with a low concentration of glucose (33) leads to a different relationship of nucleotides in the inhibited phase of respiration. In Figure 1C an ascites tumor cell suspension, which in this case has initially an ATP/ADP ratio of 7, is pre-treated with 33 µM glucose which causes small changes in ADP, ATP and phosphate.

Three minutes later, the cells are treated with a high concentration of glucose (10 mM) and independent measurements indicate respiratory inhibition as in Figure 1A. The kinetics of

* The respiratory rate falls to half maximal value without a change of oxygen concentration of 5.2 µM at an ADP/O_2 of 6. This corresponds to an ADP concentration of 31 µM.

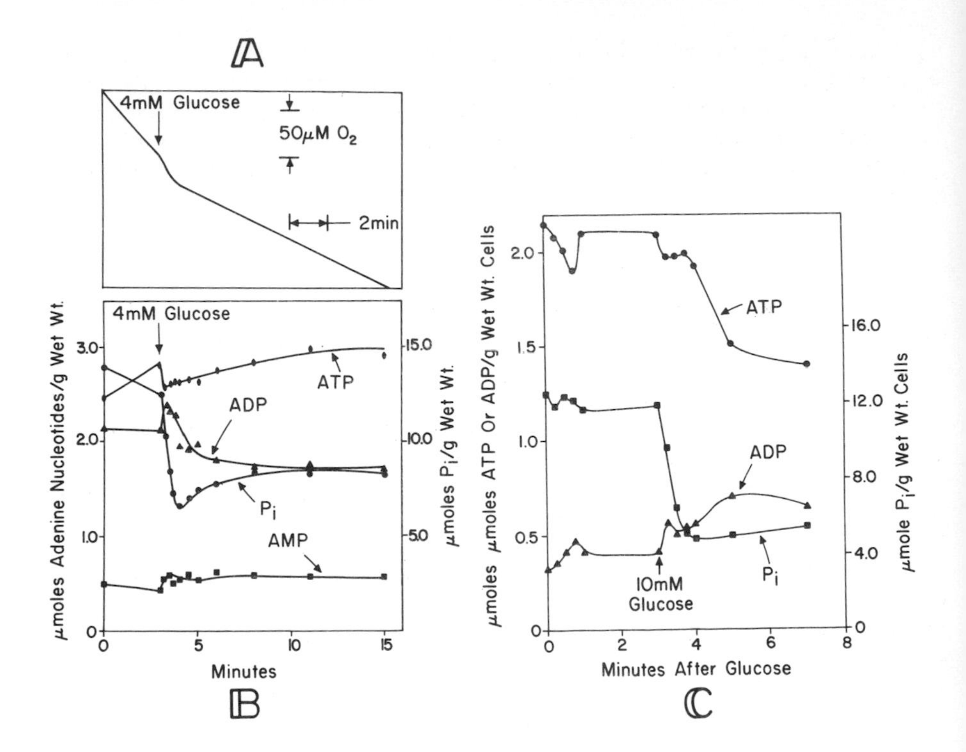

Figure 1. A) and B) Time course of changes of intracellular adenine nucleotides and P_i in an aerobic suspension of Ehrlich-Lettré hyperdiploid ascites tumor cells suspended in 20 mM triethanolamine, 154 mM NaCl, 6 mM KCl, pH 7.2, containing 5 x 10^7 cells/ml. The suspension was aerated for three minutes before taking the first sample at the start of the experiment (point marked zero time). The ordinates of Figure 1B represent intracellular materials in μmoles/gm wet weight of cells. The oxygen trace was obtained by a Clark electrode in a replicate experiment done in an airtight vessel. The units for the ordinate and abcissa are included in this graph. Temperature 23°. C) Kinetics of intracellular nucleotides in P_i in aerobic ascites tumor cells caused by consecutive addition of low (33 μM) and high (10 mM) concentrations of glucose. After harvesting the cells were aerated for 10 minutes before being diluted to 1.3 x 10^8 cells/ml and used in the experiment indicated here. (PKM 18,48).

the adenine nucleotides are very similar to those of Figure 1A for the first 20 seconds, namely a drop of ATP, a rise of ADP, and then a fall of P_i. It soon becomes apparent that the phosphate concentration has fallen to a critical level (~ 5 μmoles/gm wet weight) so that the phosphorylation of ADP is slowed. There follows a rise in the ADP level, an abrupt drop of the

ATP level and a slight decrease in the sum of ATP and ADP. (In other experiments of this type the total adenine nucleotide level is found to remain constant).

Phosphate control following addition of glucose to iodo-acetate inhibited cells, or to 2-deoxyglucose (2-DOG) to uninhibited cells can also be observed, although here the relationships of ATP, and ADP are obscured by the loss of nucleotides about a minute after adding 2-DOG. Thus, the phosphate control resulting from a glycolytic block and a phosphate trap leads to an abnormal state of ascites cells in particular, and perhaps other cells as well (13).

Kinetics of glycolytic intermediates in glucose-activated respiration. While the foregoing considerations have adequately identified the control phenomena for respiratory activation and inhibition, the cause of the inhibition of glucose utilization is a more complex phenomenon (but cf. 25,35,36). Figure 2 indicates more detailed metabolite and nucleotide assays of aerobic ascites cells. In order to more precisely define the metabolic state, three additions of glucose are made, two of low concentration. 100 and 200 μM and one of high concentration, 2 mM. Nucleotides and phosphate change (Figure 2A) as in Figure 1B where glucose additions cause cycles of increase and decrease of ADP and converse changes in ATP, together with monotonic decreases of phosphate, all typical of ADP control. The ADP levels in these cells are lower than those of Figure 1, being approximately 0.4 μmoles/gm of cells with a glucose-induced fluctuation of 0.2 μmoles/gm, the ATP/ADP ratio being approximately 10:1. Prior to the addition of a high concentration of glucose the phosphate level had fallen to 6 μmoles/g. With the addition of 2 mM glucose, phosphate falls to 4 μmoles/gm while ATP and ADP can no longer change cyclically; ADP rises to a plateau value, then rises further and ATP shows converse responses (cf. Figure 1B), indicating that phosphate control follows ADP control.

Metabolite assays of Figure 2B show that each addition of a low concentration of glucose is substantially depleted in the the two minutes that intervene between additions. However, glucose-6-P (G-6-P) accumulates to a significant level between additions (approximately 0.5 μmoles/gm). These results, combined with the rapid disappearance of glucose indicate that the hexokinase is highly active in the presence of this concentration of G-6-P. On the third addition of glucose, G-6-P rises very rapidly to 1.7 μmoles/gm and glucose (now plotted on a smaller scale) is used rapidly for one minute. Thereafter inhibition occurs*. Fructose diphosphate (FDP) and triose

* The final Q-glucose was roughly 40 % of the maximal rate.

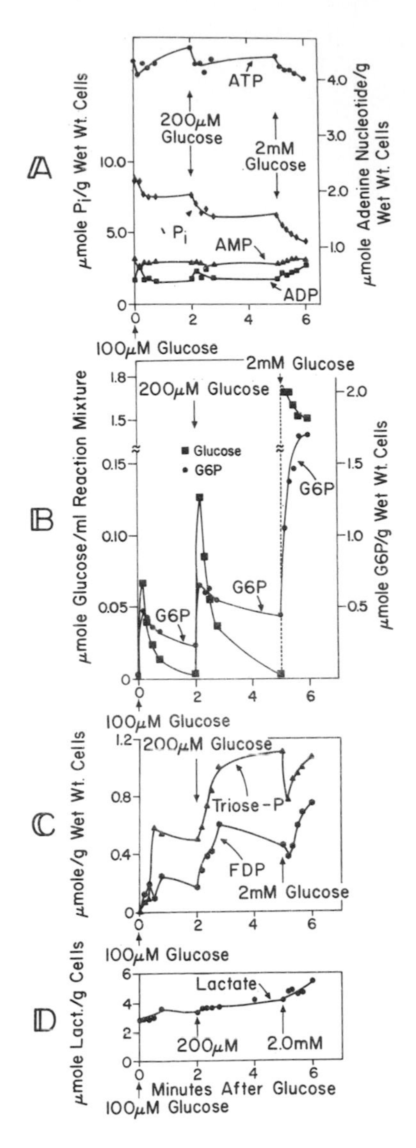

Figure 2. Effect of serial additions of 100 μM, 200 μM and 2 mM concentrations of glucose on the response of nucleotides, phosphate and glycolytic intermediates in a suspension of Ehrlich-Lettré ascites tumor cells. The medium is that described in Figure 1. The cell concentration is 5.4×10^7 cells/ml. The temperature is 23°. (PKM 54).

phosphate (triose-P)(Figure 2C) rise step-wise with the two additions of glucose. On the second addition of glucose, FDP rises to a plateau value and then rises further to a peak that decays slowly while the triose-P rises monotonically to a plateau value. The pathway G-6-P to FDP and triose-P is highly active in spite of the high ATP/ADP ratio, which might otherwise have been expected to inhibit PFK.

The third addition of 2 mM glucose causes most interesting and significant changes in the metabolite pattern. The immediate response upon adding this high concentration of glucose is a rapid rise of G-6-P to a plateau value higher than was obtained in the two previous records. It is apparent that the pathway to G-6-P is not rate-limiting under these conditions. Interesting anomalies occur in the FDP and triose-P kinetics where a small fall in the former and a large fall in the latter are recorded. It is apparent that the formation of FDP from G-6-P (and F-6-P) and the formation of triose-P from FDP is now relatively slower than their utilization; the crossover point for the activation of flux by glucose addition lies further along the glycolytic chain than triose-P, presumably at PGK, activated by the rise of the ADP concentration.

After a momentary fall, FDP and triose-P rise rapidly to the approximate range of values that were obtained before the addition of glucose. But at this point, the rate of glucose utilization has fallen and G-6-P remains high. ATP has, however, failed to return to its initial level; ADP and AMP have risen above their previous values and phosphate has fallen. It is, however, difficult to identify the metabolic control with phosphate since triose-P rises no further in the phosphate-depleted state following the addition of 2 mM glucose than prior to the addition of this higher concentration of glucose. Thus, other explanations must be sought, and one of them is the possibility that product inhibition of GAPDH is already dominating the activity of this step due to the accumulation of 1,3-diphosphoglycerate (an intermediate that was present in too small concentrations to permit an accurate assay). Thus, even when phosphate is depleted, the consequent further rise of triose-P is not observed and it is probable that the metabolic control mechanisms involve PFK, GAPDH and PGK as well.

Control of anaerobic* glycolysis in ascites tumor cells. The foregoing experiments under aerobic conditions suggest the desirability of determining the control parameters for these experimental conditions in the anaerobic state. In these experiments, the cells are treated with 0.5 mM Na_2S for three minutes prior to the addition of 0.5 mM glucose (time = 0)(see Figure 3A). This graph shows the kinetics of glucose utilization to be similar to those of the preceding figures, namely, the low concentration of glucose is rapidly and almost completely

*In the following, the term "anaerobic" will be applied to respiration-inhibited cells; insofar as metabolic control is concerned, the systems are the same.

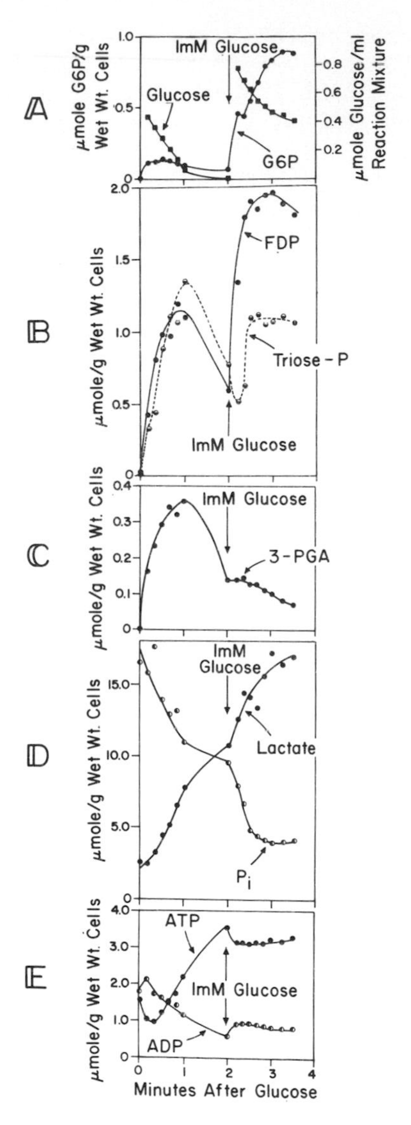

Figure 3. The effect of consecutive additions of glucose (0.5 and 1 mM) upon the kinetics of glucose utilization and metabolites, nucleotides and phosphate in a suspension of Ehrlich-Lettré ascites tumor cells pretreated with 0.5 mM sodium sulfide for 3 minutes prior to the addition of glucose. The cell concentration is 8.2 x 10^7 cells/ml. (PKM 62,63).

expended while the high concentrations of glucose show a rapid utilization for only about a minute.

It is noteworthy that the G-6-P levels are lower in the anaerobic than in the aerobic cells (compare Figure 3A with

Figure 2B). Furthermore, the level of G-6-P which remains after the utilization of glucose is also lower in the anaerobic cells than in the aerobic cells. This may be correlated with anaerobic and aerobic FDP levels. Figure 3B indicates 1.2 μM/gm wet weight of cells and Figure 2C indicates approximately .6 μM/gm wet weight of cells. It is apparent that the pathway from G-6-P to FDP is more highly activated under anaerobic conditions. It is also significant that considerable lactate is produced on the first addition of glucose. The initial low value of the ATP/ADP ratio, and its rise after the added glucose has been expended, suggests that it is responsible for the initial high activity of PFK and its inhibition after glucose has been expended. This low ATP/ADP ratio of the anaerobic system has not prevented the accumulation of triose-P to very nearly the same extent as in the aerobic cells, and it is probable that the product inhibition at GAPDH operates over a wide range of ATP/ADP ratios.

The time sequence of the rise of FDP and triose-P is in accordance with that required from the known sequence of steps in glycolysis. This result is a distinct contrast from that obtained in aerobic experiments using phosphate-labelling according to Lonberg-Holm who finds triose-P to rise before FDP (25).

The second addition of 1 mM glucose causes a further rise of G-6-P to a level which is about half that obtained under aerobic conditions. Furthermore, there is a distinct inflection point in the rise of FDP (see also Figure 2C). The same effect is observed less distincly in Figure 2C. This inflection point suggests a time sequence in which the initiation of G-6-P utilization precedes the "turning on" of G-6-P formation. Since this inflection point is not clearly shown in the FDP kinetics, it may be more closely related to the abrupt drop in triose-P concentration which lasts briefly after the addition of glucose. This drop of triose-P is shown clearly in the aerobic conditions; however, PFK is apparently activated adequately so that no drop in FDP is noted, only the inflection point in G-6-P kinetics remains. Thus, generally the kinetics of the intermediates in aerobiosis and anaerobiosis are similar, except for a greater activation at the PFK step. It is noteworthy that the level of triose-P has failed to rise after the second addition of glucose and the further depletion of phosphate (Figure 3B), which thus supports the arguments presented in connection with the aerobic results that phosphate depletion does not enhance the levels of triose-P.

Figure 3C illustrates the kinetics of 3-PGA which rise to a maximum on the first addition of glucose, but on the second addition of glucose this falling trend is delayed, but only for about half a minute. Figure 3D shows that the formation of lactate exhibits a slight induction on the first addition of glucose (presumably an interval equal to the time required for intermediates to fill the "empty spaces" in the glycolytic chain between glucose and lactate) and on the second addition of glucose, lactate production starts immediately and proceeds at a higher rate for approximately a minute, then levelling off. Thereafter the similarity of the rates of lactate formation and phosphate utilization suggests that the pool sizes are now negligible compared to the flux through the chain under anaerobic conditions, and that no step between triose-P dehydrogenase and lactate dehydrogenase limits the flux in the transient state. For example, following the first and second additions of glucose, the lactate and phosphate rates are respectively 6.5, 6.4 and 8.0, 9.0 μmoles/gm wet weight of cells.

The phosphate and nucleotide assays are included in Figures 3D and 3E. Phosphate falls monotonically with both additions of glucose and reaches approximately 4 μmoles/gm wet weight. ADP and ATP show typical responses for low glucose concentrations, namely ADP rises and falls and ATP falls and rises to give a value of about 6 for the ATP/ADP ratio as compared to the initial value of 1. The initial ATP level is, however, fully adequate to activate hexokinase and cause quantitative conversion of the lower concentration of glucose to G-6-P and other intermediates. ADP rises momentarily during the utilization of glucose but falls as glycolytic intermediates accumulate, so that the ATP/ADP ratio at the time of the second glucose addition is 6. Under these conditions, the second addition of glucose causes a fall of ATP and a rise of ADP which, during the duration of the experiment, fails to fall again.

The lactate kinetics differ from those observed in aerobic cells (see Figure 2). Here the ratio of rates before and after the higher glucose addition is 5:1, but the average of a large number of experiments suggests this rate to be generally 2:1.

Discussion

Transients in respiratory and glycolytic metabolism following the addition of glucose to aerobic suspensions of ascites tumor cells have led to a more detailed study of the reaction mechanisms involved than has been possible in the case of other systems (12). A mechanism was proposed that was consistent with the experimental data available at that time for the oxygen and glucose kinetics. Now considerably more experimental data are available, particularly on glycolytic control mechanisms and control sites not available in previous studies.

The ADP activation of resting respiration in the ascites tumor cell suspension caused by glucose addition has been verified and studied in greater detail. The resting-active transition (State 4-3 change) is characterized by synchronized changes in the mitochondrial respiratory carriers and the ATP and ADP levels, but only slight changes of AMP occur under these conditions. The termination of activated respiration at one minute may have two causes. First, the fall of ADP concentration restores respiratory control in accord with our previous conclusion (11). Secondly, it is shown here that when a high concentration of glucose is preceded by a low concentration of glucose the fall of phosphate concentration can be sufficient to inhibit phosphorylation and cause ADP to rise above the State 3 level. This type of transition is observed when 2-DOG is the substrate, or when the iodoacetate inhibits glycolysis. Phosphate control is associated with a rapid loss of nucleotides from the cell under conditions that prevent turnover of phosphorylated intermediates of glycolysis. We may summarize our viewpoint as follows: a cell with a high ATP/ADP ratio is under ADP control and will respond to glucose addition with a rise of ADP, leading to activation of respiration and possibly some glycolysis as well. This situation will persist until (1) the glucose is depleted (especially true of the experiments where the cell concentration is high), (2) the metabolite pools rise to levels where "multi-site" control of glycolysis slackens the rate, and (3) the phosphate pool is depleted in the presence of excess glucose. In cases 1 and 2 the ATP/ADP ratio will return to its initial value, while in case 3, the ATP/ADP ratio can no longer be maintained high. The sequence of events is, in any case, 1 → 2 → 3; ADP control will precede an eventual phosphate control.

In both aerobic and anaerobic cells the metabolite controls which lead to inhibition of glucose utilization one minute after the addition of a high concentration of glucose are consistent with an adequately active hexokinase; relatively high G-6-P levels can be increased rapidly by further additions of glucose. The relationship between hexokinase activity, the G-6-P concentration and the ATP/ADP ratio is apparently not a crucial one. For example, the G-6-P and FDP levels are maintained high even in the respiration-inhibited cell with an ATP/ADP ratio ranging from 1 to 6. Also the transfer from G-6-P to FDP appears adequate to carry the maximum rate of lactate production aerobically or anaerobically except for a small plateau observed in Figure 3A; then it is just equal to the task. A heavy demand is placed upon the triose-P pool on a second addition of glucose and causes a dip in concentration that suggests a momentary rate limitation at the aldolase-triose-P isomerase steps.

One of the remarkable phenomena revealed by these studies is the failure to accumulate triose-P under conditions where the phosphate concentration has fallen to the point that the ADP level rises and glucose utilization declines. We may attribute the failure to accumulate an increased amount of triose-P to the possibility that GAPDH is already mostly under control of its product. We must, nevertheless, conclude that phosphate control, if it occurs, is distributed over the glycolytic chain rather than concentrated at GAPDH. Thus, under the very conditions where we would have expected phosphate control, clear evidence of an accumulation of large amounts of triose-P is not observed. Nor is there a clear-cut crossover point between triose-P and 3-PGA. The latter is maintained at nearly a constant level during the maximum rate of lactate formation in anaerobiosis (Figure 3A). This indicates that triose-P dehydrogenase and PFK activities are at least equal to the metabolic load placed upon them by the activity of pyruvate kinase.

The generally similar kinetics and steady state levels of glycolytic intermediates in aerobiosis and anaerobiosis suggests a common denominator in the control mechanism, in spite of a more rapid initial rate of lactate formation in anaerobiosis than in aerobiosis (5-fold in Figures 2 and 3, but 2-fold on the average). At maximal flux values (indicated by the lactate rate) the responses are very similar, the most characteristic response being a drop of triose-P concentration following the second addition of a high glucose concentration as observed in Figures 2 and 3. At minimal fluxes in the inhibited phase of glucose utilization following the final addition of glucose, FDP is lower than triose-P in the aerobic cells and vice versa in the anaerobic cells. In addition, G-6-P is relatively lower in the latter case. Both results are consistent with a lower activity of PFK aerobically than anaerobically. It is difficult, however, to find clear-cut evidence for ATP, ADP or phosphate control in these two conditions; the ATP/ADP ratio is 6 in aerobiosis and 4 in anaerobiosis, and the phosphate concentrations are 4.4 as compared with 5.1 μmoles/gm wet weight of cells; the $[ATP]/[ADP][P_i]$ value is 1350 M^{-1} aerobically and 824 M^{-1} anaerobically. The available data for PFK control (37) makes it unlikely that the small changes of these components at the high levels already existing can be a significant control factor. Large changes in AMP due to adenylate kinase are not observed. Since these concentrations are averaged over the whole cell volume, it is possible that the distribution of nucleotides and orthophosphate in the cytoplasmic and mitochondrial spaces or in other cell structures is different in aerobiosis and in anaerobiosis, and that the compartmentation of adenine nucleotides may be invoked as one of the explanations of these different activities of the glycolytic system.

Control levels for ADP and phosphate. Control of metabolic flux by ADP and phosphate occurs at higher concentrations averaged over the cell volume as compared to the Michaelis constants for the control substances measured *in vitro*. Taking first, the data for ADP, it is observed in Figure 1A under the particular conditions where ADP is clearly identified as the control substance, that an increase from 2.1 to 2.4 μmoles ADP/gm fresh weight of cells leads to a State 4-3 transition and a State 3-4 transition occurs with a drop from 2.4 to approximately 1.8 μmoles/gm. These concentrations are about 10^3 times greater than the ADP concentration at which respiratory control is obtained (38); activation and inhibition of respiration comparable to that observed in Figure 1A would require a rise and a fall of the ADP concentration in the range of 50 to 1 μM. The discrepancy is even greater when the possibility of ADP localization in a specific cell compartment is considered (36). This discrepancy remains one of the most important unsolved problems in analytical biochemistry for which we have two possible explanations (36). The first is that ATP is broken down in the extraction procedure -- a hypothesis that becomes weaker and weaker as sampling methods improve and give the same analytical values (24) or secondly, and more likely, that the ADP is highly compartmented and only a few tenths of a per cent is available for the interactions of glycolysis and respiration.

A similar problem is encountered in considering phosphate control where, for example, in Figure 1C a change between approximately 6 and 4 μmoles/gm fresh weight of cells is observed to inhibit ATP formation in the cell, as compared with 50 to 100 μM phosphate, the expected value at which respiratory control would be established in isolated mitochondria. While the discrepancy is not so large as with ADP (between 50 and 100), nevertheless the same alternatives must be considered for phosphate as for ADP.

The resolution of this biochemical problem may lie beyond the sensitivity of available physical methods. However, one approach is that of microspectrophotometry of adenine nucleotides (at 260 mμ) in various compartments of a single ascites cell during the various metabolic regulations described here.

The phosphate potential (ATP/ADP) has been computed for anaerobic ascites cells on the basis of the extent of reversed electron transfer observed in terms of the oxidation of reduced cytochrome c, and values between 10^4 and 10^5 have been obtained. (39). If the intracellular phosphate concentration were 5 mM, a ratio of ATP to ADP between 50 and 500 would be computed on this basis. However, ATP/ADP ratios in anaerobic cells of less than 10 are observed (Figure 3E) suggesting that the free phosphate concentration is between 0.1 and 1.0 mM, the lower value agreeing well with that estimated from the phosphate control response shown for example, in Figure 1C for aerobic cells, or from Figure 3D for anaerobic cells.

Metabolic control by ATP compartmentation. Hypotheses for metabolic control have been based upon the assumption of compartmentation (40). Our particular version of this hypothesis attempted to explain the coincidence of inhibition of glucose utilization and of respiration to be due to compartmentation of newly phosphorylated ATP in mitochondria which was then unavailable for the initiation of the first steps of glycolysis.

Two observations indicate that ATP compartmentation may be an oversimplification of the actual control mechanism. The first of these is the observation that the initial rush and subsequent inhibition of glucose utilization observed in the aerobic cells is also found to occur anaerobically. The second consideration is that the depletion of the cytoplasm of ATP by compartmentation in the mitochondrial space is likely to lead to an activation not an inhibition of glycolytic flux, particularly under conditions where ADP is controlling (30). There appear, nevertheless, two and possibly more instances in which compartmentation is of importance, first as a general phenomenon to lower the average concentrations of ATP, ADP and phosphate as well to values which fall within the range of control properties of the mitochondrial and cytoplasmic enzymes (see paragraph above) and secondly, to provide an adequate explanation for the control of the oxidation of endogenous substrate by glucose addition (41). Here ATP compartmentation involving a special relationship between mitochondria and hexokinase appear to be required by the experimental data (41).

G-6-P control of hexokinase. In agreement with Rose and Wenner (42,43) there is a superficial agreement between the lactate rates and the G-6-P concentration in aerobiosis and anaerobiosis. Under these conditions the G-6-P ratio is 2 to 1 and the ratio of the lactate rates is 1 to 2 on the average, although in these particular experiments (Figures 2 and 3) the ratio is 1 to 5. Thus there is general agreement between these data and the data presented elsewhere on the inverse correlation of lactate rates and G-6-P concentrations.

If we now examine more critically the role of G-6-P as a regulatory substance in aerobic and anaerobic glycolysis of the tumor cells, we find that the above-mentioned relationships might be a consequence rather than a cause of metabolic control. For example, Figure 2 gives an aerobic G-6-P level of 0.5 μmoles/gm and this level is not inhibitory to a greatly accelerated production of G-6-P caused by the addition of a higher concentration of glucose. Thereupon the G-6-P level rises monotonically to 1.7 μmoles/gm when inhibition of glucose utilization occurs. Whatever the inhibitory effect of G-6-P upon hexokinase may be, the net activity is adequate to maintain a high G-6-P concentration in the inhibited phase of glycolytic activity, particularly under conditions of low phosphate concentration -- which could lead to a further inactivation of hexokinase. In fact, only once in this series of assays was evidence of a rate limitation at the hexokinase step observed, and then only in the transitory plateau in the rise of G-6-P following the addition of a high concentration of glucose (Figure 3A).

Effective control of flux by product inhibition requires the special circumstances nicely exemplified by the high sensitivity of GAPDH to 1,3-PGA where only micromolar concentrations are required. Furthermore, these concentrations are insufficient to activate the following step, PGK. In the case of hexokinase, product inhibition occurs at the concentrations of G-6-P, and is adequate to form large amounts of FDP. Thus, the chief role of product inhibition of hexokinase would appear to limit the size of the G-6-P pool, and the inverse correlation between the G-6-P level and lactate rate is probably fortuitous.

A similar example of misinterpretations of inverse relationships between pool sizes and fluxes might well have occurred in our previous studies of the respiratory chain where there is an inverse correlation between the DPNH concentration in the mitochondria and the respiratory rate. It is apparent, however, that the high concentration of DPNH is not due to product inhibition of the dehydrogenases but to other control sites in the system.

In summary, we conclude that the control of flux through the glycolytic chain is not caused by product inhibition of hexokinase, but is distributed over the glycolytic system in the multi-site fashion described above.

The Kinesine hypothesis. For some time the Leningrad group under S. A. Neifakh has proposed the release of a specific activator of glycolysis from the mitochondrial membranes (44) and the results have been published in more detail since (45). This hypothesis identifies the activation of glycolysis with the liberation of kinesine and ATP from the mitochondrial membrane, essentially an ATP-retention hypothesis but implicating a glycolysis-activating factor, in addition to ATP.

Oscillations of glycolytic intermediates in cell-free extracts show flux changes controlled by the ATP/ADP ratio (30).

Here, mitochondria are absent and the compartmentation and kinesine hypotheses are inapplicable. Nevertheless, effective control of the metabolic flow through the glycolytic system occurs repetitively during the oscillations. Only one cycle of oscillation is observed under aerobic conditions due to the high damping provided by the mitochondrial phosphorylation of ADP, a mechanism that does not appear to require the presence of kinesine or require a change in its concentration if it is present. Mitochondria appear to intensify ADP control of glycolysis simply by virtue of their high affinity for ADP.

The Pasteur reaction. Cells adequately provided with substrate, and prepared from its growth environment have in our hands, been found uniformly to be under ADP control. It is further possible to exhaust the phosphate pool of such cells by continued glycolysis in the absence of phosphate or by the addition of phosphate traps such as 2-DOG, and again to demonstrate phosphate control. It seems apparent, however, that adenine nucleotide control is of primary importance, and probably the more physiological one. Our work here, however, emphasizes the importance of the cooperative control of the glycolytic systems, which may involve the compartmentation of nucleotides and phosphate. The control at various sites along the chain is shown to be of particular importance in these studies by a cooperation of glyceraldehyde-3-phosphate dehydrogenase and PGK which respond to ADP or phosphate. While glycolysis may have its own regulatory controls, mitochondria may exert a supervisory influence which modifies the control pattern and thereby produces the Pasteur effect.

Relations to oscillations of glycolytic intermediates. Control properties of glycolysis in the ascites tumor cell suspension may usefully be compared to the properties observed in the oscillating system of glycolytic intermediates in cell-free extracts or in intact cells of *Saccharomyces carlsbergensis* (28,29,30). The multi-point control of glycolytic activity proposed here is an essential feature of the oscillatory mechanism involving the cooperation of PFK with glycerol-3-P dehydrogenase and 3-PGK. Another feature in common is that at maximal fluxes, a limitation between FDP and triose-P (aldolase or triose-P isomerase) is observed. On the other hand, the control of glucose utilization and lactate formation which is released in anaerobiosis in the ascites cell is less marked in Baker's yeast cells. A point of interest here is the observation (46) that the ATPase activity of intact yeast cells is approximately 6 times that of ascites tumor cells supplemented with dicumarol. This would lead to a higher concentration of glycolytic intermediates in the ascites tumor cell and a lower relative steady state rate of aerobic glycolysis.

Summary

1) In suspensions of ascites tumor cells, mitochondrial regulation of the intracellular ADP level allows stimulation of respiration by glucose.

2) Inhibition of glucose-activated respiration is usually due to depletion of ADP in the cytoplasm, but phosphate regulation of mitochondria and glycolytic activities may be observed when successive additions of small concentrations of glucose deplete intracellular phosphate.

3) The initial high rate of glucose utilization is followed by an inhibition which leaves high levels of glycolytic intermediates distributed along the glycolytic chain. This is a consequence of a multi-point control phenomenon centered about the GAPDH/PGK site, although the cooperation of all the kinases in this control is essential. Similar distributions of glycolytic intermediates are observed in either ADP or phosphate control as is consistent with principle control at the GAPDH/PGK site.

4) In anaerobiosis, similar control properties of the glycolytic system are observed although the flux values are considerably higher and are attributed to the larger amounts of ADP and phosphate available to the glycolytic system.

5) While compartmentation of phosphate and ADP appear essential to reconcile the analytic data and the observed metabolic controls, it is now concluded that mitochondrial compartmentation of ATP is by no means a complete explanation of metabolic control. Our view now tends towards the multi-site control found in the oscillating glycolytic system. Such controls are distributed over the kinases of the glycolytic system. The metabolic control preserves the concentration of intermediates along the whole glycolytic chain despite widely varying rates of glucose utilization and lactate production.

6) G-6-P inhibition of hexokinase activity does not appear to be rate controlling but is probably useful to limit the size of the G-6-P pool.

References

1. Chance, B., and Williams, G. R., Fed. Proc., 13, 633 (1954).
2. Connelly, C. M., and Chance, B., Fed. Proc., 13, 94 (1954).
3. Chance, B., and Hess, B., Science, 129, 700 (1959).
4. Chance, B., J. Biol. Chem., 234, 3086 (1958).
5. Ramirez, J., J. Physiol., 147, 14 (1959).
6. Jöbsis, F. F., J. Gen. Physiol., 46, 905, 929 (1963).

7. Chance, B., and Weber, A. M., J. Physiol., 169, 263 (1963).

8. Chance, B., and Hess, B., J. Biol. Chem., 234,2404 (1959), I.

9. Chance, B., and Hess, B., J, Biol. Chem., 234, 2413 (1959), II.

10. Chance, B., and Hess, B., J. Biol. Chem., 234, 2416 (1959), III.

11. Chance, B., and Hess, B., J. Biol. Chem., 234, 2421 (1959), IV.

12. Chance, B., Garfinkel, D., Higgins, J. J., and Hess,, B., J. Biol. Chem., 235, 2426 (1960), V.

13. Maitra, P. K., and Estabrook, R. W., Biochem. Biophys. Res. Commun., 9, 1 (1962).

14. Estabrook, R. W., and Maitra, P. K., J. Biol. Chem., in the press.

15. Chance, B., and Hess, B., N. Y. Acad. Sci., 63, 1008 (1956).

16. Lynen, F., in J. Liebig, Annalen der Chemie, 546, 120 (1941).

17. Johnson, M. J., Science, 94, 241 (1941).

18. Wu, R., and Racker, E., in B. Wright (ed.), Control Mechanisms in Respiration and Fermentation, Ronald Press, Co., New York, 1963, p. 265.,

19. Ibsen, K. H., Coe, E. L., and McKee, R. W., Biochim. Biophys. Acta, 30, 384 (1958).

20. Wenner, C. E., Cerijo-Santalo, R., Arch. Biochim. Biophys., 98, 67 (1962).

21. Chance, B., in W. D. McElroy and B. Glass (eds.), The Mechanism of Enzyme Action, Johns Hopkins, Baltimore, 1954, p. 399.

22. Chance, B., unpublished data.

23. Chance, B., and Hess, B., Science, 129, 700 (1959).

24. Chance, B., in IUB/IUBS Rapid Mixing and Sampling Techniques in Biochemistry, (B. Chance, Q. H. Gibson, R. Eisenhardt, and K. K. Lonberg-Holm, eds.), Academic Press, New York, 1964, p. 39.

25. Lonberg-Holm, K. K., Biochim. Biophys. Acta, 35, 464 (1959).

26. Bergmeyer, H. U., Methods of Enzymatic Analysis, Academic Press, New York, 1963.

27. Maitra, P. K., and Estabrook, R. W., Anal. Biochem., 7, 472 (1964).

28. Chance, B., Estabrook, R. W., and Ghosh, A., Proc. Nat. Acad. Sci., 51, 337 (1964).

29. Chance, B., Hess, B., and Betz, A., Biochem. Biophys. Res. Commun., 16, 182 (1964).

30. Chance, B., Schoener, B., and Elsaessar, S., J. Biol. Chem., 240, 3170 (1965).

31. Estabrook, R. W., and Maitra, P. K., Anal. Biochem., 3, 369 (1962).

32. Fiske, C. H., and Subba Row, Y., J. Biol. Chem., 66, 375 (1925).

33. Hess, B., and Chance, B., J. Biol. Chem., 234, 3031 (1959).

34. Ibsen, K. H., Coe, E. L., and McKee,, R. W., Cancer Research, 22, 182 (1962).

35. Hess, B., in Proceedings of the Vth International Congress of Biochemistry, Pergamon Press, New York, 1963, p. 313.

36. Chance, B., in G. E. W. Wolstenholme, (ed.), Ciba Foundation Symposium on the Regulation of Cell Metabolism, Little, Brown and Company, Boston, 1959, p. 91.

37. Garfinkel, D., this volume, p. 101.

38. Chance, B., and Williams, G. R., J. Biol. Chem., 217, 383 (1955), I.

39. Chance, B., and Maitra, P. K., in B. Wright (ed.), Control Mechanisms in Respiration and Fermentation, Ronald Press Company, New York, 1963, p. 307.

40. Lynen, F., and Koenigsberger, R., Ann. Chem., 573, 60 (1951).

41. Chance, B., in Cold Spring Harbor Symposia on Quantitative Biology, 26, 289 (1961).

42. Rose, I. A., this volume, p. 177.

43. Wenner, C. E., this volume, p. 199.

44. Niefakh, S. A., in Proceedings of the VIth International Congress of Biochemistry, IX-16, New York, 1964.

45. Niefach, S. A., Biochim. Biophys. Acta, 100, 329 (1965).

46. Maitra, P. K., unpublished data.

THE CONTROL OF HEXOKINASE IN ASCITES TUMOR GLYCOLYSIS*

Irwin A. Rose

The Institute for Cancer Research
Philadelphia, Pennsylvania

The rate of glucose utilization in a cell which has rapid glucose transport and which has little or no glucose-6-P hydrolysis depends on the rate of the hexokinase step. These two conditions have been shown to hold rigorously in the ascites cells, Sarcoma-37, which we have been studying. Hence we feel that, in an intact cell experiment, the conversion of C^{14}-glucose to anions, material that is held on Dowex 1-acetate, can be taken as a measure of the hexokinase rate. This is true because the losses of radioactivity due to incorporation into polysaccharides and oxidation to CO_2 are negligible.

The hexokinase of S-37 is found to be associated with both the mitochondrial and soluble fraction of the .25 M sucrose homogenate. Of the 30 per cent of the whole cell activity that is found to be soluble about two-thirds is specifically bindable to mitochondria that have been freed of bound enzyme. Hence, by the criterion of its being bound or bindable to mitochondria, at least 90 per cent of the hexokinase activity is due to a single enzyme. Indeed the soluble and mitochondrial enzymes have grossly similar catalytic properties. As reported by McComb and Yushok (1) the tumor enzyme resembles brain hexokinase (2,3) in being strongly inhibited by G-6-P. Our data agrees with that of Fromm and Zewe (4) for the brain enzyme in finding that inhibition by G-6-P is accurately competitive with ATP in the presence of excess Mg^{++}. Using freshly prepared mitochondria in the presence of excess glucose and Mg^{++} the results shown in Table I are obtained. The value of K_m for ATP in the absence of G-6-P is similar to that reported for brain (4). The effect of G-6-P on this K_m is very large, and the Kdiss for G-6-P and enzyme at zero ATP would be in the range 0.005 - 0.015 mM.

* This work has been supported by a grant (P-340) of the American Cancer Society, and in part by USPHS CA 06927.

TABLE I

Kinetic properties of fresh Sarcoma-37 mitochondrial hexokinase

G-6-P	P_i	K_m^{ATP}	K_i^{G-6-P}
mM	mM	mM	mM
0	0	0.28	
.015	0	0.59	.014
.05	0	2.2	.007
.05	1	0.73	.031
.05	2	0.54	.053

Conditions of incubation: ^{14}C-glucose (4.6 x 10^6 cpm/µmole) 0.3 mM, imidazole buffer pH 7.2, 0.05 M, ATP 0.3-10 mM, Mg^{++}, 10 mM, and mannitol to osmolarity. The hexokinase and time of incubation at 35° were such that the G-6-P formed in the reaction should not have caused significant inhibition. The reaction was stopped with 1000 µmoles of unlabelled glucose, the whole solution placed on Dowex 1-Acetate and the ^{14}C-anions eluted with 1N NCl from the well washed column.

The finding that P_i offsets the inhibitory effect of G-6-P was first made by Tiedemann and Born (5) with Ehrlich ascites cell homogenates. These authors showed that consumption of glucose but not mannose or deoxyglucose was stimulated by added P_i and therefore correctly concluded that it was the specific inhibition by G-6-P that was being overcome by P_i. They also suggested that this might have an important relation to the Pasteur effect. Without being aware of this observation which appears not to have been followed up we traced the effect of P_i in stimulating glucose utilization in human red cells to this property of P_i (6). Figure 1 is taken from this work. Here a series of glycolyzing whole cell incubation with different amounts of methylene blue reach different steady state levels of G-6-P. A plot of 1/V utilization vs. G-6-P gives a straight line, proving the wide range regulation by G-6-P. If two such experiments are done at different levels of medium P_i the extrapolation to zero G-6-P gives a value in close agreement with the total measured hexokinase content of the cell. This agrees with our finding that P_i had little or no effect on the rate of hexokinase in the assay with TPN-glucose-6-P dehydrogenase, i.e., in the absence of G-6-P. On the other hand, the effect of P_i was to raise the apparent K_i of G-6-P. This effect is shown for the tumor mitochondrial enzyme as well. The effect of P_i is so strong as to be better than an equivalent amount of ATP. Thus, 1 mM P_i lowers the K_m ATP from 2.2 to 0.73 in the presence of .05 mM G-6-P (Table I). It should also be mentioned that the P_i effect is not shown by such other phosphate compounds as PEP, AMP and ADP.

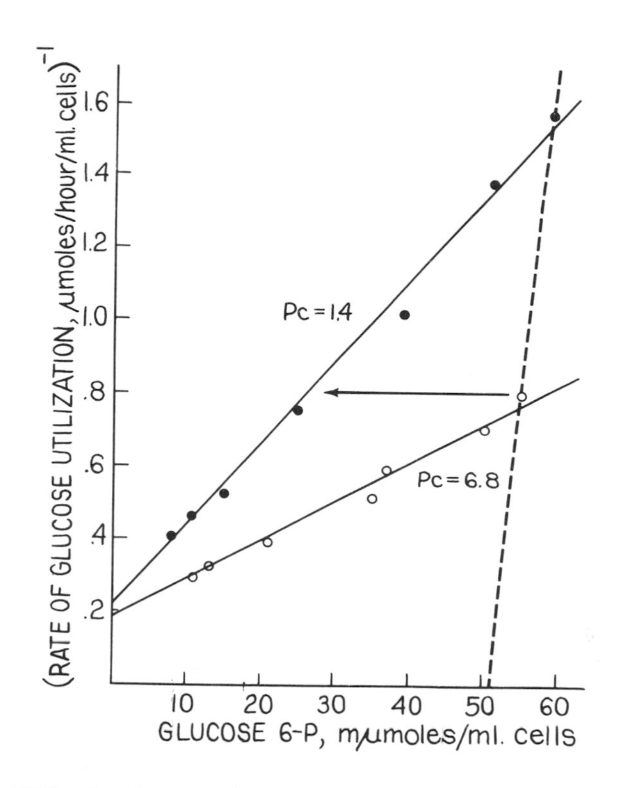

Figure 1. Effect of P_i on glucose utilization as a function of G-6-P levels of the cell. Each point represents an incubation of red blood cells with varying amounts of methylene blue and 20 mM P_i added to the medium of the "open circled" points. The steady state level of G-6-P decreased with the increasing dye. For details see Reference 6.

If, in Figure 1, the two points obtained from incubations without methylene blue but differing in cellular P_i were used to draw a line then it is clear that 1/V is not a rational function of G-6-P concentration. From these two pieces of data we can say that under the conditions of these incubations the stimulatory effect of P_i on steady state glucose utilization is about 95 percent non-classical -- that is, not due to lowering of G-6-P.

The reason I consider using only the two points of the red cell data is that when it comes to Sarcoma-37 we are unable to get a nice standard curve of 1/V utilization vs. G-6-P. For the tumor cell the glycolytic path, via PFK, is the only substantial avenue for metabolism of G-6-P so that methlyene blue or other activators of the pentose-P shunt produce only minor changes in the G-6-P concentration of the cell.

When S-37 cells were incubated aerobically in 0.1 M glycylglycine medium, pH 8.0 (invariant) the effect of added P_i first reported by Wu and Racker (7) on ascites cells is noted. In our case, with 5 mM P_i, there was a 1.7-fold increase in the steady state rate of utilization, no change in ATP and a 24 per cent fall in G-6-P. The two points with the coordinates (G-6-P, 1/V) give a line with a negative intercept on the ordinate, as seen in Figure 2. Thus, the decrease in G-6-P was inadequate to explain the increased rate. If we assume a maximal rate equal to the rate of utilization in the first 10 seconds fol-

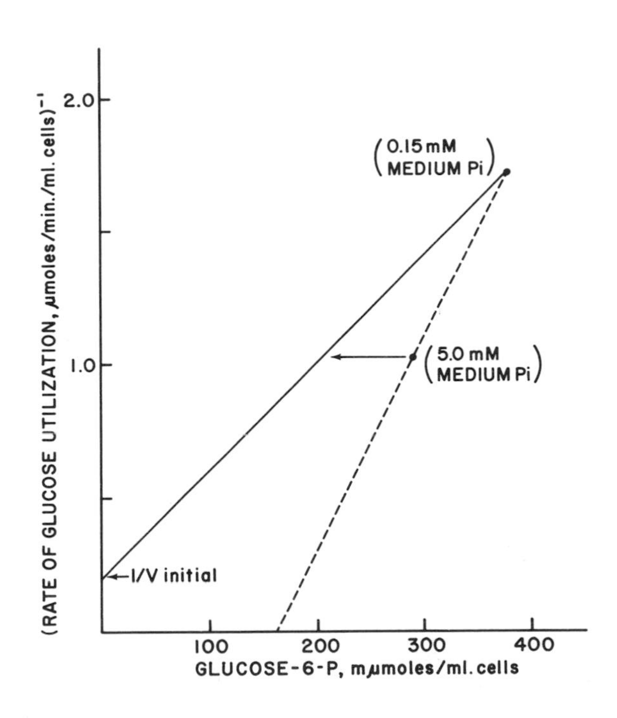

Figure 2. Cells were incubated in a 5 per cent suspension in the basal medium: 0.1 M glycylglycine, pH 8.0, .034 M NaCl, 0.02 M KCl, .002 M $MgCl_2$, and .006 M glucose-6-^{14}C. P_i was present in the medium as noted.

lowing the addition of glucose, 1/V initial, we can say that about 65 per cent of the increased rate occurred by virtue of some activation of the enzyme in the inhibited state. Now it seems a fair assumption that this additional effect is due to a direct effect of P_i. However, to place this problem in perspective it should be mentioned that in the normal aerobic state the glycolytic rate is only about 4 per cent of the total hexokinase present.

One may ask, to what extent is this tremendous inhibition due to G-6-P and whether the P_i effect might be due to overcoming some segment of the inhibition that might not be due to G-6-P. Figure 3 shows early time rates of glucose utilization by cells previously incubated with or without P_i, 15 mM. The initial ATP levels of the two incubations were the same as were the initial rates, up to 10 seconds, of utilization. The difference in rates only shows up later, when inhibition due to G-6-P becomes a factor. This result is consistent with the behavior of tumor hexokinase developing its own G-6-P (see Figure 4). Here two incubations of mitochondrial hexokinase were identical except for the presence of 3 mM P_i in one. Product inhi-

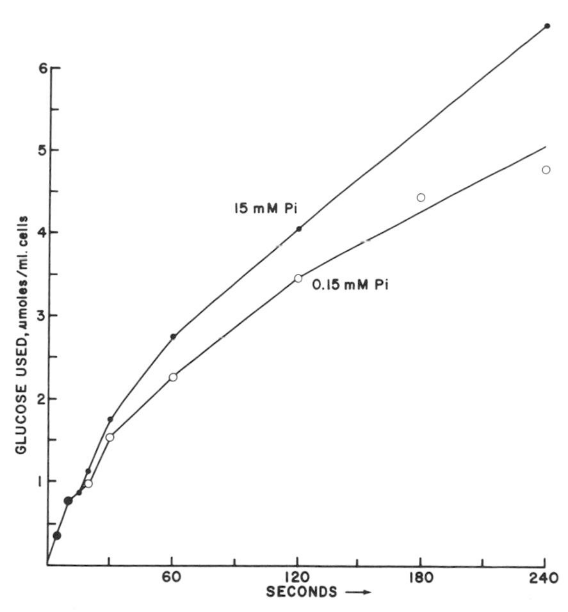

Figure 3. The basal medium, Figure 2, was supplemented with P_i as noted. Cells in a 5 per cent suspension were equilibrated at 33° prior to the addition of glucose-^{14}C to give .02 M. The reaction was "stopped" by unlabeled-glucose addition. The cells were homogenized (Dounce) rapidly and the whole mixture placed on Dowex 1-Acetate for recovery of ^{14}C-anions.

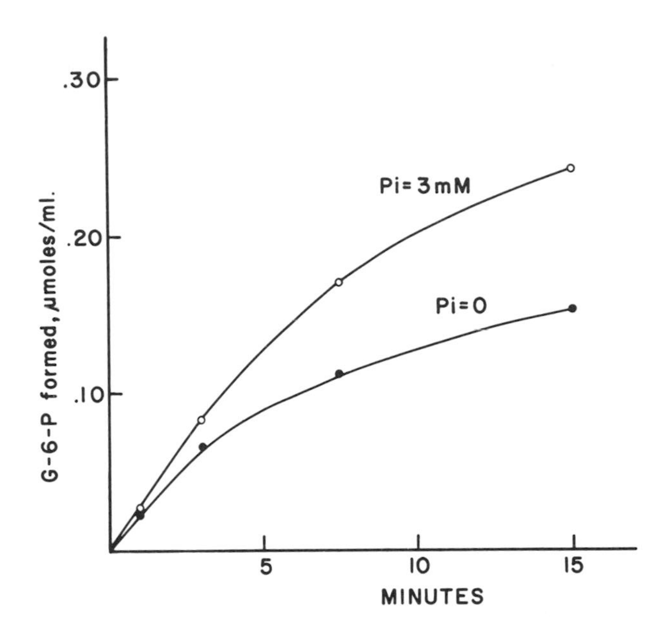

Figure 4. Effect of P_i on the rate of hexokinase. The two incubations contained imidazole (50 mM, pH 7.2), $MgCl_2$ (5mM), ATP (0.8 mM), creatine-P (3 mM), glucose-6-^{14}C (0.5 mM, 320,000 cpm/μmole), EDTA (1 mM), 0.03 units of fresh mitochondrial hexokinase and 0.2 units of creatine kinase in 0.5 ml. P_i was present in one incubation at 3 mM.

bition, due to G-6-P only, is evident at a lower product concentration and is much more intense in the absence of P_i.

Perhaps the most interesting fact seen in Figure 3 is that the initial rate of utilization which is about 8 times the steady state aerobic rate is only about one-third the assayed rate in the whole homogenate. Why the cell uses only 30 per cent of its hexokinase capacity in the absence of G-6-P is an intriguing question. Could this be related to the fact that only 30 per cent of the enzyme is soluble?

Finally it might be worthwhile to say a few words about the Pasteur effect. Cells poisoned with carbon monoxide use up the glucose 70 per cent faster than aerobic cells, Figure 5. The ATP level is 10 per cent lower so that, judging from the high K_m of ATP under these inhibited conditions one would expect the hexokinase to react 10 per cent more slowly anaerobically. The G-6-P is down 40 per cent in the anaerobic cells which should increase the rate of hexokinase about 40 percent.

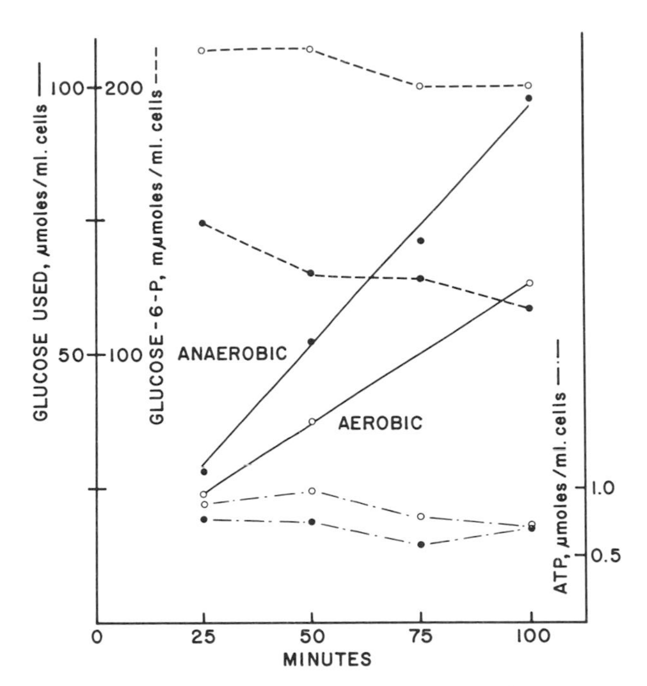

Figure 5. The basal medium, Figure 2, with 8.5 mM glucose-6-^{14}C and 5 per cent cell suspension were shaken at 33° in either air (O) or carbon monoxide atmosphere (●).

As usual we are assuming that these amounts of ATP and G-6-P are what they seem, namely relative concentrations, and that we are not incorrect in ignoring such ideas as local compartmentation of these metabolites. With this assumption, using a 1/V vs. G-6-P plot, Figure 6, one can see that the decrease in G-6-P is adequate to explain about 70 per cent of the increased anaerobic rate of glucose utilization. About 30 per cent of the increase would have to be due to other factors that change in going to anaerobic conditions. As recognized by previous workers, only by invoking separate mitochondrial and soluble pools of ATP can nucleotide control of hexokinase be made a justifiable hypothesis since the net change in ATP concentration is in the wrong direction. Furthermore, ADP and AMP are relatively ineffective modifiers of the hexokinase rate and they too would provide changes of rate in the wrong direction, for their concentration changes in going from the aerobic to the anaerobic steady state. The change in P_i is in the right direction but is only about 10 per cent and would not be sufficient alone to explain the additional stimulation of hexokinase anaerobically.

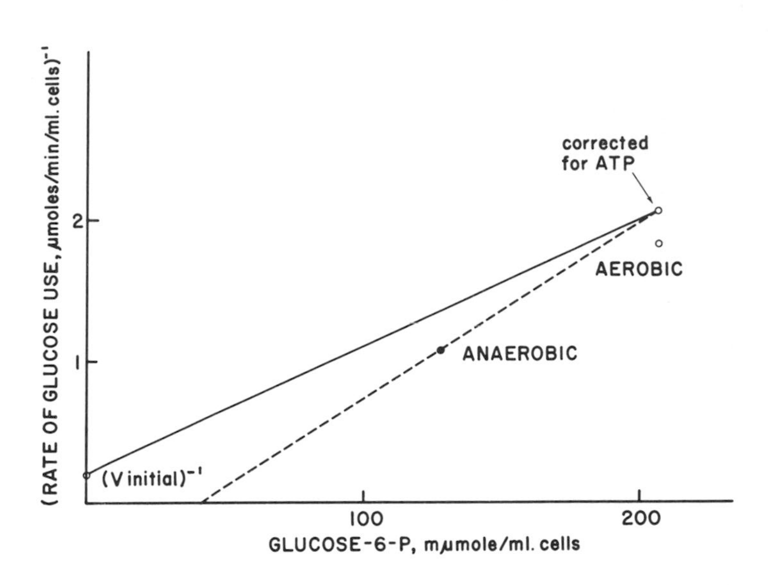

Figure 6. Replot of 1/V vs. G-6-P from Figure 5. The average aerobic rate (O) reduced 10 per cent due to lower ATP in the anaerobic set (●) in order to evaluate the contribution of G-6-P alone to the increased anaerobic rate of the hexokinase step.

Since it is well known that P_i accumulates in isolated mitochondria along with the respiration-dependent uptake of cations it may reasonably be asked whether the distribution of P_i in the aerobic and anaerobic cells may be sufficiently different to favor the hexokinase reaction anaerobically. This possibility is under investigation. That G-6-P may accumulate during cation uptake in mitochondria has been tested and found not to be the case.

Table II summarizes the graphed data (experiments 1, 2) and also shows results with dinitrophenol, (experiment 3). The conclusion in all these cases is the same: the decrease in G-6-P concentration due to the more rapid phosphofructokinase reaction is responsible for 50-70 per cent of the stimulation of hexokinase. However, other factors also change which act by decreasing the inhibitor effect of G-6-P or by making additional enzyme molecules available, or by independently activating the enzyme.

TABLE II

Exp.	Condition	Steady State Values V utilization	ATP	G-6-P	"Expected" G-6-P*
		μmoles/min/ml	μmoles/ml		μmoles/ml
1	Basal	.58	1.2	.38	
	+ P_i (5 mM)	.98	1.2	.29	.20
2	Basal	.52	.83	.205	
	+ CO	.89	.68	.125	.10
3	Basal	.42	.90	.218	
	+ DNP (0.5 mM)	1.14	.71	.112	.055

* "Expected" G-6-P: This is the concentration of G-6-P that would be required if control of the hexokinase rate were to be exercised solely by the G-6-P concentration.

REFERENCES

1. McComb, R.B., and Yushok, W.D., Biochim. Biophys. Acta, 34, 515 (1959).

2. Weil-Malherbe, H., and Bone, A.D., Biochem. J., 49, 339 (1951).

3. Crane, R.K., and Sols, A., J. Biol. Chem., 203, 273 (1953).

4. Fromm, H.J., and Zewe, V., J. Biol. Chem., 237, 1661 (1962).

5. von Tiedemann, H., and Born, J., S. Naturforsch., Pt. b., 14, 477 (1959).

6. Rose, I.A., Warms, J.V.B., and O'Connell, E., Biochem. Biophys. Res. Comm., 15, 33 (1964).

7. Wu. R., and Racker, E., J. Biol. Chem., 234, 1029 (1959).

8. Sauer, L.A., Biochem. Biophys. Res. Comm., 17, 294 (1964).

ON THE CONTROL OF GLYCOLYSIS IN NOVIKOFF ASCITES TUMOR CELLS*

Ray Wu

Department of Biochemistry, The Public Health Research Institute of the City of New York, Inc., New York 9, N. Y.

Control of Anaerobic Glycolysis

In analyzing the rate-limiting factors of glycolysis in Novikoff ascites tumor cells, a striking parallel between the rate of anaerobic glycolysis and the level of intracellular P_i was observed. As can be seen in Figure 1, the rate of lactate production, as well as the level of P_i was high during the first two minutes after the addition of glucose. A drop in both the level of P_i and the rate of lactate production occurred between two and four minutes. However, the drop in the P_i level preceded the drop in the rate of glycolysis, suggesting that the intracellular P_i level controls the rate of lactate production. After 4 minutes, both the level of P_i and the rate of glycolysis began to increase to a similar extent.

The large decrease in the intracellular P_i was due mainly to an increase in the cellular concentration of fructose-1,6-di-P which accounted quantitatively for the loss of P_i. The presence of high levels of fructose-1,6-di-P and glyceraldehyde-3-P together with the very low level of 3-P-glycerate (Table I, CO_2-N_2) suggested that the lactate production was limited by P_i in the reaction catalyzed by glyceraldehyde-3-P dehydrogenase. This suggestion was supported by the observed decrease in the level of 3-P-glycerate at 4 minutes when the P_i level reached its minimum. As a consequence only suboptional amounts of 3-P-glycerate and P-enolpyruvate were available for the 3-P-glycerate kinase and pyruvate kinase steps. The activity of these two phosphorylating enzymes was apparently limited by substrate rather than by ADP, since the level of ADP was found to be high and fairly constant throughout the incubation periods. In fact, no correlation between the levels of adenine nucleotides and the rate of glycolysis was found.

* This investigation was supported by Public Health Service Grant No. CA-05706 from the National Cancer Institute.

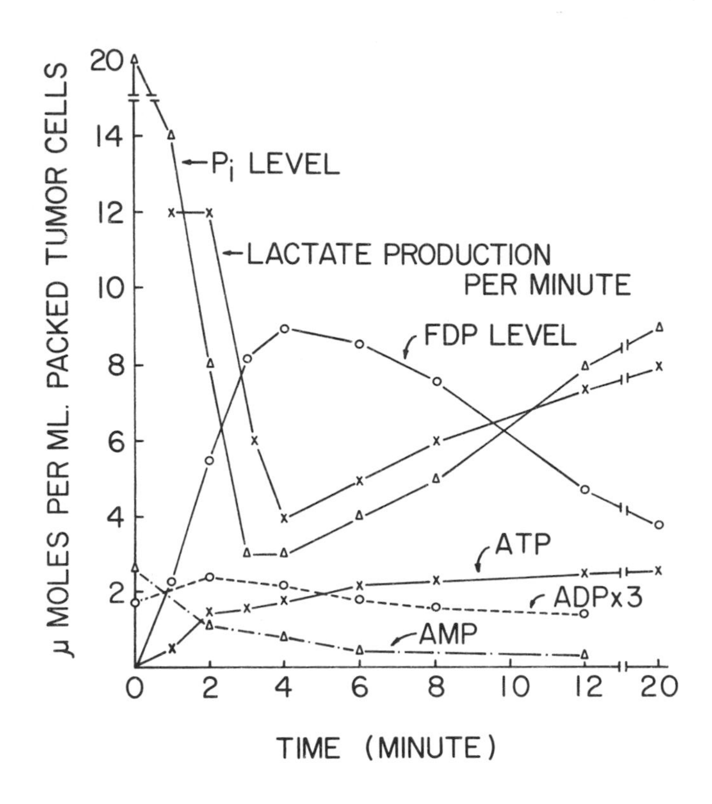

Figure 1. Relations between the intracellular P_i level and the rate of anaerobic lactate production in Novikoff ascites tumor cells. Novikoff ascites tumor cells (14 mg of cell protein) were incubated in 2 ml of Krebs Ringer bicarbonate buffer. After 10 min of gassing, glucose was tipped in from the double sidearm of the Warburg vessel. To terminate the incubation at various time intervals, 0.08 ml of 10 N $HClO_4$ was tipped into the main compartment from the single sidearm. An identical set of Warburg vessels was used for the determination of P_i in the medium in order to correct for the intracellular P_i content. At the end of the incubation, the tumor cells were poured into chilled centrifuge tubes and centrifuged immediately for 2 min; the supernatant solution was deproteinized with trichloroacetic acid and used for the determination of P_i in the incubation medium. Methods for the determination of lactate, glucose, adenine nucleotides and glycolytic intermediates were the same as previously described (2, 4). The ADP level, as indicated, is drawn to a 3-fold larger scale (e.g., ADP at 8 min was actually 0.6 mM). Results are expressed as μmoles per ml of packed cells (120 mg of protein).

TABLE I

Rate-limiting factors for aerobic and anaerobic glycolysis in Novikoff ascites tumor cells

Experimental conditions were the same as described in Figure 1.

Gas phase	Incubation time	Glucose[f] added	Glucose uptake		Lactate prod.		Intracellular concentration			
			per min[a]	% Pasteur effect[b]	per min[a]	% Pasteur effect[b]	HMP[c]	FDP[d]	3PGA[e]	P_i
	(min)	(mM)								
CO_2-O_2	0	0					0	0	0	13
			8.0[g]		5.2					
	1	1.5[g]					3.3	2.3	0.05	6
			1.2	88	3.0	75				
	2	2.0					3.1	2.2	0.05	7
			1.6	60	3.4	44				
	3	2.0					2.5	2.3	0.05	8
			2.6	13	3.6	10				
	4	2.0					2.1	2.2	0.05	9
			2.3	8	4.4	12				
	6	2.5					1.7	1.9	0.09	11
			2.5	17	4.5	25				
	8	2.5					1.7	1.7	0.09	11
			2.7	29	4.7	37				
	12	3.0					1.7	1.5	0.09	14
			2.7	31	4.0	50				
	20	5.0					1.5	1.0	0.08	15
CO_2-N_2	0	0					0	0	0	20
			11		12					
	1	2.5					0.50	2.2	0.14	14
			10		12					
	2	2.5					0.60	5.6	0.14	8
			4		6					
	3	2.5					0.60	8.2	0.10	3
			3		4					
	4	3.0					0.62	9.0	0.07	3
			2.5		5					
	6	3.5					0.60	8.6	0.07	4
			3.0		6					
	8	4.0					0.60	7.6	0.07	5
			3.8		7.5					
	12	4.0					0.66	4.8	0.07	8
			3.9		8.0					
	20	6.0					0.80	3.9	0.08	9

a Per minute between two time intervals. Expressed as μmole per 120 mg of protein.

b per cent Pasteur effect = 100 X (anaerobic rate - aerobic rate / anaerobic rate).

c HMP = Hexose monophosphates, which were consisted of glucose-6-P (75 per cent) and fructose-6-P (25 per cent).

d FDP = Fructose 1,6-diphosphate, which included triose phosphates in amounts to be expected from the aldolase equilibrium. The ratio of dihydroxyacetone-P and glyceraldehyde-3-P was approximately 10.

e 3-PGA = 3-Phosphoglyceric acid.

f In order to increase the accuracy in the measurements of glucose uptake, different amounts of glucose were added at zero time for different lengths of incubation. The initial glucose concentration for each experiment (run in individual Warburg vessels) was chosen such that an appreciable portion of the glucose would be utilized but its final level would be higher than 0.4 mM. Preliminary experiments indicated that the rate of glycolysis in this tumor was independent of the glucose concentration at 0.4 mM or higher.

g 1.5 mM glucose (3 μmoles in 2 ml of incubation medium in the Warburg vessel) were tipped in at zero time for this experiments which was terminated 1 minute later. During the 1 minute incubation, 0.93 μmoles of glucose were utilized in this experiment (with 14 mg of tumor cell protein), which is equivalent to 8.0 μmoles of glucose utilized per 120 mg of protein.

The rate of anaerobic glucose uptake during the first 8 minutes also paralleled the levels of intracellular P_i (Table I). Since P_i has been shown to partially counteract the glucose-6-P inhibition of hexokinase of red blood cells (1) and of Novikoff ascites tumor cells (Table II), the severe inhibition of glucose uptake observed after 3 minutes could be explained by the sharp drop of the P_i level. Since the glucose-6-P level remained constant between 1 and 8 minutes, it became a more effective inhibitor of hexokinase when the P_i reached its lowest level at 3 minutes.

TABLE II

Effect of P_i on the glucose-6-P inhibition of Novikoff ascites tumor hexokinase

Addition		Hexokinase activity*
Glucose-6-P (mM)	P_i (mM)	
0		39
0.5		7.3
1.0		4.0
0	6	34
0.5	6	14
1.0	6	5.2
0	16	30
0.5	16	17
1.0	16	6.6

Hexokinase activity was determined by measuring the uptake of ^{14}C-glucose according to slight modification (2) of the method of Rose and O'Connell (3). The incubation mixture contained, in a final volume of 0.3 ml, ^{14}C-glucose-U (0.4 mM, 1 x 10^6 cpm per µmole), triethanolamine chloride (0.05 M, pH 7.4), imidazole (0.05 M, pH 7.4), ATP (1 mM), $MgCl_2$ (2.5 mM), dialyzed bovine serum albumin (30 µg) and Novikoff ascites tumor homogenate (0.05 mg protein per test tube). Incubation was carried out at 28° for 5 minutes, and reaction was terminated by addition of 1 ml of 1 N $HClO_4$.

* Expressed as mµmoles of ^{14}C-glucose phosphorylated in 5 minutes per 0.05 mh of homogenate protein.

Control of Aerobic Glycolysis

As shown in Table I, both the rate of aerobic glucose uptake and lactate production were slowest between 1 and 2 minutes after glucose addition. The slow rate of glucose uptake may be correlated with the very high intracellular levels of glucose-6-P which inhibited hexokinase, and the relatively low level of P_i to reverse this inhibition (1). The slow rate of lactate production may be correlated with the relatively low levels of P_i which partly limits glyceraldehyde-3-P dehydrogenase.

The rate of aerobic glycolysis became higher after 6 minutes and was correlated with a higher level of P_i and lower levels of glucose-6-P. A slight increase in the activity of glyceraldehyde-3-P dehydrogenase was indicated by an 80 per cent increase in the level of 3-P-glycerate found at 6 minutes as compared to 4 minutes. This increase, occurring at a time when the rate of lactate formation was also increased, clearly indicated that the glyceraldehyde-3-P dehydrogenase step was accelerated.

The aerobic levels of ATP (3.5 mM), ADP (0.4 mM) and AMP (0.25 mM) at 0, 2, 6 and 12 minutes remained essentially constant and showed no correlation with the rate of aerobic glycolysis at different time intervals.

The Pasteur Effect in Novikoff Ascites Tumor Cells

The results in Table I illustrate the importance of specifying the time interval during which the Pasteur effect was measured since, regardless of whether glucose uptake or lactate production was measured, the per cent Pasteur effect varied continuously during the 20 minute incubation period. The relatively large Pasteur effect, which occurred between 1 and 3 minutes, could be attributed to a decreased inhibition of hexokinase by the lower level of glucose-6-P under anaerobic conditions. The lower anaerobic glucose-6-P level, in spite of a faster rate of glucose phosphorylation can be attributed to a faster rate of hexose-P utilization by P-fructokinase.

A marked decrease in the Pasteur effect was observed between 3 and 8 minutes. Although the level of glucose-6-P is lower anaerobically, P_i was also much lower. The net effect of these compounds on hexokinase indicated that this enzyme was nearly as strongly inhibited anaerobically as aerobically. This would account for the almost similar rates of glucose phosphorylation. Since the levels of fructose-1,6-di-P remained high and almost constant during this incubation period, it seems clear that lactate production was controlled by a step after the formation of fructose-1,6-di-P. The rate of lactate production seemed to be controlled by P_i, since the concentration of P_i and the rate of lactate formation paralleled each other. In view of the higher aerobic level of P_i and the lower rate of aerobic lactate production, it appeared that the effective concentration of aerobic P_i was much lower than the P_i content actually found in the cell.

The Pasteur effect on lactate production was between 37 and 50 per cent after 8 minutes. The difference in the aerobic and the anaerobic level of glucose-6-P was not nearly as great as between 1 and 3 minutes. Furthermore, the anaerobic levels of P_i were lower than the aerobic levels after 8 minutes. As a result, the rate of anaerobic glucose phosphorylation was only 30 per cent higher than under aerobic conditions.

In summary, the rate-limiting factors for glycolysis, the Pasteur effect and the levels of intracellular intermediates were found to change continuously with the time of incubation. Intracellular P_i appeared to be the most important factor in controlling glycolysis. However, the relative importance of P_i in the control of activities of hexokinase, P-fructokinase and glyceraldehyde-3-P dehydrogenase varied with the time of incubation. The coordinated control of two or three of these key glycolytic enzymes of P_i has already been reported in studies with red blood cells (1), with Ehrlich ascites tumor cells (2), and in reconstructed systems (5,6).

REFERENCES

1. Rose, I. A. Warms, J. V. B. and O'Connell, E. L., Biochem. Biophys. Res. Commun., 15, 33 (1964).
2. Wu, R., Biochem. Biophys. Res. Commun., 18, 402 (1965).
3. Rose, I. A., and O'Connell, E. L., J. Biol. Chem., 239 12 (1964).
4. Wu, R., Biochem. Biophys. Res. Commun., 14, 79 (1964).
5. Racker, E., Mechanisms in Bioenergetics, Academic Press, New York, 1965, p. 252.
6. Uyeda, K., and Racker, E., this colloquium, p. 127.

THE CONTROL OF GLYCOLYSIS IN YEAST

Kendall Pye

Johnson Research Foundation, University of Pennsylvania
Philadelphia, Pennsylvania

Working with Professor Eddy in Manchester, I obtained some indirect evidence that ADP rather than P_i controls the rate of glycolysis in yeast. Using a single strain of S. cervisiae we were able to alter the Pasteur Quotient displayed by the yeast by culturing it on growth media containing different concentrations of fermentable carbohydrate. The cells, while utilizing glucose, were then subjected to an aerobic-anaerobic transition in the manner of the classical experiments described by Lynen (1), and the glycolytic intermediates assayed in samples of the cells. The experiments were performed on yeast displaying a small, an intermediate and a large Pasteur effect respectively (2).

The data showed that the behavior of ADP was typical of that expected of a control component since on changing to anaerobic conditions it rose to a new steady-state level within the time taken for the glycolytic rate to increase (Figure 1). Also the rise in level in each case was proportioned to the increase in glycolytic rate. This striking correlation between the ADP level and the glycolytic rate was further revealed when a plot of the Pasteur Quotient of the yeast, that is the ratio of the aerobic to the anaerobic glycolytic rates, against the ratio of the aerobic to the anaerobic ADP levels showed them to be directly proportional.

The behavior of P_i on the other hand was similar in each of the three types of cells (Figure 2) and showed no trend which could be related to the Pasteur effect displayed by the cells. On changing to anaerobic conditions the level of P_i rose by a small amount and then continued to rise even though the rate of glycolysis appeared to be steady. This was in contrast to the ADP level which remained reasonably constant during steady-state glycolysis.

If ADP is the controller of glycolysis in yeast then an activation of glycolysis by an uncoupler should also be accompanied by a proportional increase in the level of ATP. This

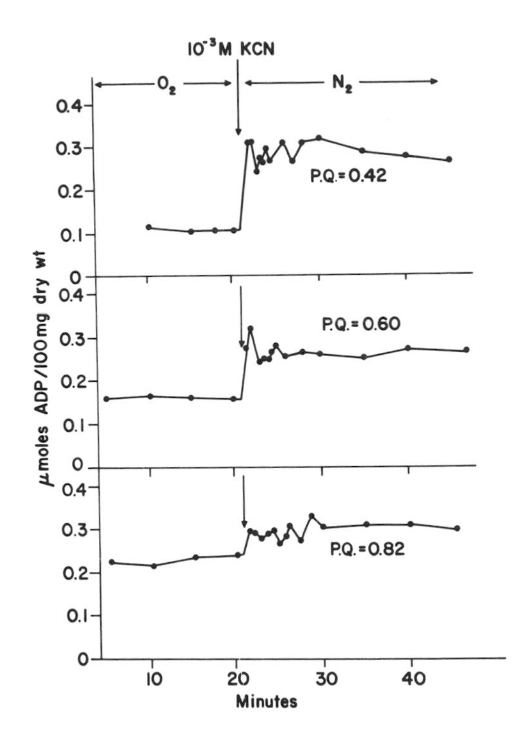

Figure 1. The effects of a change from aerobic to anaerobic conditions on the level of ADP in yeast. Cells displaying Pasteur Quotients as shown were suspended in 0.05 M potassium maleate buffer, pH 6.4, and 3.5 per cent glucose added at zero time. To produce anaerobic conditions 10^{-3} M KCN was added and the gas phase changed from oxygen to nitrogen.

proved to be the case for on addition of 2.4 dinitrophenol to the yeast under aerobic conditions both the glycolytic and the ADP level rose by approximately the same amount.

The behavior of the glycolytic intermediates was consistent in every case with a theory for the regulation of glycolysis via the availability of ADP as a substrate for 3-phosphoglycerate kinase and pyruvate kinase, and the presence of secondary regulatory sites of the phosphofructokinase and sugar entry steps.

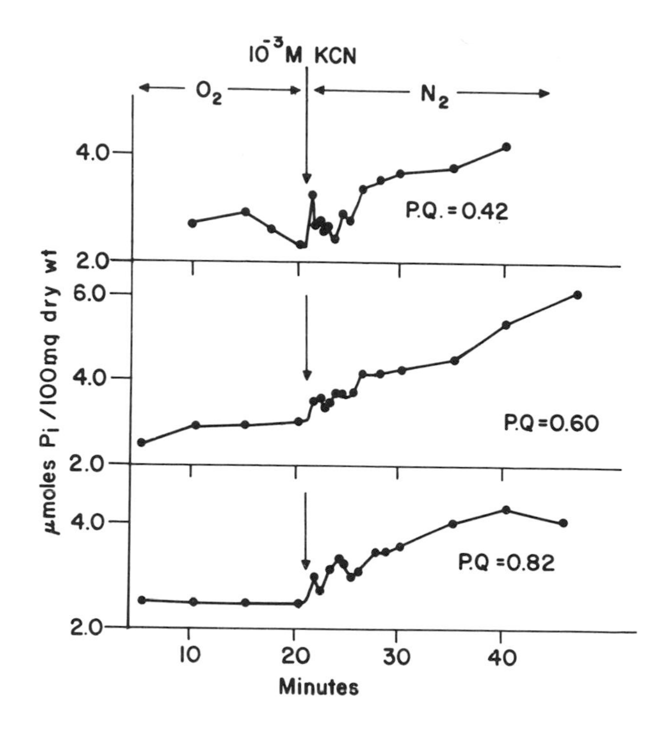

Figure 2. The effects of a change from aerobic to anaerobic conditions on the level of P_i in yeast. The conditions were the same as in Figure 1.

REFERENCES

1. Lynen, F., Hartmann, G., Netter, K. F., and Schuegraf, A., in Regulation of Cell Metabolism, Ciba Foundation Symposium, G. E. W. Wolstenholme, Ed., J. and A. Churchill, Ltd., 1959, p. 256.

2. Pye, E. K., "Studies on the Mechanism of the Pasteur Effect in Yeast." Ph.D. Thesis, University of Manchester, 1964.

DISCUSSION

Hess: In discussing ADP vs. phosphate control, one must realize that there is a strong implication of an ADP control in the GAPDH reaction, because the GAPDH is strongly inhibited by its own product, 1,3-diphosphoglycerate. The inhibitor constant for 1,3-diphosphoglycerate of the muscle enzyme is 8×10^{-7} M according to Velick (Velick, S. and Furfine, C., in The Enzymes, (S.P. Colowick and N. Kaplan, eds.), Academic Press, New York, p. 243, 1963, Vol. III). I think this mechanism is important also for yeast glycolysis as can be shown by the titration of a yeast extract showing oscillating glycolysis with 1,3-diphosphoglycerate and PGK:

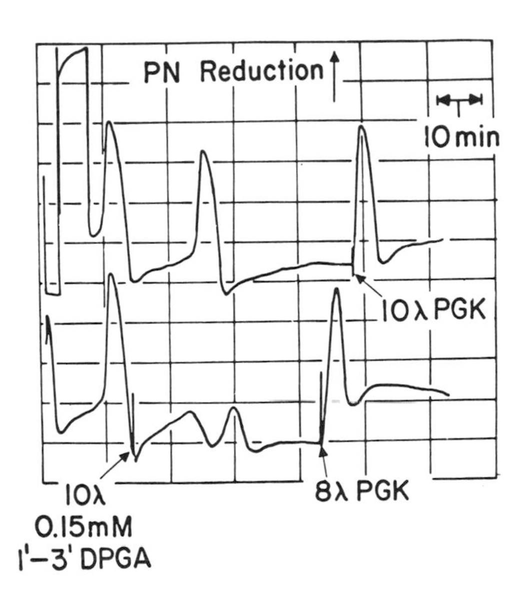

Figure 1. Spectrophotometric traces of two equally treated samples of an extract of Saccharomyces carlsbergensis, simultaneously recorded by two filter double-beam spectrophotometers (340-400 mμ, 1 mm light path, 100 μl volume)(Cassuto, Hess, unpublished experiments, 1965).

On addition of 1,3-diphosphoglycerate, reduction of pyridine nucleotide is inhibited as compared to the control (upper trace) where the system displays a full oscillation cycle leading first to a strong reduction until the system turns to the oxidation phase of the period. Then on addition of PGK (see upper and lower traces) a full cycle of reduction and oxidation is induced which we ascribe to the lowering of the steady state level of 1,3-diphosphoglycerate and therefore to the de-inhibition of GAPDH which is then free to react with DPNH and phosphate. The reduction of pyridine nucleotide cannot be due to an increase of the ATP level because this normally leads to an oxidation of pyridine nucleotide and not to a reduction. Thus any ADP control at the PGK level would be fed back to the GAPDH level automatically because of the intrinsic control coupling of both enzymes. For this reason phosphate control must be secondary to ADP control in a system where a strong feedback inhibition of GAPDH by 1,3-diphosphoglycerate is operating. Work is under way in our laboratory to assay the kinetics of the intermediates of this reaction, especially 1,3-diphosphoglycerate during an appropriate transition.

Chance: It is of interest to note that Dr. Pye's data show that there may be an oscillation in the metabolites under conditions where you demonstrate ADP control independently. Also ADP control of the oscillations in the cell-free extract can readily be established. Apparently the oscillations are characteristic of adenine nucleotide rather than phosphate control.

Rose: Dr. Chance, can you propose any mechanism for ADP control of hexokinase?

Chance: Yes, if there is a compartment.

Rose: Now my problem is that it is evident that ATP as a substrate can regulate the rate of hexokinase. How will ADP regulate the rate of hexokinase, by feedback or otherwise?

Chance: One simply invokes an ATP compartment in which ADP is the means of entry into that compartment, and is phosphorylated therein. We, of course, considered this compartment to be the mitochondrial space (Chance, B., in Ciba Foundation Symp. on the Regulation of Cell Metabolism (G.E.W. Wolstenholme, ed.), Little, Brown and Company, Boston, p. 122 (1959)).

Rose: Meaning that ATP is compartmented either with or without the hexokinase?

Chance: Yes, according to the mechanism we proposed in 1959 (Chance, B. and Hess, B., Science, 129, 700 (1959)).

Rose: But in the light of our more recent ideas of PFK control, doesn't the notion of ATP compartmentation as a control factor need to be abandoned? That is, if the rate of G-6-P removal is governed by the degree to which ATP inhibits PFK and this, in turn is primarily responsible for determining the hexokinase rate, then any decrease in the amount of ATP available to the soluble compartment during aerobic conditions should serve to stimulate rather than to limit glucose utilization and lead to an inverse of the Pasteur Effect.

Chance: Assays of ATP in ascites cells (see Chance, B. and Maitra, P. K., this volume, p. 157) may show a rise or fall in the average concentration of ATP in the cell in the inhibited phase of glucose utilization, and various mechanisms in addition to ATP control, including compartmentation of ATP, need to be considered.

Lowry: It is often difficult to change ADP without changing AMP even more, particularly when ATP is high. The changes in AMP are bound to be 2 to 3 times greater than the changes of ADP, whether ADP is added from the outside or whether it is generated in the system.

Chance: AMP as well as ADP may control at PFK, but I would like to point out that the changes of AMP are not greater than those of ADP in ascites cells (See Fig. 1, Maitra and Chance, this volume, p. 160). The ADP change is almost twice that of AMP according to assays of the cell suspensions.

H. Krebs: To elaborate Dr. Lowry's question, both Dr. Chance and Dr. Bücher measured ATP, ADP and AMP. Have you titrated whether these three nucleotides are always in equilibrium? We have done many experiments, and they always are. This equilibrium depends somewhat on the magnesium concentration, but the ratio ATP times AMP over ADP-squared should be between 0.5 and 0.8. This is, of course, a variety of the constant proportion theme, but it's a bit different.

Bücher: Myokinase mass action ratios may shift in the liver by a factor of 10. The fact is that what we measure in liver changes by a factor of 8, so we have to look for an explanation for this.

Hess: The steady state ratio of the myokinase reactants in Ehrlich Ascites Tumor Cells is displaced from equilibrium by a factor of 10 (Hess, B., *Proc. Vth Intern. Congr. Biochem.*, Moscow, 1961, Vol. V, p. 313; Hess, B., *Koordination von Atmung und Glykolyse in Funktionelle und Morphologische Organisation der Zelle herausg.* (P. Karlson) Springer Verlag, 1963, p. 163.).

Control experiments have shown that this cannot be due to a change of the magnesium concentration. The state of the myokinase reaction is a sensitive indicator of the metabolic state of the cell and can be used as a control of the experimental conditions (Hess, B., in IUB/IUBS Symp. on Rapid Mixing and Sampling Techniques in Biochemistry (B. Chance, Q.H. Gibson, R. Eisenhardt, and K. Lonberg-Holm, eds.), Academic Press, New York, 1964, p. 267.).

Bücher: But may I have another question. In the paper of Chance and Hess on Ascites tumor cells (Science, 129, 700 (1959)), the Chance effect of glucose was explained by a transportation of ATP from extramitochondria into the mitochondrial compartment. Do you still hold to this hypothesis?

Chance: Partially. There is substantial evidence for the compartmentation in mitochondria (Ciba Foundation Symp. on the Regulation of Cell Metabolism (G.E.W. Wolstenholme, ed.), Little Brown and Company, Boston, p. 122 (1959); Hommes, F., Fed. Proc., 21, 142 (1962)). However, our paper with Maitra (this volume, p. 157) suggests that glucose utilization may have other controls as well. It is probable that a cooperative effect is involved.

Wenner: In considering the requirements of P_i and ADP in the regulation of metabolism, I would like to call attention to the α-glycerophosphate shuttle. When extramitochondrial DPNH is oxidized by the shuttle, only two phosphorylations are involved since the electrons from α-glycerophosphate are transferred to cytochrome b. Since ascites tumor cells have been widely used for the study of control mechanisms and the occurrence of this cycle in neoplastic cells has been disputed, I would like to present evidence that the α-glycerophosphate cycle is operative in the intact cells.

As seen in Figure 1, when ELD ascites cells are treated with an inhibitor of DPNH oxidation (rotenone), respiration almost ceases. It was observed that the addition of glucose partly restored respiration after a slight lag which can be attributed to the formation of α-glycerophosphate. A decrease in respiration was produced by the further addition of pyruvate which would lower DPNH availability for α-glycerophosphate formation by virtue of the competing lactic dehydrogenase.

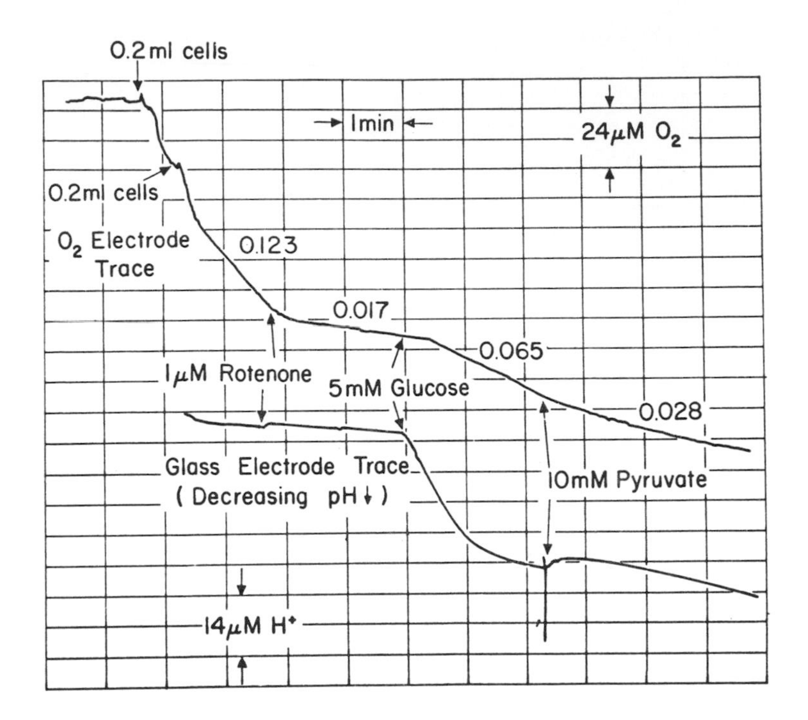

Fig. 1. Partial recovery of oxygen utilization upon glucose addition to rotenone-inhibited ELD ascites-tumor cells.

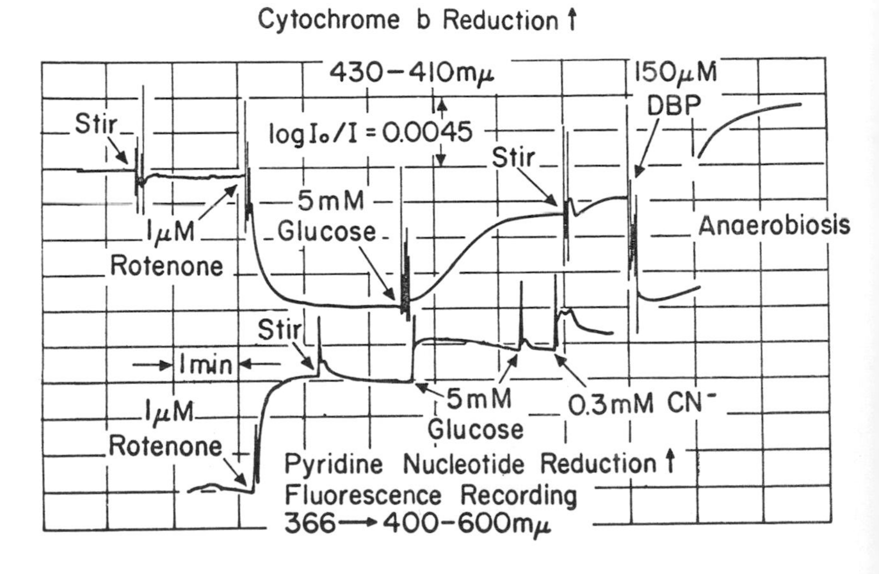

Fig. 2. Reduction of cytochrome b upon glucose addition to rotenone-treated ascites tumor cells (ELD).

Dr. Estabrook and I were able to obtain confirming evidence by following the spectroscopic changes with the intact cells as seen in Figure 2. Thus, the inhibition by rotenone was observed to involve an oxidation of DPNH and a reduction of cytochrome b. When glucose was added, it is seen that cytochrome b was reduced as expected from α-glycerophosphate oxidation via the α-glycerophosphate oxidase. This data is then in accord with previous evidence which indicated that α-glycerophosphate is readily formed by the supernatent fraction of these cells, and that ascites tumor mitochondria are capable of oxidizing α-glycerophosphate (P. Borst, Biochim. et Biophys. Acta, 57, 270 (1962); Wenner, C.E., and Cereijo-Santalo, R., J. Biol. Chem., 238, 1584 (1963)).

Garfinkel: I would like to make a few remarks about different hexokinases to add to what Dr. Rose has said about ascites hexokinase. Apparently, different hexokinases do have different reaction mechanisms; at least two that have been investigated in detail, those from yeast and those from brain, have distinctly different mechanisms. The yeast enzyme has a rapid equilibrium random mechanism with no phosphorylated enzyme being formed, whereas the brain mechanism is different and might possibly involve the formation of a phosphorylated enzyme, although this is not proven. One useful point that has been made about the ascites enzyme is that, according to Dr. Maitra (personal communication), the hexokinase inhibition by G-6-P is not as fast in time as its relief; in other words, it takes some time to go inhibited, but if phosphate is present, it will recover faster.

Wenner: I'd like to show a slide related to a linear inverse relationship between G-6-P levels and the rate of glucose utilization in the $6C_3HED$ Lymphoma ascites. This is a slowly glycolyzing tumor, and we have not been able to observe this relationship in Ehrlich ascites cells or under conditions where we have a high rate of aerobic glycolysis. The G-6-P levels have been measured under conditions where glucose utilization is modified by respiratory inhibitors and by β-hydroxybutyrate as an inhibitor of glycolysis.

The relationship is linear under the conditions of the experiment as can be seen in Figure 3. It is possible that the relationship between G-6-P levels and glucose utilization is secondary to a change in some intermediate or effect which varies directly with G-6-P, such as F-6-P or PFK activity. However, the data do suggest that product inhibition of the hexokinase reaction is a factor in regulating glycolysis in these cells.

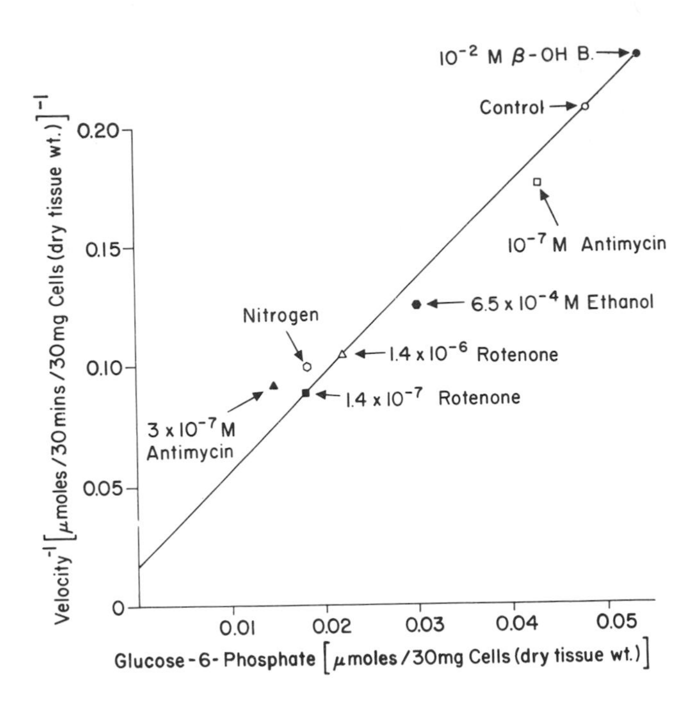

Figure 3. Inverse relationship between glucose-6-phosphate levels and glucose utilization in $6C_3HED$ lymphoma ascites.

Moore: In ascites cells, the secondary inhibition of respiration after glucose addition is indeed related to the inhibition of the bound hexokinase by the G-6-P formed, as stated by Drs. Rose and Wenner, and is also inherent in the findings of Sauer (Sauer, L.A., Biochem. and Biophys. Res. Commun., 17, 294 [1964]). This relationship of respiratory behavior to hexokinase activity in tissues in which this enzyme is mostly mitochondrially bound is attested to by our unpublished findings of a year ago with brain mitochondria.

A transient activity of hexokinase bound to mitochondria prepared from rat (or rabbit) brain cortex can be demonstrated by use of the platinum electrode where stimulation of respiration is proportional to the rate of ADP formed during the phosphorylation of glucose.

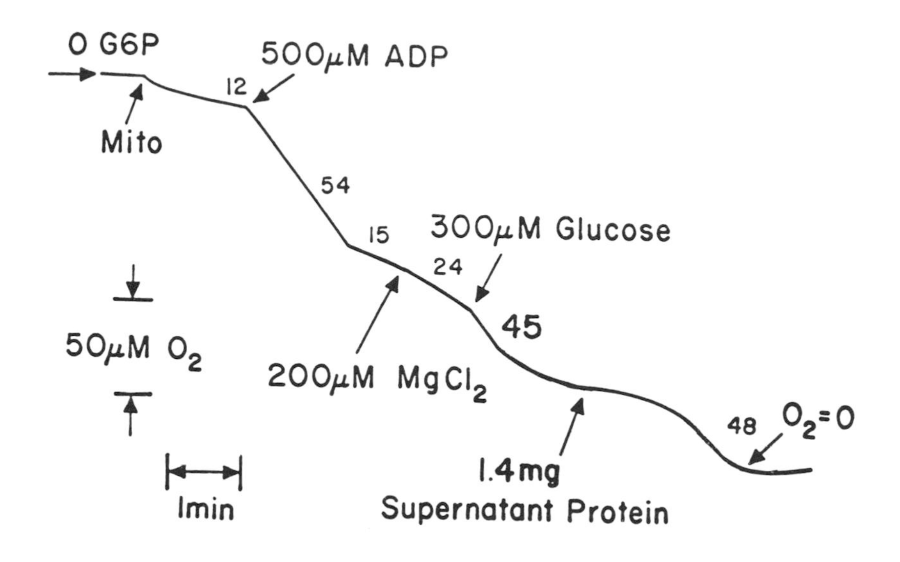

Figure 4. A polarographic tracing of brain mitochondrial respiration carried out at 22° C, pH 7.4, in a medium containing 22.5 mM Mannitol, 7.5 mM sucrose, 5.0 mM Tris, 50.0 mM K-PO_4, 0.2 mM EDTA, 1 mg/ml bovine serum albumin and 0.07 mM $MgCl_2$. The concentrated cortical extract was obtained by homogenization of 3 gm cortex in 2.5 ml of a solution containing 22.5 mM mannitol, 7.5 mM sucrose, 0.2 mM EDTA, 0.10 mM nicotinamide, 1 mg/ml bovine serum albumin, and 5 mg/ml $KHCO_3$.

Figure 4 shows the polarographic tracing using rat brain mitochondria. The stimulation of respiration by addition of 500 µM ADP demonstrates respiratory control in the State 4-3-4 transition of these mitochondria. In order to activate the hexokinase activity, 200 µM $MgCl_2$ is added, and this is followed by 300 µM glucose. The resultant respiratory rate approaches the State 3 level, but after 30 seconds tapers off toward the State 4 level. While there is still adequate glucose present, there is a definite slowing of the ADP formation. This is not due to an initial lack of ATP, since added ATP has no stimulatory effect at this point or at the start of the experiment. This effect is due rather to an inhibition of the hexokinase activity by the approximately 115 µM G-6-P formed. A concentration of 150 µM G-6-P was enough to inhibit the glucose stimulation of respiration in the presence of 250 µM glucose at an initial phosphate concentration of 50 mM.

Dr. Rose has shown in Table I that approximately 50 per cent inhibition of his system could occur with 50 μM G-6-P at 2 mM phosphate.

The slow release of the inhibition by the addition of a concentrated cortical extract prepared as described above and which contains the bulk of the glycolytic enzymes can also be seen in Figure 4. This extract obtained by high speed centrifugation had little or no effect in control experiments in the absence of added glucose.

The possibility of the bound hexokinase playing a dual role in cortical metabolism has some basis in that the enzyme could produce G-6-P for extramitochondrial oxidation, as well as intramitochondrial ADP necessary for maintenance of oxidative phosphorylation.

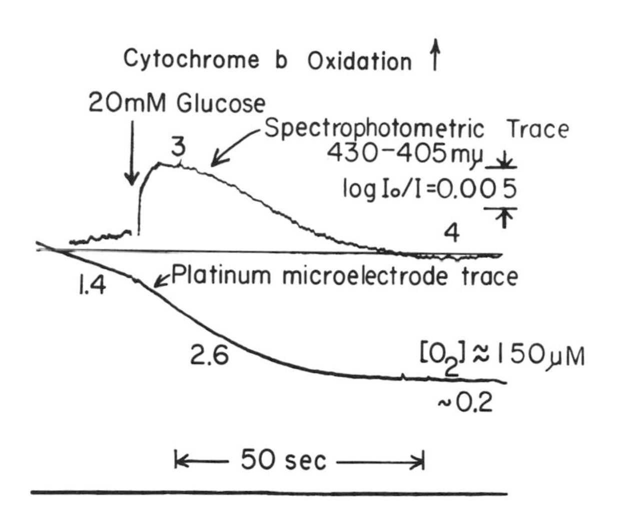

<u>Figure 5</u>. Illustrating the rapid use of intracellular ADP on addition of glucose to ascites tumor cells. [Figure appeared originally in J. Biol. Chem., <u>129</u>, 705 (1959)].

<u>Chance:</u> Dr. Rose has pointed to the difficulty of measuring the initial value of hexokinase activity when ATP is high and G-6-P is low. A rapid measurement of this type is feasible by observing the time required for the State 4-3 transition to occur, in suspensions of ascites tumor cells. When glucose is suddenly added (Figure 5) its phosphorylation and the consequent release of ADP causes the oxidation of cytochrome <u>b</u>

together with the stimulation of respiration. In vitro, we have found that the State 4-3 transition can occur in about one tenth of a second at room temperature and presumably the same reaction time applies to the in vivo situation. In this particular record, where mixing was accompanied by a stirring rod, it is seen that the State 4-3 transition occurs in about 1/2 second, meaning that the intracellular ADP level rose to at least 50 μM in this time. It is further apparent from this type of recording that the glucose utilization rate soon declines. (Note decrease of respiratory stimulation and the increased reduction of cytochrome b.

H.Krebs: In respect to the stimulating effect of inorganic phosphate on hexokinase, I should like to ask Dr. Rose if he has any experience with liver tissue. My reason for asking this is that it has long been known -- Rosenthal, I think, was the first who showed it -- that if one keeps a liver slice in a saline medium aerobically for 20 minutes and then introduces anaerobic conditions, the anaerobic glycolysis (the sugar disappearance) is about 4 or 5 times greater than in liver slices placed immediately in anaerobic conditions. Something happens on aerobic incubation for a short time which appears to stimulate the activity of hexokinase. This effect has recently been rediscovered by Negelein and Noll, but no major new observations have been added. We ourselves looked at various possible stimulators, for example the ATP/ADP ratio, or the relative concentrations of DPN and DPNH, and nothing we found could explain the effect. Perhaps inorganic phosphate provides the key.

Rose: Liver, of course, is confusing because it presumably does not work on the principle of hexokinase inhibition by low levels of G-6-P. Liver is also different because it has a very active G-6-Phosphatase which is not present in many other cells. By way of partial answer to your question, there may be an interrelation between the phosphatase and the hexokinase of the liver which could be important since the phosphatase apparently is very strongly regulated.

Lowenstein: Did I understand you to say that liver hexokinase is not inhibited by glucose-6-phosphate?

Rose: Well, at least the glucokinase is not.

Lowenstein: Glucokinase is exceptional because it is mainly concerned with glucose removal in relation to glycogen deposition. It would be interesting to look at liver hexokinase.

Moore: Liver hexokinase is inhibited by glucose-6-phosphate as are most hexokinases, but the liver glucokinase is not inhibited by glucose-6-phosphate. (Viñuela, E., Salas, M., Sols, A., J. Biol. Chem, 238, 1175 [1963]; Sharma, C., Manjeshwai, R., and Weinhouse, S., Diabetes, 12, 359 [1963]; Vester, J., and Reino, M. L., Science, 142, 590 [1963]).

VI

The Role of Cations in Metabolic Control

CATION FLUX ACROSS THE MITOCHONDRIAL MEMBRANE AS A POSSIBLE PACEMAKER OF TISSUE METABOLISM*

Howard Rasmussen and Etsuro Ogata

Department of Biochemistry
University of Pennsylvania, Philadelphia

A number of cations and anions are transported across the mitochondrial membrane (1-7). Recent evidence indicates that the primary species transported is the cation (4, 7, 8), and that the inner mitochondrial membrane is the one across which the ions are transported. However, the rate of cation influx and the net accumulation of cations within the mitochondrion depends upon the anionic composition of the medium (6, 7, 8). The best available evidence indicates that cation influx is energy-dependent and linked intimately with the oxidative energy-producing system (2), whereas cation efflux is a passive process (7). Cation transport is supported by energy derived from the high-energy intermediates of oxidative phosphorylation and in fact these intermediates may be the cation carrier (2, 7, 8). In any case, it is important to distinguish between the accumulation and the influx of cation. It is possible to demonstrate cation-dependent respiration with or without net ion accumulation (9), the net accumulation depending upon such factors as pH, external cation and anion concentrations, and the nature of the ions involved (10).

Of considerable interest is the question of the physiological significance of this mitochondrial activity. Several interpretations are possible.

One is that this *in vitro* activity has no counterpart *in vivo*. This is not the case, it being possible to demonstrate the accumulation of divalent cations (by electron microscopy) in intact cells *in vitro* or in tissue obtained directly from

* Supported by a grant from the Atomic Energy Commission (AT-(30-1)3489).

experimental animals (11, 12). Furthermore, the accumulation of calcium by some intact cellular preparations has very similar characteristics to that of the mitochondrial accumulation of calcium (13).

A second and conservative proposal is that this mitochondrial activity is important in maintaining ionic compartmentation within the cell (12). That such compartmentation does in fact exist has been established (14). The functional significance of this compartmentation is not readily apparent, although numerous possibilities suggest themselves. For example, it is now well established that free calcium ions have profound effects upon metabolism including the initiation of muscular contraction, glandular secretion, and enzyme activation, to mention a few. This being the case, the accumulation of calcium by mitochondria may serve to control the intracellular-extramitochondrial concentration of this important ion. Similar arguments can be applied to other cations.

A third, more radical proposal is that in those tissues in which net transport of ions occurs, the mitochondrial system is an integral part of the transcellular ion transporting system (15). This proposal is based upon the similarity in the effects of the parathyroid hormone upon ion transport across the renal tubule and ion transport across the mitochondrial membrane, and also upon the striking structural polarity of the renal tubular cells with the localization of the mitochondria in the basal portion of these cells, each mitochondria being surrounded over a considerable extent of its surface by infoldings of the plasma membrane of the cell. There is evidence that close apposition of two membranes in this fashion leads to a marked alteration in their functional properties (16). Nevertheless, considerably more evidence is needed before this proposal can be seriously considered.

A final possibility is that an alteration in ionic fluxes across the mitochondrial membrane can act as a physiological uncoupler and thereby stimulate metabolism. This possibility has come from a recent extension of our work upon the effects of parathyroid hormone upon ion transport in mitochondria. This is the possibility which I should like to consider this morning.

Figure 1 is primarily by way of orientation and demonstrates the response of isolated rat liver mitochondria to the addition of calcium and the subsequent addition of phosphate in an acetate medium. It is taken from work carried out with

Drs. Chance and Ogata (7). The important point in this figure is that the addition of calcium leads to a controlled response, a cycle of pyridine nucleotide oxidation-reduction and a burst of respiration, after which the rate of respiration returns to a control level. By independent measurements it is apparent that all the calcium has gone into the mitochondria. Under these conditions, there is a swelling of the mitochondria (Figure 1). If phosphate is now added, there is no change in the rate of respiration (no utilization of energy) but the mitochondria contract. During this contraction, if you measure phosphate and acetate, you find that the acetate which was accumulated with the calcium returns to the medium and the phosphate enters the mitochondria. Our interpretation is that there has been a non-energy dependent anion exchange between the external phosphate and internal acetate, leading to the precipitation of the calcium within the mitochondria (2, 7, 8). This in turn has led to an increase in light scattering (a decrease in mitochondrial volume), as confirmed by electron microscopy.

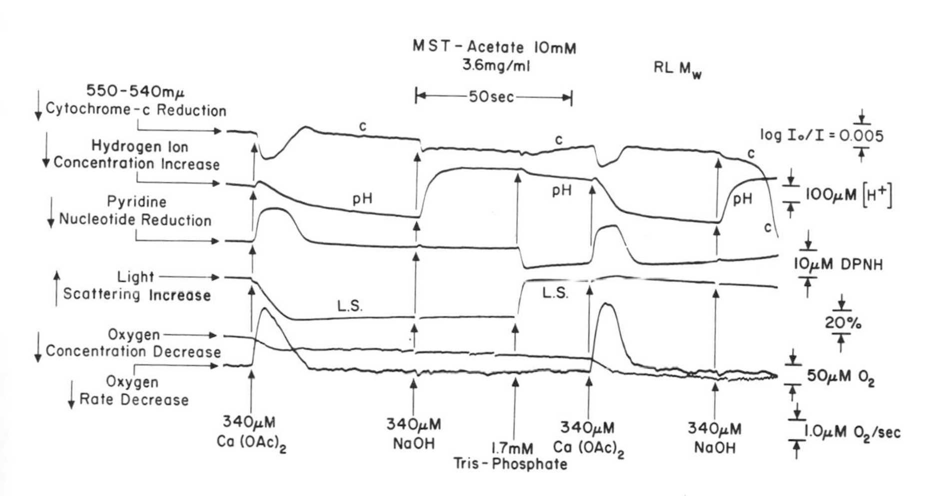

Figure 1. The response of rat liver mitochondria to the additions of $Ca(OAc)_2$ and Tris-Phosphate in an acetate medium. The medium consisted of Mannitol - 225 mM, Sucrose - 75 mM, and Tris-Acetate - 10 mM, pH 7.4. NaOH was added at two points to calibrate the H^+ evolution. The calcium addition leads to a burst of respiration, an oxidation-reduction cycle of pyridine nucleotides, the ejection of hydrogen ion, and a decrease in light scattering. Phosphate addition led to an increase in light scattering without respiratory activation. (990 6 IV)

These data suggest that mitochondrial swelling, under some circumstances at least, is an osmotic phenomenon. They raise the interesting possibility that, in studies with ascites tumor cells, the change in mitochondrial volume observed may occur by a similar mechanism (17).

With this orientation I would like to turn to a consideration of the parathyroid hormone studies.

In brief, it had been shown that this hormone stimulates the net accumulation of either magnesium or potassium in the presence of appropriate anions (6, 18). From a variety of data, the conclusion has been reached that the primary effect of the hormone is to alter the Mg^{++} and K^{+} permeabilities of the mitochondrial membrane (19). This leads to an increased rate of energy-linked ion influx with a consequent stimulation of respiration.

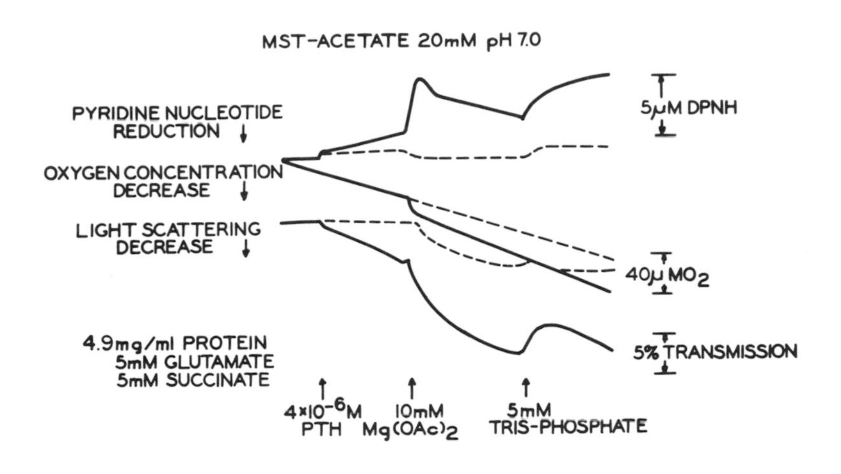

Figure 2. The response of mitochondria to the addition of $Mg(OAc)_2$ and Tris-Phosphate in the absence (- - -) and presence (———) of 4×10^{-6}M parathyroid hormone. Pyridine nucleotides were measured by fluorescence (366 → 450 mμ). Note that an initial burst of respiration is followed by a sustained increase in rate.

The next figure (Figure 2) illustrates the response of mitochondria to the addition of magnesium in the presence of parathyroid hormone. The dotted lines are the responses one observes in the absence of hormone. The response to magnesium is qualitatively similar in the presence of hormone to that observed to calcium in the absence of hormone. But there is one important difference. Once respiration is activated by Mg^{++}, there is a continued stimulation of respiration, in contradistinction to the situation with calcium where respiratory activation is limited and rapidly returns to the basal rate. This sustained stimulation of respiration is apparent even after ion accumulation has become maximal, suggesting a continual recycling of ions (9). The ratio of net accumulation of magnesium phosphate over oxygen consumed can vary over a wide range depending upon the pH of the incubation medium (9). This indicates that a bidirectional flux of ions occurs across the membrane. This in turn led to the proposal that, under appropriate conditions, marked stimulation of respiration (and uncoupling) could be induced without net ion accumulation. This possibility was verified experimentally (9). In fact, in the case of magnesium and phosphate transport across the mitochondrial membrane in the presence of the parathyroid hormone, it was possible to show that the K_m for the maximal stimulation of respiration by Mg^{++} is between 0.5-0.75 mM, whereas that for accumulation is 8-10 mM (18).

The question then became one of deciding whether such an uncoupling effect had any physiological significance, i.e., could it be demonstrated _in vivo_. It was possible to produce marked uncoupling _in vitro_, but at the outset it appeared most unlikely that such a marked change could be observed _in vivo_. This being the case, the likelihood of detecting a small difference in the rate of oxygen consumption between control and hormone-treated or hormone-deficient tissue seemed remote. However, an alternative approach to the problem was suggested by the work of Aurbach, Houston, and Potts (20). These workers were able to demonstrate a marked stimulation of the production of $^{14}CO_2$ from succinate-1,4-^{14}C when mitochondria were incubated with parathyroid hormone in an appropriate medium. They were inclined to believe that this effect of hormone was unrelated to its effects upon ion transport (20). However, a careful analysis of the requirements of the two systems indicates that the increased $^{14}CO_2$ production from labeled succinate is a consequence of the uncoupling effect of the hormonally-stimulated ionic movements (21). For example, as illustrated in Table I the nature of the anion is of critical importance. Phosphate and, to a lesser degree, acetate supported this conversion but chloride did not. This is completely analogous to the effects of these anions upon magnesium or potassium accumulation and magnesium or potassium stimulated respiration (6, 19).

TABLE I

$C^{14}O_2$ EVOLUTION FROM 1, 4 - C^{14} SUCCINATE BY RAT LIVER MITOCHONDRIA IN PRESENCE AND ABSENCE OF BOVINE PARATHYROID HORMONE.

	Control	PTH
A. Complete Medium	9.5	65
B. - Mg and K	10.6	46.5
C. - Pi + Cl	12.0	11.8
D. - Pi + OAc	9.5	27

30 minutes incubation. A - sucrose 160 mM, K_2HPO_4 32 mM, DPN 0.8 mM, Tris-succinate 8mM, 0.1 uc C^{14} succinate, $MgCl_2$ 5.3 mM, oligomycin 5α/ml, pH 7.6, parathyroid hormone 40α/ml. B - $MgCl_2$ and K_2HPO_4 replaced by Tris Cl, and Tris-phosphate. C - K_2HPO_4 replaced by Tris Cl. D - K_2HPO_4 and $MgCl_2$, replaced by Tris-acetate and $Mg(OAc)_2$.

Among the advantages of using $^{14}CO_2$ production from labeled succinate, as an index of hormonal activity is the fact that a considerable amplification of the response is obtained. Thus it is possible to observe effects with as little as 10^{-9} M hormone (20, 21). Using this response as a measure of hormonal activity, the effect of changes in hormonal status upon $^{14}CO_2$ production by rat liver slices, homogenates, and mitochondria was investigated. As shown in Table II, the surgical removal of the parathyroid glands from animals four hours prior to the experiment led to a significant decrease in $^{14}CO_2$ production by all three preparations, slices, homogenates and mitochondria, compared to the rate of production observed by similar preparations obtained from sham-operated animals. These preliminary observations must be confirmed and extended. However, they do suggest that hormonally induced alterations in succinate oxidation occur _in vivo_. Our tentative conclusion is that under appropriate conditions an alteration in ionic fluxes across the mitochondrial membrane can lead to significant changes in electron transport and Krebs Cycle activity and thus serve a pacemaker function in metabolism.

TABLE II

EFFECT OF PARATHYROIDECTOMY UPON $C^{14}O_2$ EVOLUTION FROM RAT LIVER SLICES, HOMOGENATES AND MITOCHONDRIA.

	Sham	PTX
Slices cpm/mg dry wt.	23.0	14.5
Homogenates cpm/mg protein	27.4	14.8
Mitochondria cpm/mg protein	13.0	8.9

40 minute incubation. A - Krebs-Ringer phosphate with 1 mM $CaCl_2$, 8 mM Tris - succinate and 0.2 uc/ml C^{14}-1, 4 - succinate. B and C - sucrose 160 mM, K_2HPO_4 32 mM, DPN 0.8 mM, $MgCl_2$ 5.3 mM, Tris - succinate 8 mM, oligomycin 5α/ml, 0.1 uc C^{14}- succinate, pH 7.6.

REFERENCES

1. C. S. Rossi and Lehninger, A. L., J. Biol. Chem., 239, 3971 (1964).

2. B. Chance, J. Biol. Chem., 240, 2729 (1965).

3. C. Moore and Pressman, B., Biochem. Biophys. Res. Comm., 15, 562 (1964).

4. J. B. Chappell, Cohn, M. and Greville, G. D., in B. Chance (Editor), Energy-Linked Functions of Mitochondria, New York, 1963, p. 219.

5. N. W. Saris, Societas Scientiarum Fennica, Commentationes Physico-Mathematical, 28, 11 (1963).

6. H. Rasmussen, Fischer, J. and Arnaud C., Proc. Nat. Acad. Sci. (U. S.), 52, 1198 (1964).

7. H. Rasmussen, Chance, B. and Ogata, E., Proc. Nat. Acad. Sci. (U. S.), 53, 1069 (1965).

8. B. Chance and Yoshioka, T., Fed. Proc., 24, 425 (1965).

9. M. Fang and Rasmussen, H., Endocrinol., 75, 434 (1964).

10. G. S. Christie, Ahmed, K., McLean, A. E. M. and Judah, J. D., Biochim. Biophys. Acta, 94, 432 (1965).

11. L. D. Peachey, J. Cell Biol., 20, 95 (1964).

12. H. Rasmussen and DeLuca, H. F., Ergeb. Physiol. Chem. u. Exptl. Pharmakol., 53, 1 (1963).

13. H. Rasmussen, Waldorf, A., DeLuca, H. F. and Dziewiatkowski, D. D., Biochim. Biophys. Acta, 75, 250 (1963).

14. R. E. Thiers and Vallee, B. L., J. Biol. Chem., 226, 911 (1957).

15. H. Rasmussen, in P. Karlson (Editor), Mechanisms of Hormone Action, George T. Verlag, Stuttgart, 1965, p. 131.

16. Y. Kanno and Lowenstein, W. R., Science, 143, 959 (1964).

17. L. Packer and Golder, R. H., J. Biol. Chem., 235, 1234 (1960).

18. J. D. Sallis, DeLuca, H. F. and Rasmussen, H., J. Biol. Chem., 238, 4098 (1963).

19. H. Rasmussen and Ogata, E., in preparation.

20. G. D. Aurbach, Houston, B. A. and Potts, J. T., Jr., Biochem. Biophys. Res. Comm., 17, 464 (1964).

21. E. Ogata, Delluva, A. and Rasmussen, H., in preparation.

A ROLE OF SODIUM AND POTASSIUM IN METABOLIC CONTROL

R. D. Keynes

Agricultural Research Council, Institute of Animal Physiology
Babraham, Cambridge, England

All living cells have to a greater or lesser degree the ability to bring about and maintain an internal ionic composition which may be very different from that of the surrounding medium. Typically, they accumulate potassium in their cytoplasm and keep the levels of sodium and chloride relatively low. Another ion whose intracellular concentration is small is calcium. In order to build up these concentration differences, osmotic work has to be performed at the expense of cellular metabolism, and if the energy requirement for ion pumping is large, it may have a major influence in determining the metabolic activity of the cell. The extent of this influence will depend on the nature of the cell, being relatively small in a tissue where there is only a slow resting leakage of ions to be made good, and perhaps exercising a dominating control in a tissue like nerve whose function depends on the occurrence of a large interchange of ions, or in a tissue which is specialized for secretory activity.

In 1957 Skou (1) showed that the microsomal fraction from minced crab nerves contained an ATPase activated by magnesium, sodium and potassium ions, and he suggested that this might form part of a system responsible for the active transport of these cations. This suggestion has been followed up by many other workers, and the presence of Na- and K-activated ATPase has been demonstrated in a very wide variety of tissues. Perhaps the best evidence for associating the activity of this enzyme with active transport comes from the work of Whittam (2) and Glynn (3) on reconstituted erythrocyte ghosts, showing a close parallel between the ionic requirements for ATPase activity, and those for active transport - that is to say a high internal concentration of sodium, and the presence of some potassium outside the cells. Another important feature of the transport ATPase, which is often used to differentiate it from other ATPases, is that it resembles the active transport of sodium and potassium in being blocked by low concentrations of cardiac glycosides like ouabain. Bonting and Caravaggio (4) have shown that there is a close correlation between the Na-, K-ATPase activity in different tissues and their ability to transport sodium, the two richest sources of the ATPase being brain and the electric organ. In suitably treated preparations from the electric organ, over 95 percent of the total ATPase activity is sensitive to removal of K^+ ions or treatment with ouabain (5, and unpublished observations in my own laboratory), and in this tissue active transport exerts an over-riding control over the consumption of phosphate-bond energy and hence of metabolism.

In the course of their work on the restoration of the sodium efflux in cyanide-poisoned squid axons by the injection of ATP, arginine phosphate and related compounds, Caldwell, Hodgkin, Keynes and Shaw (6) arrived at a value of about 0.7 for the ratio of Na^+ ions transported to ~P bonds consumed. However, this result was recognized as a limit rather than a really reliable estimate of the stoichiometry, since it assumed that the transport ATPase accounted exclusively for the ATP that was split. Baker (7) has now shown that about 75 per cent of the total ATPase in a squid axon is to be found in the axoplasm, and is not associated with the cell membrane or with active transport. This means not only that the estimate for the Na/~P ratio must be raised to about 3 (which is a surprisingly high value because it implies that the efficiency of the sodium pump is close to 100 per cent), but also that in these giant axons only 25 per cent of the total metabolic activity is controlled by the intracellular ionic concentration. The observation that the oxygen consumption of a squid axon cannot be increased by more than about 10 per cent by stimulation (10) is quite consistent with these facts, because in a cell with such a small ratio of surface to volume it is difficult to raise the internal sodium concentration very far, even by rapid tetanization.

In crab nerve, Baker (7) finds that about half the normal metabolic activity seems to be linked with active transport and hence with cation concentrations. Here the surface/volume ratio is very much larger, so that passage of even a few impulses can raise the internal sodium concentration enough to cause a considerable enhancement of metabolism.

One point of interest in this connection is the steepness of the relationship between sodium concentration and rate of sodium transport. If the Na/~P ratio is normally as large as 3, this would suggest that Na^+ ions might be transported three at a time, and the rate of splitting of ~P bonds would be proportional to the cube of the sodium concentration rather than its first power. There is, indeed, evidence in frog muscle (8,9) that under some conditions the sodium efflux does vary as the cube of the internal sodium concentration. I have also tried to see whether the activity of electric organ ATPase varies with $[Na]^3$, but was unable to achieve more than rather vague indications that at low [Na]'s the enzyme activity does increase in a non-linear fashion. This question seems to me to deserve further study.

To recapitulate, I would suggest that in any tissue where ionic transport across the cell membrane is functionally important, at least part of the metabolism is controlled by the following sequence of cause and effect:

(1) The functional activity of the organ determines the rate at which the ionic concentration gradients are run down. This rate is controlled by outside events, e.g. by the frequency of passage of impulses along a nerve fiber, or by hormonal control of secretion in a secretory tissue.

(2) The changes in internal sodium concentration affect the rate at which ions are pumped through the cell membrane, and hence the rate at which ~P bonds are split.

(3) Aerobic or anaerobic metabolism is accelerated in a way which has been described by Dr. Chance and others so as to resynthesize ATP at an appropriate rate.

REFERENCES

1. Skou, J.C., Biochim. Biophys. Acta, 23, 394 (1957).
2. Whittam, R., Biochem. J., 84, 110 (1962).
3. Glynn, I.M., J. Physiol., 160, 18P (1962).
4. Bonting, S.L., and Caravaggio, L.L., Arch. Biochem. Biophys., 101, 37 (1963).
5. Glynn, I.M., J. Physiol., 169, 452 (1963).
6. Caldwell, P.C., Hodgkin, A.L., Keynes, R.D., and Shaw, T.I., J. Physiol., 152, 561 (1960).
7. Baker, P.F., J. Physiol., in the press (1965).
8. Keynes, R.D., and Swan, R.C., J. Physiol., 147, 591 (1959).
9. Keynes, R.D., J. Physiol., 178, 305 (1965).
10. Connelly, C.M., and Cranefield, P.F., Abstr. XIX, Int. Physiol. Congr., Montréal, p.276 (1953).

THE ROLE OF NA^+ AND K^+ ON α-AMINOISOBUTYRIC ACID TRANSPORT IN STRIATED MUSCLE+

David M. Kipnis

Metabolism Division, Department of Medicine
Washington University School of Medicine
St. Louis, Missouri

Considerable evidence has now accumulated which indicates that Na^+ is essential for the active carrier-mediated transport* of a variety of organic solutes across the cell membrane. Riklis and Quastel (12) were the first to demonstrate this Na^+ dependency in their study of sugar transport by the guinea pig intestine. These original observations have subsequently been confirmed and extended by numerous investigators (3,5,6,7,11,19) to the active transport of other organic solutes (e.g. - amino acids, uricil) in intestine and other tissues. In contrast to these findings with active transport systems it was recently demonstrated in our laboratory that Na^+ dependency is not a characteristic feature of non-active carrier-mediated transport processes such as that involved in glucose movement across the muscle cell membrane. One possible explanation for this differential effect of Na^+ on active and non-active transport systems may be that these processes differ primarily with respect to the properties of the carrier molecule; Na^+ affecting the carrier in active transport systems but not altering carrier properties in non-active processes. In this paper, the results of a series of experiments using the intact rat diaphragm preparation are reported which are consistent with this hypothesis. In addition, data are presented which further clarify the interrelationships between the Na^+ pump in striated muscle and the amino acid transport system involved in α-aminoisobutyric acid (AIB) penetration.

*Active transport, in contradistinction to non-active transport, in this paper, refers to movement or accumulation of solute against an electrochemical gradient.

+Supported by PHS AM-1921.

Effects of Na^+ on AIB Transport

The non-metabolizable amino acid analogue, α-aminoisobutyric acid-1-C^{14} (AIB), was selected for these studies because 1) this amino acid does not exhibit significant homo- or heteroexchange diffusion; hence the rate of its intracellular accumulation serves as a direct measure of the rate of net transport, and 2) all intracellular radioactivity represents the free amino acid.

The iso-osmotic replacement of sodium by choline markedly depresses the basal penetration of AIB in both the intact and cut rat diaphragms and abolishes the insulin response (Table I). Furthermore, the ability to transport AIB against a concentration gradient, as represented by an intracellular/extracellular AIB concentration ratio 1, is no longer apparent. It should be noted that choline chloride

TABLE I

Effect of Na^+ on α- minoisobutyric Acid (AIB) Penetration into the Rat Diaphragm*

Medium	Rat diaphragm Preparation	Na^+ meq/L	Intracellular/Extracellular AIB ratio: Control	Insulin
Krebs-phosphate	Intact	137	0.83 ± 0.05	1.73 ± 0.05
Tris-choline	Intact	0	0.52 ± 0.02	0.59 ± 0.07
Krebs-phosphate	Cut	137	1.83 ± 0.58	3.32 ± 0.69
Tris-choline	Cut	0	1.07 ± 0.03	1.10 ± 0.08

*Intact rat diaphragms were incubated in 4.8×10^{-6} M AIB-1-C^{14} for 60 minutes at 37° C; cut diaphragms were incubated in 1×10^{-6} M AIB-1-C^{14} for 60 minutes at 37° C. All values represent the mean ± S. D. of 4 to 12 experiments.

does not, in itself, affect either the total tissue water or extracellular space of the diaphragm, permeability of the cell membrane to non-permeant solutes (e.g. - insulin, sucrose, raffinose) or the rates of either galactose or 2-deoxyglucose penetration in this tissue.

The AIB concentration gradient which the transport system is capable of maintaining in diaphragm muscle appears to be related directly to the extracellular [Na^+] (Figure 1). The only effective monovalent cation is Na^+; Li^+ is inactive and K^+ is inhibitory. Since changes in the steady-state level of intracellular [AIB] can result from either increased influx and/or decreased efflux, the effect of Na^+ on these two processes was assessed. As seen in Figure 2, Na^+ markedly

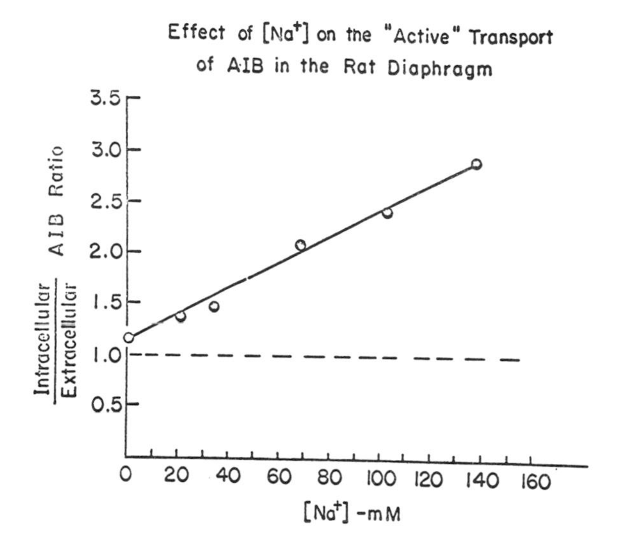

Figure 1. Effect of Na^+ on the active transport of AIB in the rat diaphragm. Cut diaphragms were incubated for 1 hour in the presence of insulin (0.4 μ /ml) in varying concentrations of Na^+. NaCl was replaced by choline chloride, isosmolarity being maintained at 300 mOsm/L. AIB concentrations, 1.5×10^{-5} M. Each point represents the mean ± SEM of 3 or more experiments. (from J. Clin. Invest., 43, 1994 (1964)).

accelerates influx, whereas net efflux was only minimally influenced by this cation. It is also of interest to note that in the absence of extracellular Na^+, exchange diffusion can be demonstrated (Figure 2, curve 3).

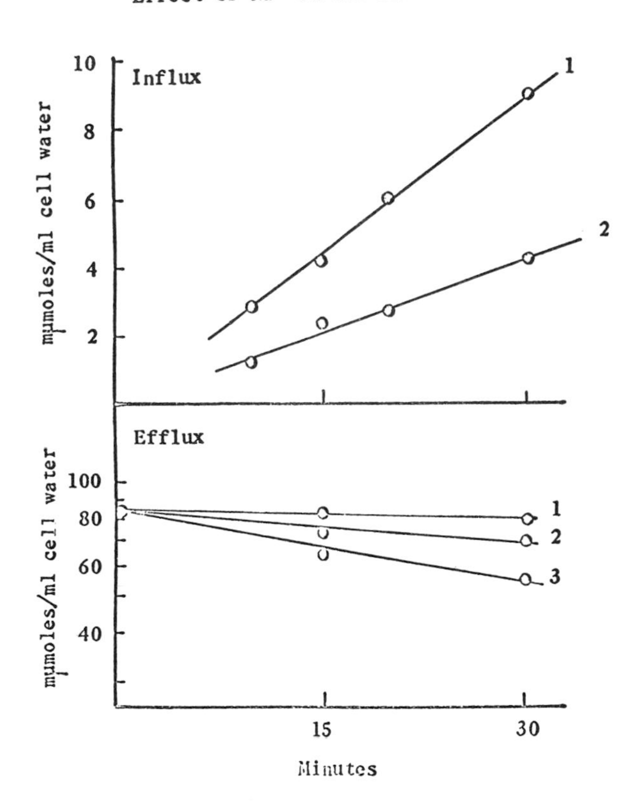

Figure 2. Effect of Na^+ on AIB influx and efflux in the intact rat diaphragm. Influx: Diaphragms were incubated in Krebs-phosphate (curve 1) or TRIS-Choline Cl (curve 2) in the presence of insulin (0.4 U/ml) for 10-30 minutes. AIB concentration, 1×10^{-5} M. Efflux: Diaphragms were pre-incubated in AIB, 1×10^{-3} M, for 45 minutes in the presence of insulin (0.4 U/ml) and then transferred to Krebs-HCO_3 without AIB (curve 1), TRIS-Choline Cl without AIB (curve 2) and TRIS-Choline Cl with AIB, 1×10^{-3} (curve 3) and incubated an additional 15-30 minutes.

AIB transport in both the intact rat diaphragm and an isolated lymph node cell preparation previously used in this laboratory (1,8) can be described in terms of Michaelis-Menton kinetics. The expressions K_m and V_{max}) are used in this study only in an operational sense; an analogy is not intended between the molecular events of transport and enzyme action although such may ultimately prove to be the case. K_m represents the concentration of AIB giving half maximal entry rates and V_{max}) is the maximal entry rate as determined from the Lineweaver-Burke plot. The effect of sodium on AIB influx appears to be due primarily to an effect of the cation on the K_m of the carrier system, V_{max} remaining unaltered (Figure 3).* In the isolated lymph node cell preparation used in these studies, K_m increased from 1.1×10^{-4} M at $[Na^+]$ = 140 mEq/L to 4×10^{-3} M at $[Na^+]$ = 50 mEq/L. Of further

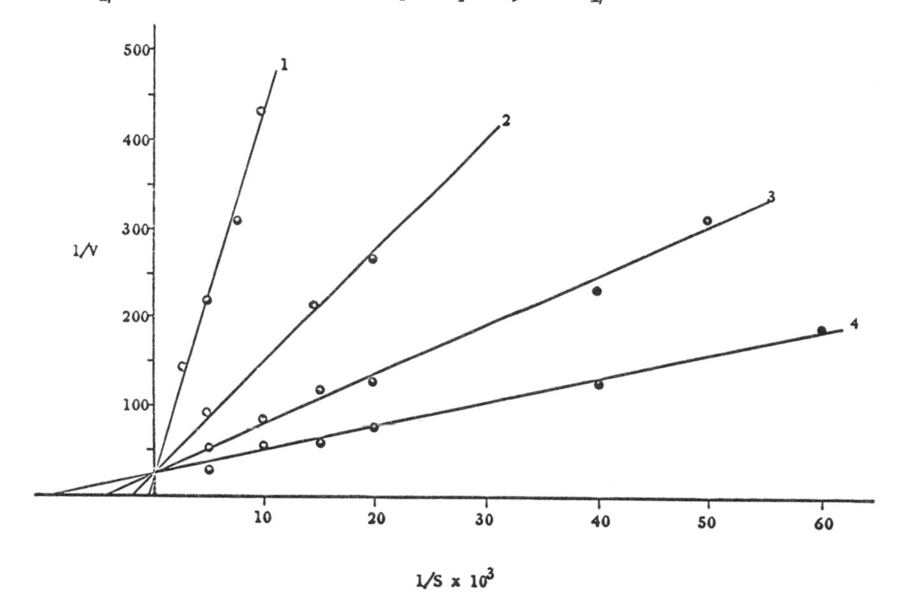

Figure 3. Effect of Na^+ on the K_m of the carrier for AIB in isolated rabbit lymph node cells. Velocities are expressed as μmoles/ml of intracellular water/minute. Lymph node cells incubated for 15 minutes (rate measurements approximate initial velocities) in varying concentrations of Na^+ - 50 mM (curve 1), 75 mM (curve 2), 100 mM (curve 3), and 140 mM (curve 4). NaCl was replaced by choline chloride, isosmolarity being maintained at 300 mOsm/L.

*Similar observations have recently been made with respect to active sugar transport in the intestine by R. Crane, Department of Biochemistry, Chicago Medical School, personal communication.

interest is the linear relationship observed in the double reciprocal plot of 1/AIB entry versus $1/[Na^+]$, a relationship which would be expected if one Na^+ ion functions as a co-substrate with AIB in the transport process (Figure 4). Vidaver (15) using the same method of analysis observed a linear relationship of 1/V (glycine entry) and $1/[Na^+]^2$ in pigeon red cells and concluded that two sodium ions were co-substrates with glycine at some step of glycine entry.

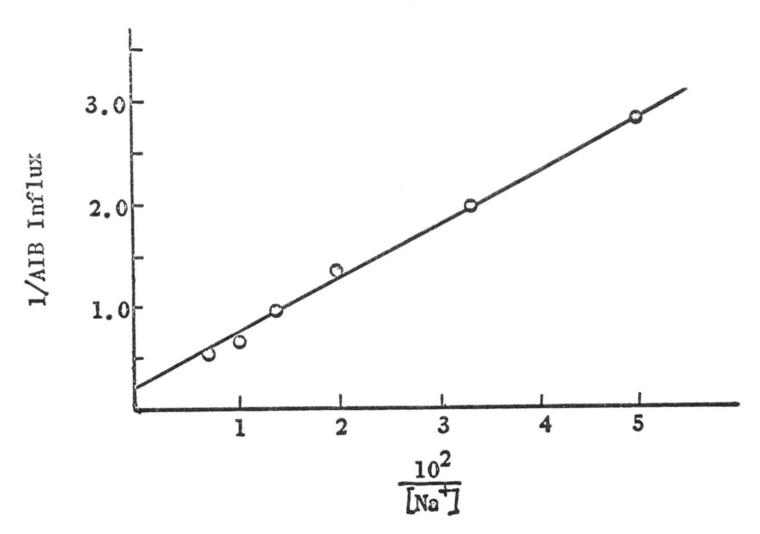

In operational terms, these results indicate that the rate-limiting event in AIB influx is represented by the binding of AIB to the carrier and that sodium affects this complex formation. Helmreich and Kipnis (8) have reported that AIB transport in isolated lymph node cells appears to be functionally irreversible and suggested that in kinetic terms, this is a consequence of marked asymmetry of the cell membrane with respect to the K_m of the carrier on the outer cell surface (K_2) such that $K_2 \gg K_1$. Since Na^+ appears to be a major determinant of K_m, it is possible to explain, at least in part, the membrane asymmetry with respect to these carrier properties. The intracellular $[Na^+]$ of the intact rat diaphragm varies between 25-35 mEq/L of cell water. On the basis of the data in Figure 3, one would predict that K_2 (i.e., the K_m of the carrier on inner cell surface) would be at least 100-fold greater than K_1. Since measurements of total intracellular $[Na^+]$ may lead to an overestimate of the $[Na^+]$ on the inner cell surface, in view of recent evidence suggesting that the distribution of Na^+ within the cells is compartmentalized and preferentially concentrated in the nucleus (2,14), the ratio of K_2/K_1 may even be greater than that estimated.

Relation of the Na^+ Electrochemical Gradient and AIB Transport

Christensen and coworkers (4,13) were the first to suggest that the energy required for active amino acid transport may be derived from the sodium electrochemical gradient established across the cell membrane. Recently Vidaver (15-18) has published a series of studies on the effect of sodium on glycine transport in pigeon cells, which have been interpreted as confirming this hypothesis. This investigator reported that the absolute level of Na^+ either in the external or internal fluid phase was not a determinant in glycine entry, rather the Na^+ electrochemical gradient was of primary importance.

Our studies are not in complete agreement with this conclusion. As noted previously (Figure 1), AIB influx is markedly diminished as the extracellular $[Na^+]$ is progressively decreased. Under these conditions, the intracellular $[Na^+]$ proportionately decreased although the transmembrane potential remained remarkably constant (Table II). Indeed incubation of the intact diaphragm preparation in Na^+-free Tris-choline Cl buffer (containing Ca^{++} - 2.5 mM and K^+ - 5 mM) for periods up to 60 minutes did not result in a significant change in membrane potential.

The energy represented by the Na^+ electrochemical gradient can be calculated from the equation:

$$V = \frac{RT}{ZF} \ln (C_o/C_i) - E_m$$

where R is the gas constant, T the absolute temperature, F the Faraday, Z the valence of the cation, C_o and C_i the Na^+ in the extracellular and intracellular water and E_m the membrane potential.

Under the conditions recorded in Figure 2 and Table II, the energy represented by the sodium electrochemical gradient is not changed, yet AIB influx is decreased approximately 80 per cent. The results indicate that the absolute level of sodium on both the inner and outer cell surface is of primary importance in maintaining the active transport of AIB.

TABLE II

Relation of AIB Influx to Extracellular [Na^+] and the Na^+ Electrochemical Gradient

Extra-cellular [Na^+]	Intra-cellular [Na^+]	Membrane Potential	Na^+ Electro-Chemical Gradient	AIB Influx*
meq/L	meq/L	mv	mv	mμmoles/min
140	30.0 ± 3.4		-105	0.33
115	23.0 ± 2.2		-116	0.27
70	17.3 ± 1.4	-72 ± 1.5	-110	0.18
40	11.8 ± 1.1		-106	0.07

All values represent mean ± S.E.M. of 4 or more determinations.

*Influx measured in presence of insulin (0.4 U/ml incubation medium). AIB = 1 x 10^{-5} M.

Effect of K^+ on AIB Transport

The effect of potassium on AIB transport is more difficult to assess since replacement of extracellular sodium by potassium is associated with marked changes in the rate of AIB penetration merely as the result of the decreased [Na^+]. To obviate this difficulty, the effect of potassium was studied using either buffers totally deficient in sodium or Krebs-HCO_3-Choline Cl solutions containing a fixed level of Na^+ and substituting K^+ for the choline moiety. Under these circumstances, significant depression of AIB transport, in the presence and absence of insulin, was observed when external [K^+] ~ 70 mEq/L (Table III). Further increases in external [K^+] resulted in even greater impairment of AIB penetration. The high temperature coefficient of AIB transport (> 2.0) was not affected by these high levels of K^+ and, furthermore, glycine still competed with AIB for entry. These results indicate that the penetration of AIB observed under these conditions is still carrier-mediated, although transport against a concentration gradient no longer occurs.

TABLE III

Effect of K^+ on AIB Transport in the Presence and Absence of Insulin in the Intact Rat Diaphragm

Exptl. Conds. Procedure†	Na^+ meq/L	K^+ meq/L	Intracellular/Extracellular (AIB) ratio* Control	Insulin‡
1	115	5	0.40 ± 0.02	0.98 ± 0.07
	115	10	0.45 ± 0.06	-
	115	15	0.39 ± 0.04	0.97 ± 0.05
	115	20	-	1.02 ± 0.11
	115	35	0.38 ± 0.06	-
2	70	0	0.82 ± 0.10	1.57 ± 0.14
	70	70	0.56 ± 0.08	0.53 ± 0.09
3	70	0	0.74 ± 0.07	1.05 ± 0.10
	70	70	0.57 ± 0.10	0.54 ± 0.11
4	140	0	0.83 ± 0.05	1.73 ± 0.05
	0	0	0.52 ± 0.02	0.59 ± 0.07
	0	140	0.31 ± 0.06	0.37 ± 0.02

*Extracellular AIB - 1×10^{-5} M.

‡Insulin - 0.4 units/ml.

†Procedure 1. Intact diaphragm incubated in Krebs-HCO_3 buffer containing Na^+ - 115 meq/L, K^+ - 5 meq/L and Na^{22} for 45 minutes. K^+ then added to give final concentration recorded in column 3 and incubated additional 30 minutes.

Procedure 2. Intact diaphragm incubated in either Krebs-PO_4-Choline Chloride or high K^+-Krebs-PO_4 buffer for 60 minutes.

Procedure 3. Cut diaphragm incubated in either Krebs-PO_4-Choline Cl or high K^+-Krebs-PO_4 buffer for 30 minutes.

Procedure 4. Intact diaphragm incubated in either Krebs-PO_4, Tris-Choline Chloride or Tris-high K^+ buffer for 60 minutes.

Effect of K^+ on AIB Influx and Efflux

Extracellular potassium affects both AIB influx and efflux. Influx was measured during short periods of incubation when the rate of AIB accumulation was linear and the intracellular level was low (efflux is therefore negligible). As seen in Figure 5, AIB influx is markedly depressed in the presence of high external $[K^+]$; correspondingly, efflux is significantly increased (curve 3) and exchange diffusion is readily demonstrated (curve 4). These observations suggest that K^+ increases the K_m of the carrier for AIB, an effect opposite to that observed with Na^+. A concomitant change in V_{max}, however, cannot be excluded until more detailed kinetic studies are carried out. On the basis of these studies, the marked asymmetry of the cell membrane with respect to carrier characteristics can be explained in terms of the unequal distribution of Na^+ and K^+ between the intracellular and extracellular compartments. The high $[Na^+]$ and low $[K^+]$ in the extracellular field results in a low K_1, and the low $[Na^+]$ and high $[K^+]$ in the intracellular water results in a high K_2.

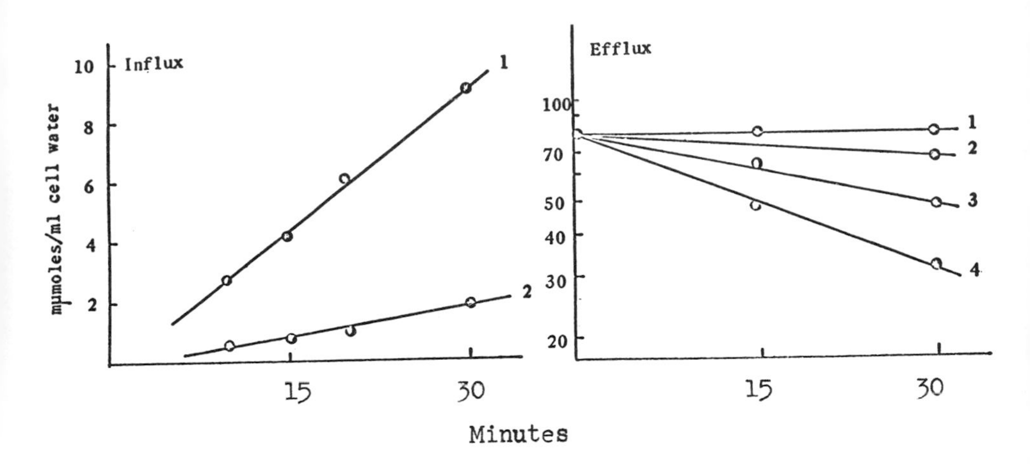

Figure 5. Effect of K^+ on AIB influx and efflux in the intact rat diaphragm. Influx: Diaphragms were incubated in Krebs-HCO_3 (curve 1) or Tris-KCl (150 mM) - curve 2, in the presence of insulin (0.4 U/ml) for 10-30 minutes. AIB concentration, 1×10^{-5} M. Efflux: Diaphragms were pre-incubated in AIB, 1×10^{-3} M, for 45 minutes in the presence of insulin (0.4 U/ml) and then transferred to Krebs-HCO_3 without AIB (curve 1), Tris-Choline Cl without AIB (curve 2), Tris-KCl (150 mM) without AIB (curve 3), and Tris-KCl (150 mM) with AIB, 1×10^{-3} M (curve 4) and incubated an additional 15-30 minutes.

Relation of the Na^+ Pump to AIB Transport

In this series of studies, the steady state intracellular [Na^+] has been used as an index for assessing Na^+ pump activity in a variety of experimental conditions. In the course of determining the effect of potassium on AIB transport, the intracellular [Na^+] was noted to decrease markedly as the extracellular [K^+] was increased from 5 to 20 mM (Table IV). This decrease in [Na^+] was not secondary to expansion of the intracellular volume since similar fluid shifts produced by incubation in hypotonic buffer did not result in equivalent changes in Na^+ content. Since there was a net loss of Na^+ from the cell against a Na^+ electrochemical gradient, the change in the steady state level of Na^+ was interpreted as indicating the acceleration of the Na^+ pump induced by increasing the extracellular [K^+]. This interpretation has been confirmed recently by studies of Horowicz (9). Concomitant measurement of the AIB penetration rates under these conditions demonstrated that despite an acceleration of Na^+ pump activity as well as an approximately 20 per cent decrease in the Na^+ gradient potential, AIB influx was unaffected.

TABLE IV

Relation of AIB Influx to Extracellular Na^+, K^+, Membrane Potential and Na^+ Electrochemical Gradient

Extracell. Na^+ meq/L	Extracell. K^+ meq/L	Intracell. Na^+ meq/L	Membrane Potential mv	Na^+ Electrochem. Gradient mv	AIB Influx* mμmoles/min.
115	5	23.1 ± 0.8	-69	-109.5	0.27 ± 0.06
115	7.5	22.8 ± 0.9	-65	-105.8	
115	10.0	21.8 ± 1.1	-59	-101.0	0.28 ± 0.04
115	12.5	19.7 ± 1.6	-50	- 94.5	
115	15.0	18.9 ± 1.2	-45	- 90.5	0.24 ± 0.07
115	20.0	14.9 ± 0.8	-40	- 91.6	0.25 ± 0.06

All values represent mean ± S. E. M. of 4 or more determinations.

*Influx measured in the presence of insulin (0.4 U/ml incubation medium)

The effect of decreased Na^+ pump activity on AIB transport was also studied (Table V). Low concentrations of the cardiac glycoside, strophanthin K (1×10^{-5} M), inhibit the Na^+ pump, as reflected in the increasing levels of intracellular $[Na^+]$ but do not affect either the basal or insulin stimulated rate of AIB transport. Na^+ pump activity was also depressed by producing hyperpolarization of the cell membrane by incubating the diaphragm in hyper-osmotic buffers (osmolarity increased to 450 mOsm/L by addition of sucrose) yet maintaining extracellular $[Na^+]$ constant. Under these conditions AIB influx remained unchanged. Since neither stimulation of the sodium pump nor its inhibition cause significant changes in AIB transport, it would seem unlikely that the Na^+ pump in striated muscle is either directly linked to or involves the same carrier mechanism as that responsible for AIB entry.

TABLE V

Effect of Depressing Na^+ Pump Activity on AIB Transport in the Intact Rat Diaphragm

Experimental Conditions	Intracellular Content of AIB	Intracellular Content of Na^+
	$m\mu$moles/ml	μmoles/ml
Control		
Before incubation	---	23.2 ± 1.8
After incubation	4.2 ± 0.14	24.0 ± 1.2
Strophanthin K 1×10^{-5} M	4.1 ± 0.25	44.4 ± 0.6
Hyperosmotic Buffer (450 mOsm/L)	3.9 ± 0.36	31.5 ± 3.8

*Intact rat diaphragms were incubated at 37° C for 60 minutes in AIB, 2×10^{-6} M. All values represent the mean $\pm$ SEM of 3 to 6 experiments.

SUMMARY

The various kinetic models which have been proposed for active transport systems generally assume participation of a "carrier" and differ only with respect to the mobility of the carrier-solute complex. To account for movement against an electrochemical gradient, it is assumed that the carrier is inactivated on the cell surface adjacent to the phase in which the solute is concentrated and is reactivated as it returns to the opposite surface. The differences in carrier activity on the inner and outer cell membrane surface may be expressed, in kinetic terms, as differences in the K_m of the carrier for the solute. The observations reported in this paper indicate that these changes are, at least in part, a consequence of the unequal distribution of Na^+ and K^+ across the cell membrane; Na^+ activating the carrier and K^+ functionally inactivating the carrier. The ability of the cationic environment to affect carrier properties is not an unexpected finding if one assumes, in an operational sense, an analogy between transport and enzyme mechanisms. Allosteric cation activation and inhibition of enzyme activity is a well known phenomenon. Whether similar molecular mechanisms, such as conformational changes in carrier structure, are mediated by cationic environment must await specific chemical identification of the carrier moiety.

These studies also suggest that although the Na^+ electrochemical gradient may be a source of energy for active amino acid transport, the absolute levels of both Na^+ and K^+, irrespective of the gradient, are also a major factor in regulating the transport process. It should also be pointed out that although transport mechanisms may be similar in various tissues, the specific properties of the carrier may vary. For example, K^+ has a marked inhibiting effect on the carrier in muscle but is apparently inactive in pigeon cells (15). The relation of the Na^+ pump in muscle to Na^+ dependent amino acid transport does not appear to be one in which the systems are either stoichiometrically linked or share a common carrier. Rather, the Na^+ pump appears to be involved in terms of maintaining an unequal distribution of Na^+ and K^+ between the cell and its environment. Consequently, any significant impairment in its activity will eventually result in impaired amino acid transport.

ACKNOWLEDGMENTS

The author wishes to express his appreciation to Dr. Harry Fozzard, Cardiology Division, Washington University School of Medicine, for performing the measurements of membrane potential recorded in this paper. He is also grateful to Mrs. Kathleen Keithly for her valuable and expert technical assistance.

REFERENCES

1. Akedo, H. and Christensen, H.N., J. Biol. Chem., 237, 118 (1962).

2. Allfrey, V.G., Neudt, R., Hopkins, J.W. and Mirsky, A.E., Proc. Natl. Acad. Sci. (Wash.) 47, 907 (1961).

3. Bihler, I. and Crane, R.K., Biochim. Biophys. Acta, 59, 78 (1962).

4. Christensen, H.N., Riggs, T.R., Fischer, H. and Palatine, I.M., J. Biol. Chem., 198, 1 (1952).

5. Crane, R.E., Miller, D. and Bihler, I. Membrane Transport and Metabolism. Academic Press Inc., New York, 1961, p.439.

6. Csaky, T.Z., Am. J. Physiol., 201, 999 (1961).

7. Csaky, T.Z., Fed. Proc., 22, 3 (1963).

8. Helmreich, E. and Kipnis, D.M., J. Biol. Chem., 237, 2582 (1962).

9. Horowicz, P. and Gerber, C., J. Gen. Physiol., 48, 489 (1965).

10. Kleinzeller, A. and Kotyk, A., Biochim. Biophys. Acta, 54, 367 (1961).

11. Parrish, J.E., and Kipnis, D.M., J. Clin. Invest., 43, 1994 (1964).

12. Ricklis, E. and Quastel, J.H., Canad. J. Biochem., 36, 347 (1958).

13. Riggs, T.R., Walker, L.M. and Christensen, H.N., J. Biol. Chem., 233, 1479 (1958).

14. Vallee, B.L. and Hock, F.L., Int. Rev. Cytol., 8, 345 (1959).

15. Vidaver, G.A., Biochem., 3, 662 (1964).

16. Vidaver, G.A., Biochem., 3, 795 (1964).

17. Vidaver, G.A., Ibid., 3, 799 (1964).

18. Vidaver, G.A., Ibid., 3, 803 (1964).

19. Yunis, A., Arimura, G.K. and Kipnis, D.M., J. Lab. and Clin. Med., 60, 1028 (1962).

DISCUSSION

<u>Bücher</u>: Dr. Chance reports that in the salt gland, the ratio of Na^+ to ~P is about 8 (Chance, B., Lee, C-P., Oshino, R., and van Rossum, G.D.V., Am. J. Physiol., 206, 461, [1964]). If there is a similar mechanism in the electric organ, one could assume that 8 Na^+ are transported.

<u>Lardy</u>: Dr. Keynes pointed out the high efficiency of the Na^+ transport, but I believe he did not calculate into this the fact that K^+ is transported out simultaneously. Wouldn't this make the system too efficient?

<u>Keynes</u>: No, because the K^+ is very nearly at the same electrochemical potential on both sides of the membrane; relatively little work would have to be done on the K^+. Could I ask Dr. Chance if he knows what gradient the salt gland is working against?

<u>Chance</u>: Dr. S. Thesleff of Lund University has attempted to insert electrodes into the salt gland cells to measure their membrane potential, but has not been completely successful. The salt gland is highly invaginated tissue, and it is difficult to be sure just where the electrode is located. (S. Thesleff, personal communication; Thesleff, S. and Schmidt-Nielson, K., Am. J. Physiol., 202, 597 [1962]).

<u>Keynes</u>: I think that Ussing has pointed out that estimates on the Na^+/~P ratio in kidney work at something like 28 (Ussing, H.H. and Windhager, E.E., in "Water and Electrolyte Metabolism," Elsevier, Amsterdam, [1964], p.3). There, of course, most of the Na^+ is being transported against a zero osmotic gradient when it is absorbed in the proximal tubule, so you must explain how the mechanism has the capability of changing its gear ratio, rather than how it works at high efficiency.

<u>Kipnis</u>: In muscle, we obtain a ratio of about 3.5 for the Na^+ ions transported per ATP.

<u>Pressman</u>: I have one other figure to add to this efficiency picture, although in deference to the fact that we do not know what the potentials are in mitochondria, let us just call it an "ion transport yield". In the valinomycin-stimulated K^+

transport, the yield supplying energy from ATP is approximately 6 K^+ transported per ~P. Either there are different mechanisms which involve different stoichiometries of ions transported to ~P consumed, or else there is one mechanism with a very flexible stoichiometry which accommodates itself for the various gradients against which it has to work. We prefer the latter hypothesis.

Salganicoff: I would like to point to another mechanism by which ions can induce control properties and compartmentation in cells. Glutamic acid concentration in brain is of the order of 0.1 M and is shown by isotopic data and computer analysis to be compartmented in two pools. This amino acid is also known by its strong depolarizing action on individual neurons (Curtis, D.R. and Watkins, J.C., J. Physiol., London, 150, 656 [1960]),leading to spreading depression if applied to the surface of the brain (Van Hareveld, A., in "Inhibition in the Nervous System and γ-Aminobutyric Acid", Roberts, E., Ed., Pergamon Press, Oxford, 1960, p. 454). γ-aminobutyric acid (GABA (GABA), when tested by its neurophysiological effects, has an effect opposite to that of glutamic acid. There is an enzyme, glutamic decarboxylase (GAD) unique to the central nervous system, which produces GABA in an irreversible reaction. 50 per cent of the total content of GAD is localized in the nerve endings complex, 13 per cent in the microsomal fraction, and 30 per cent in the supernatant of total homogenate. We have been able to show that the enzyme activity appearing in the supernatant fraction depends on the concentration of electrolytes particularly Ca^{++} present in the homogenizing medium. Even after solubilization in the absence of electrolytes, GAD may be bound again to subcellular structure, Ca^{++} again having an important quantitative effect (Salganicoff, L., and De Robertis, E. D., J. Neurochem., 12, 287 (1965)).

These results, apart from showing that the soluble enzyme is an artifact due to the absence of ions in the homogenization medium, lead to a hypothesis for the compartmentation of glutamic acid and the control of its depolarizing action on neuronal surfaces. It is possible to envisage GAD fixed to cellular membranes through Ca^{++} bonds as the biochemical barrier by which glutamic acid is kept away from the surface of neurons. In this sense, its labile fixation would lead to an understanding of the importance of Ca^{++} levels in blood and tissue and their influence on the neurological symptoms characteristic of the hypocalcemic state. It might also lead to partial clarification of the powerful excitatory action of chelating agents in vivo (Curtis, D. R., Perrin, D. D., and Watkins, J. C., J. Neurochem., 6, 1 (1960)), a mechanism shown to differ from the excitatory action of neurotransmitters and amino acids by the 5-second delay in the initiation of depolarization.

VII

Control Due to Changes of Enzyme Content

ON TRANSITORY AND PERIODIC SYSTEMS IN BACTERIA[+]

Arthur B. Pardee

Department of Biology, Princeton University
Princeton, New Jersey

Intermittent events are among both the most significant and the least explained in biological systems. These can take place in response to an outside stimulus, as in the changes in the transport of ions in nerve cells, or the release of calcium ion in muscle. Or they can occur periodically (for example, divisions of a growing cell). In this communication, using bacteria as model cells, we will draw attention to some relations between these important physiological events and the regulatory properties of enzyme formation and function.

First we will present an example of a system which shows an overshoot when subject to an outside stimulus. This is the transport of sulfate ions into *Salmonella typhimurium*, investigated by Dreyfuss. Normally, when bacteria are exposed to a molecule which is actively transported, the kinetics show the transported material approaching a final maximum concentration within the cell, asymptotically (1). However, sulfate ions first enter the bacterium, and then, having reached a maximum concentration, a large part flow out again (Figure 1) (2).

According to generalized models for overshoots (3) the active transport mechanism must be modified during transport in order that this should occur. An hypothesis consistent with this behavior (4) is that some compound derived from internal sulfate inhibits the inflow mechanism; as this compound is gradually formed, inward flow diminishes until it is slower than outward flow. Curves of the experimentally observed sort are easily constructed with such a model system (Figure 2). Feedback inhibition of activity (5) is the basic principle involved.

Overshoot at the completely different level of gene function and enzyme formation has been known for some time. Gorini and Maas (6) demonstrated that ornithine transcarbamylase, an

[+] This work was aided by USPHS AI 04409.

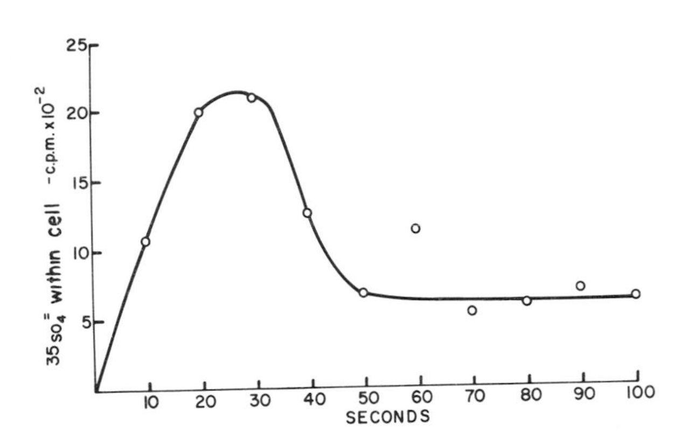

Figure 1. Sulfate transport of Mutant CYS CD-519. Cells were grown on djenkolic acid, harvested, and washed once with medium E. Cells representing 400 µg of protein (0.05 ml) were incubated at 37° for the desired time interval in 2.0 ml of medium E containing 1 x 10^{-4} sulfate, 30 µg of chloramphenicol per ml, and 2 x 10^6 C.P.M. of $^{35}SO_4^{=}$ per ml. After incubation, 1.0 ml of the cell suspension was filtered through a 0.45 µ millipore filter. The cells were then washed with 5 ml of ice-cold glucose free medium E. Under these conditions, the sulfate pool is not removed. The millipore filter was then dried and counted.

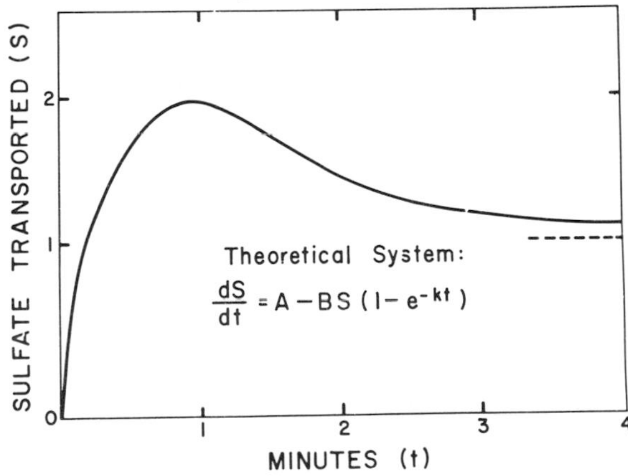

Figure 2. A theoretical curve for sulfate transport. The curve is a plot of the equation given in the figure. Values for the constants used at A = 3.5; B = 3.5; and K = 0.7. The sulfate transported is indicated in arbitrary units.

enzyme of arginine biosynthesis, appears very rapidly when bacteria are deprived of an external supply of arginine. After about one division, enzyme formation ceases abruptly; the enzyme that has been formed is gradually diluted out as the cells continue to grow and divide. The maximal enzyme concentration is thus much higher than at final equilibrium. Their explanation for this observation is that a high concentration of arginine (or some compound related to arginine) is gradually built up by the enzyme, and this compound eventually inhibits (represses) formation of the enzyme. Thus, the well-known phenomenon of enzyme repression (7) explains this overshoot satisfactorily.

The period formation of enzyme during the bacterial division cycle (Figure 3) has recently been observed (8,9,10). In a synchronously dividing culture, some enzymes are formed only at certain times within the cycle, but not at others. Since rapid enzyme formation occurs once in each division cycle, it is suggested that an overshoot of enzyme production, similar

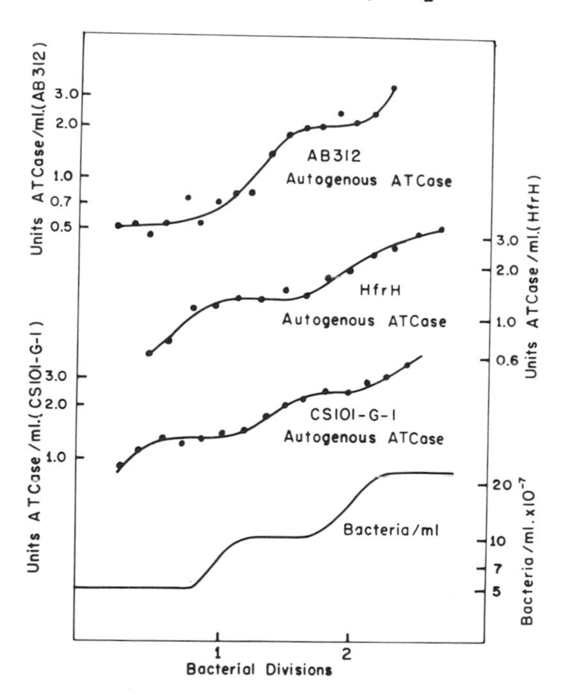

Figure 3. The autogenous activity of aspartate transcarbamylase in synchronous cultures of three E. coli HRF strains. The data from three separate experiments are normalized with respect to both bacterial concentration and generation time. Semi-log plot.

to that observed by Gorini and Maas, occurs in each cycle. The perturbation which sets up this overshoot is assumed to be the duplication of the gene corresponding to this enzyme, at the time in the cycle when its replication occurs. Each gene seems to replicate at a definite time during chromosomal growth (11); and chromosomal division appears to be related to cell division (see, for example, 12).

A mathematical model can be set up for this overshoot (10). First, consider the consequences of only one gene replication. The model is based on the familiar scheme of enzyme repression by the co-repressor, a substance produced by the enzyme. Let us suppose that such a system starts off in a non-balanced state, following replication of the gene. Then, according to the model, it will follow the course shown in Figure 4. The enzyme is synthesized periodically through several cycles, in each of which the volume of the system doubles. The amount of co-repressor passes through several damped oscillations. This model shows that such oscillations can occur when further cell division or gene replication is prevented.

Now let us suppose that at "Interval" mark on the figure the gene is allowed to replicate once more. At this point, each of the components of the system has doubled; therefore,

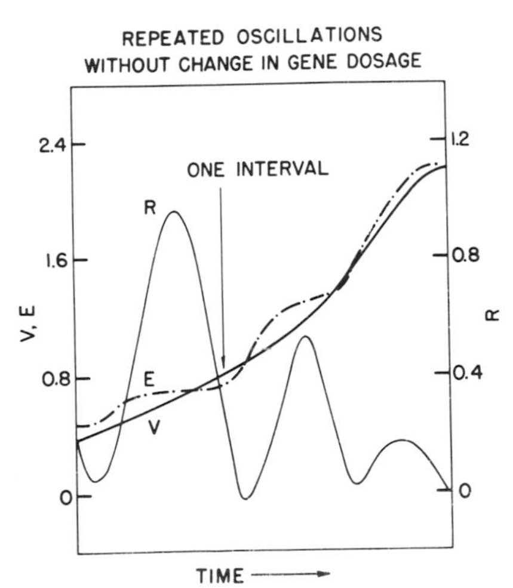

Figure 4. Theoretical curves of the overshoot in enzyme production. These were obtained with an analog computer, using the equations

$$dE/dt = 0.004\ V/R; \quad dR/dt = 0.495\ E - 0.545\ V; \quad dV/dT = 0.01V$$

E is the total amount of enzyme; T is time; V is the total volume of the system; R is the total repressor.

when the cell divides each is brought back to the initial situation. The system goes through the same cycle over and over again. This model shows the periodic enzyme synthesis actually observed (see Figure 3). It is actually too simple, since it requires special starting conditions; otherwise, it tends not to converge with a stable repetitive behavior. However, a model of this general sort with some stabilizing factors introduced might well account for the observed periodic enzyme formation.

An interesting possibility is that the above model might account for periodic cell divisions. Schaecter _et al_. (12) have shown that cell division is a quite precisely timed event, with a coefficient of variation of the order of ± 20 per cent. Furthermore, it is related to the periodic chromosomal separation which can be observed in the cells (12). Let us suppose that this latter event is initiated by a minimum (or maximum) concentration of some special regulating substance within the cell, produced in the manner indicated above (Figure 4). In turn, chromosomal replication would later produce another minimum of repressor. These events, one following the other, would set up periodic chromosomal replications, and as a consequence periodic cell divisions. These stable oscillations would be much like those set up by the interactions of the mainspring and balance wheel of a watch; the former's energy, being released periodically by the escapement controlled by the latter, keeping the otherwise damped oscillation of the balance wheel in constant motion.

A model of this sort would account for many of the observations on bacterial cell division. The involvement of nutritional conditions in determining cell division (reviewed by Kuempel and Pardee, 13), would show themselves in the rates of repressor formation. Under very rich nutritional conditions Yoshikawa _et al_. (14) have shown that replication can be initiated at more places than one. Furthermore, according to Pritchard and Lark (15), thymine starvation starts new chromosomal replications. Evidence obtained from cell division mutants by Jacob _et al_. (16) would be consistent with our model also.

In summary: Overshoot phenomena have been observed in growing bacteria, in the function of an enzyme-like transport mechanism, with a period of about a minute. Also at the level of enzyme formation, enzymes have been shown to be made intermittently, with periods of about an hour. In both cases, explanations can be provided in terms of known control mechanisms (feedback inhibition and induction-repression, respectively). The former events have implications for physiological transport mechanisms of transitory duration; the latter have implications for cell and chromosomal division.

REFERENCES

1. Hoffman, J.F. (Ed.), The Cellular Functions of Membrane Transport, Prentice-Hall, Inc., New Jersey, 1964.

2. Dreyfuss, J., J. Biol. Chem., 239, 2292 (1964).

3. Burton, A.C., J. Ce.. Comp. Physiol., 14, 327 (1939).

4. Dreyfuss, J., and Pardee, A.B., in preparation.

5. Umbarger, H.E., Cold Spring Harbor Symp. Quant. Biol., 26, 301 (1961).

6. Gorini, L. and Maas, W.K., Biochim. Biophys. Acta, 25, 208 (1957).

7. Vogel, H.J., in D.M. Bonner (Ed.), Control Mechanisms in Cellular Processes, The Ronald Press Co., New York, 1961, p. 23.

8. Masters, M., Kuempel, P.L. and Pardee, A.B., Biochem. Biophys. Res. Comm., 15, 38 (1964).

9. Gorman, J., Taruo, P., LaBerge, M. and Halvorson, H., Biochim. Biophys. Res. Comm., 15, 43 (1964).

10. Kuempel, P.L., Masters, M., and Pardee, A.B., Biochem. Biophys. Res. Comm., 18, 858 (1965).

11. Yoshikawa, H., and Sueoka, N., Proc. Natl. Acad. Sci., U.S., 49, 559 (1963).

12. Schaecter, M., Williamson, J.P., Hood, J.R., Jr. and Koch, A.L., J. Gen. Microbiol., 29, 421 (1962).

13. Kuempel, P.L. and Pardee, A.B., J. Cell. Comp. Physiol., 62 (Supp. 1), 15 (1963).

14. Yoshikawa, H., O'Sullivan, A. and Sueoka, N., Proc. Natl. Acad. Sci., U.S., 52, 973 (1964).

15. Pritchard, R.H. and Lark, K.G., J. Mol. Biol., 9, 288 (1964).

16. Jacob, F., Brenner, S., and Cuzin, F., Cold Spring Harbor Symp. Quant. Biol., 28, 329 (1963).

ACKNOWLEDGEMENT

We are indebted to Mr. Robert Klahn for programming the digital computer and to Dr. Joseph Higgins for putting the model onto the analog computer. Drs. J. Dreyfuss and P.L. Kuempel performed the experiments on sulfate transport and ATCase, respectively.

ON THE DIRECTION OF PYRIDINE NUCLEOTIDE OXIDATION-REDUCTION REACTIONS IN GLUCONEOGENSIS AND LIPOGENESIS+

Henry A. Lardy

Institute for Enzyme Research and Department of Biochemistry
University of Wisconsin, Madison

A matter of considerable importance in determining whether the liver cell synthesizes fat or carbohydrate, is the direction taken by the malic dehydrogenase reaction of the cytosol.* This subject can be discussed more succinctly after considering the path that carbon takes from pyruvate to either fatty acids or hexoses.

Liver mitochondria carboxylate pyruvate to form oxaloacetate (OAA), but the latter does not diffuse through the membrane to the cytosol (1). The OAA is in part reduced to malate, in part transaminated to form aspartate and some of it is converted to citrate by condensing with acetylCoA. These di- and tri- carboxylic acids can diffuse from the mitochondria.

Under conditions that predispose the liver to gluconeogenesis, malate must be oxidized by DPN in the cytosol and the OAA is converted to phosphoenolpyruvate (PEP) by PEPcarboxykinase. Aspartate yields OAA by transamination with α-ketoglutarate -- a reaction that requires no pyridine nucleotide.

In contrast, during lipogenesis the OAA produced in the citrate-cleavage reaction in the cytosol is probably reduced to malate by DPNH and malic dehydrogenase. The malate is converted by malic enzyme to pyruvate and CO_2, generating TPNH which is required for reductions in fatty acid synthesis. Evidence for a transhydrogenation from DPNH to TPN, and involving

*The term cytosol will be used to designate that portion of the cell which is found in the supernatant fraction after centrifuging the homogenate at 105,000 x g for 1 hour. It refers specifically to the cytoplasm minus mitochondria and endoplasmic reticulum components.

+Our experimental work on gluconeogenesis has been supported by NSF, NIH and the Eli Lilly Co.

OAA and the enzymes of rat liver cytosol has been published (2).

The question that arises is whether the O-R state of the cytosol DPN determines the direction taken by the four-carbon acids, or whether the disposal of the acids by one route or the other drives the pyridine nucleotide more oxidized or more reduced.

Table I

Rat liver pyridine nucleotides

Status	DPN/DPNH
Control fed rats	8.6
Fasted 24 hrs.	4.5
Fasted 72 hrs.	5.1
Fasted 72 hrs., glucose 2 hrs.	9.7
Adrex. fed	9.9
Adrex fasted 24 hrs.	8.2
Adrex. fasted; HC* 3 hrs.	8.0
Adrex. fasted; HC 24 hrs.	4.3
Diabetic (alloxan)	5.3
Diabetic (mannoheptulose)	9.6
Diabetic (allox) 5 μ Insulin 2 hrs.	8.4
Diabetic (allox) 20 μ Insulin 24 hrs.	9.6

*Hc = Hydrocortisone

Table I (from 3) summarizes the oxidation-reduction state of DPN in livers of rats subjected to various treatments. TPN/TPNH values were close to unity and did not vary as a result of any of the treatments. Several of the findings are in agreement with data reported by Burch, Lowry and their collaborators. Their analytical and sampling techniques were used throughout.

Fasting, a condition accompanied by enhanced gluconeogenesis, causes a striking increase in the reduced form of DPN. This effect is very rapidly reversed by feeding glucose. The adrenalectomized rat is defective in its ability to mobilize protein reserves for gluconeogenesis and moreover, is incapable of driving its pyridine nucleotides more reduced during fasting. Following hydrocortisone administration to the fasted adrenalectomized rat, blood sugar increases within one or two hours and glycogen deposition is significant by three hours (4). Liver DPN does not become more reduced in three hours, but is 24 hours after hydrocortisone administration. The alloxan-diabetic rat's liver produces excessive amounts of glucose and has a low DPN/DPNH ratio. The "instant diabetes" produced by mannoheptulose is not accompanied by alteration of the O-R state of pyridine nucleotides.

The data might be explained by assuming that malate delivers not only a C_4 compound for gluconeogenesis, but also reducing equivalents to the cytosol. The reducing power is of great importance in driving phosphoglycerate back to triose phosphate. Glucose administration to the normal fasted animal might shut off this production of malate and permit DPN/DPNH to return to its normal value of 8 to 10. Hohorst, Kreutz and Reim (5) have shown that malate concentration in the liver of the fasted animal is greatly enhanced in comparison with the normal. The question of how glucocorticoids regulate gluconeogenesis is not clear. Hydrocortisone is without effect on the DPN/DPNH (total) ratio in fasted adrenalectomized rats within three hours (Table I) but it very rapidly increases the malate content of the liver (5). In the diabetic, adrenalectomized rat, prednisolone caused a decrease of OAA concentration without significant alteration of the malate concentration (5). This change occurred within one hour and was associated with a relatively minor change of glycerol-1-phosphate/dihydroxyacetone phosphate. Can this mean that glucocorticoids exert their influence on gluconeogenesis by "pulling" oxaloacetate to PEP?

The role of insulin seems much clearer. Insulin administration to the diabetic is followed by a drop in malate concentration without change in the already low concentration of OAA. Glycerol-1-phosphate concentration is also decreased whereas lactate is not (5). These findings are in agreement with a role for insulin in shutting off malate synthesis from pyruvate in the liver mitochondria. Although insulin enhances fat synthesis and might therefore be supposed to deplete malate via the malate shuttle of Young *et al.* (2) (see discussion elsewhere in this symposium), it should be recalled that the repair of the defect in fat synthesis after insulin administration is relatively slow, and the acquisition of malic enzyme requires more than 24 hours (6).

Therefore the effect of insulin seems to be mediated via decreased malate formation. This postulate is being examined in our laboratory by Mr. Verner Paetkau using normal and diabetic rats and by Dr. Paul Walter using *in vitro* systems. In any event, the role of reversed electron transfer for the generation of reducing power within the mitochondria (7), and indirectly in the cytosol, is obvious.

REFERENCES

1. Lardy, H., Paetkau, V. and Walter, P., Proc. Natl. Acad. Sci., June 1965, in the press.

2. Young, J., Shrago, E. and Lardy, H. A., Biochemistry, 3, 1687 (1964).

3. Wang, S. and Lardy, H. A., manuscript to be submitted.

4. Ray, P., Foster, D. and Lardy, H. A., J. Biol. Chem., 239, 3396 (1964).

5. Hohorst, H. J., Kreuts, F. H. and Reim, M., Biochem. Biophys. Res. Commun., 4, 163 (1961).

6. Shrago, E., Lardy, H. A., Nordlie, R. and Foster, D., J. Biol. Chem., 238, 3188 (1963).

7. Chance, B. and Hollunger, G., Nature, 185, 666 (1960).

ON THE "BIOCHEMICAL IMPRINTING" OF METABOLIC EXPERIENCE IN LIVER CELLS+

Jay Tepperman and Helen M. Tepperman*

State University of New York, Upstate Medical Center,
Syracuse, New York

During the past 10 or 15 years the great molecular biology spectacular symbolized by the Watson-Crick DNA model has tended to obscure important concurrent developments in biochemical thought. This conference attests to advances in metabolic control theory made on many salients. One aspect of metabolic control which has received increasing attention recently is that which can be characterized by the phrase "biochemical imprinting".

For some, the word "imprinting" may conjure up the distracting image of a confused duckling marching after a moving catcher's mitt in the mistaken belief that it is following its mother. I use the word here to signify adaptive increases in enzyme activities that occur along specific metabolic pathways when there is a large and sustained increase in substrate traffic through them. The experience of accommodating large amounts of substrate is often reflected in a characteristic imprint on the enzyme pattern of the cell. Indeed, it is commonplace (although, perhaps, not always justified) for some of us to infer from changes in enzyme pattern which metabolic route a substrate is likely to have taken under a given set of physiologic circumstances.

Among enzymes which have been demonstrated to fluctuate widely in liver, adipose tissue and mammary gland are the dehydrogenases of the direct oxidative pathway and the TPN malic enzyme. In an earlier report (1) we described how estrogen and thyroxine treatment influence the activities of the hexose-monophosphate shunt dehydrogenases and the malic enzyme differentially. This implies that the system of signals and

+Aided by NIH grant A-5410 and by Smith, Kline and French. One phase of this work was presented at a meeting of the American Physiological Society in April 1956.
*With the technical assistance of J. Pownall and A. Branch.

modulators which elicit new enzyme activity must be far more complex than we had supposed them to be, for we had begun those experiments with the naive idea that the soluble TPN linked enzymes of the liver fluctuate in a coordinate manner.

We can now add two additional experiments which emphasize the complex nature of the enzyme response to thyroxine and to a drug. When one studies the time course of the response of the malic enzyme and the individual shunt dehydrogenases to thyroxine administration (Fig. 1), it is immediately apparent that malic enzyme activity increases significantly long before 6-phosphogluconate dehydrogenase activity does. In this experiment, glucose-6-phosphate dehydrogenase did not increase very much. Differential effects on the enzymes of the first two steps of the HMP pathway have been described by Lee, Debro and Lucia (2) and by Huggins and Yao (3).

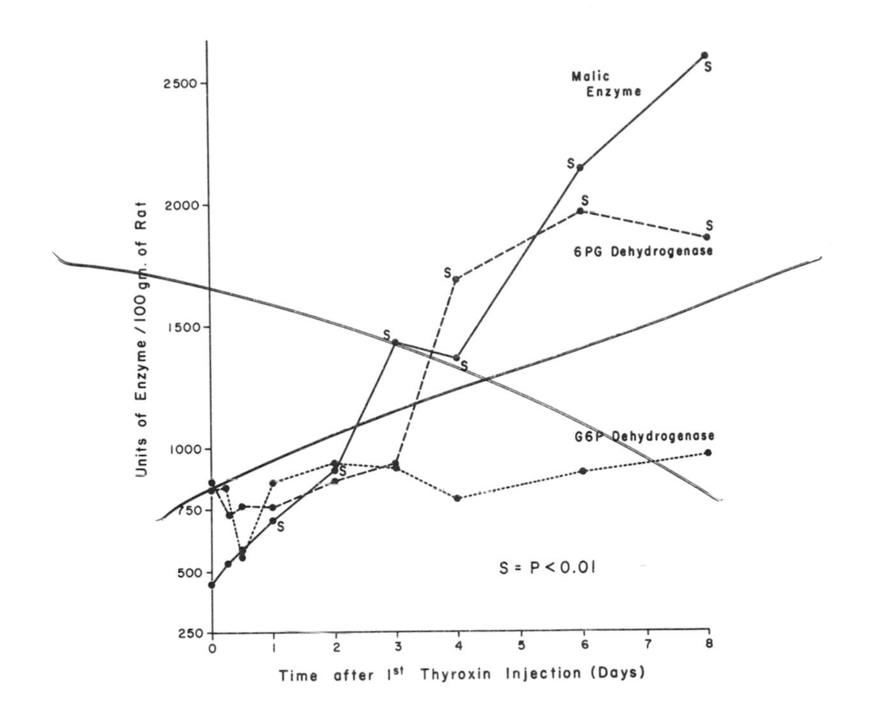

Figure 1. The effect of the daily administration of 80 mcg of thyroxine on the activities of the individual HMP dehydrogenases and on TPN malic enzyme. (Each point represents the mean value for 6-8 rats.)

Stimulated by the reflections of Pette *et al.* (4) we began to view the TPN malic enzyme increase produced by thyroxine as an event secondary to a primary effect of the hormone on mitochondrial metabolism. Accordingly, it was of interest to examine the effect of dinitrophenol (DNP) on enzyme patterns which had been shown to be affected by thyroid hormone. In Table I the results of one dinitrophenol experiment can be seen. In this case, there was a statistically significant increase in TPN malic enzyme activity, but no significant effect on the HMP dehydrogenases. The cold exposed controls were included because the DNP animals were exposed to cold for one-half hour after each injection. It is of some interest that DNP, like thyroxine, appears to have a more easily demonstrable effect on the malic enzyme than on the shunt dehydrogenases, and that both this drug and thyroxine may have their primary transaction with elements of the mitochondrion.

TABLE I

Group N Treatment	Body Weight (gms)		O_2 Consumption ml O_2/100 cm^2 per hour	Liver Enzyme Activity units per mg. liver N	
	Initial	Δ/day		HMP DeHase	Malic Enzyme
C (9) No treatment	251 ± 2.3	4.7 ± .21	119 ± 6.5	3.5 (6) ± .28	1.6 (6) ± .15
E (9) Cold exposed	248 ± 3.3	3.9 ± .34	119 ± 7.7	3.9 (6) ± .35	1.8 (6) ± .10
CI (8) Cold exposed oil injected	268 ± 1.9	3.3 ± .33	120 ± 4.2	2.9 ± .27	1.9 ± .12
DNP (14) Cold exposed DNP injected	266 ± 1.4	1.4*** ± .22	157*** ± 9.5	3.2 ± .44	4.1*** ± .43

*** $P < .01$ compared to CI

Effect of dinitrophenol injection (30 mg/kg b.d. for 18-22 days) on body weight, oxygen consumption of the whole animal and the activity of TPN-linked liver enzymes in the mature rat.

Indifferent success in finding patterns does not inhibit us from searching for others. I would like to take the remaining time to describe three apparently unrelated physiologic circumstances associated with increases in hexosemonophosphate shunt dehydrogenase activity. In all three of these conditions it is possible to demonstrate an accelerated rate of oxidation of TPNH. We believe that this increase in the rate of TPNH utilization may be the common denominator which provides at least a component of the signal for eliciting new dehydrogenase activity in the cell.

1) Lipogenesis and the HMP dehydrogenases.

The association between high rates of lipogenesis and increased activity of the HMP dehydrogenases is too well known to require more than brief mention. In Figure 2 we have plotted the recovery and overshoot of lipogenesis activity by liver slices (operationally defined as the rate of incorporation of Acetate-1-C^{14} into long chain fatty acids) and the appearance of the new HMP dehydrogenase activity. If these

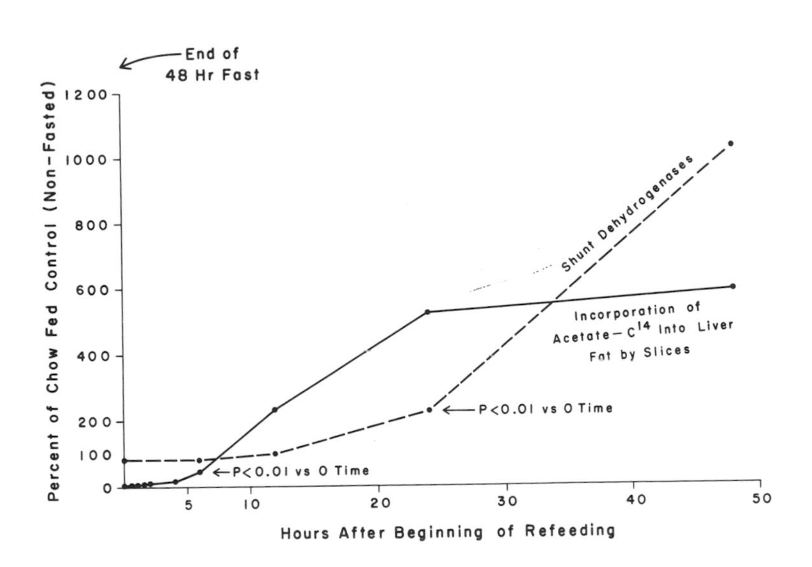

Figure 2. Recovery of lipogenesis by surviving liver slices and the appearance of new (combined) HMP shunt dehydrogenase activity during refeeding a fat-free, high carbohydrate diet after a 48 hour fast.

processes are related the time course shown here suggests that the lipogenesis recovery is the primary event which generates some sort of signal for the dehydrogenases to increase in activity. We (1) and others (5) have shown that TPN malic enzyme also increases in this type of experiment, and a number of investigators, including Pande (6) et al., Wise and Ball (7) and Lardy (8) have suggested that the malic enzyme reaction may generate some of the TPNH required for lipid synthesis.

2) Microsomal "detoxifying" system induction and TPNH generating systems.

Last year Bresnick and Yang (9) reported that increases in the activity of microsomal drug-detoxifying enzyme systems by phenobarbital treatment was associated with increases in activity of the HMP dehydrogenases. Figure 3 confirms that fact and shows that malic enzyme is also increased under these circumstances. Gillette et al. (10) demonstrated that phenobarbital induction of new microsomal "detoxifying" activity is associated with an increase in TPNH oxidase. This condition, like hyperlipogenesis, is probably associated with increased rates of oxidation of TPNH.

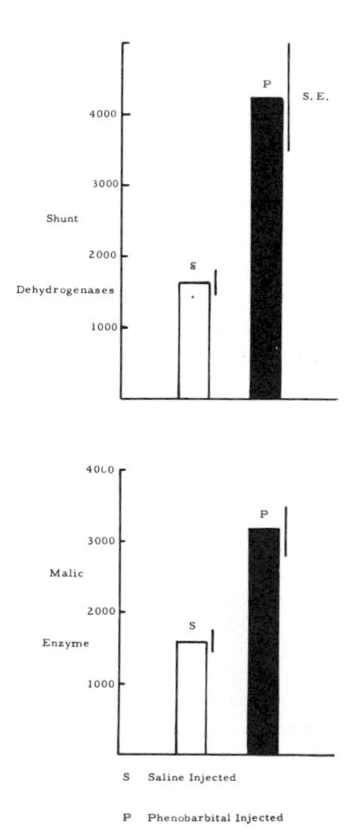

Figure 3. Effect of phenobarbital injection on HMP dehydrogenases and on TPN malic enzyme (n - 8).

3) Essential fatty acid deficient diets and TPN dehydrogenases.

Some months ago, stimulated by experiments of Allman and Gibson (11), we began a series of experiments which were designed to answer the question: is lipogenesis inhibited more by corn oil than by isocaloric amounts of hydrogenated fat? During the course of attempting to answer this question we made the serendipitous discovery shown in Fig. 4. When isocaloric amounts of fat were fed, particularly in the presence of some dietary carbohydrate in the diet, the animals on the essential fatty acid deficient diet showed very high levels of hepatic hexosemonophosphate shunt dehydrogenase activity. Under these conditions the rate of acetate carbon incorporation into fatty acids was low and similar in both groups. We were so intrigued by this unexpected finding that we lost sight of our original problem and began to concentrate on the new one.

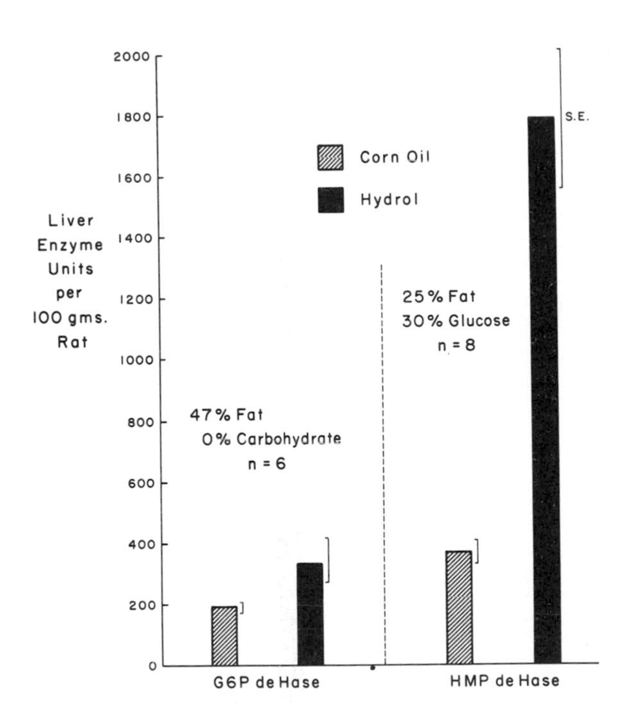

Figure 4. Effect of dietary carbohydrate on response on liver enzymes to feeding diets containing satured fat.

We had been conditioned to suspect that, for some reason, the livers of the hydrogenated oil fed rats use more TPNH than do those of the corn oil fed animals. All we had to do was to identify the appropriate TPNH-utilizing reactions in order to establish the circumstantial evidence for assigning this instance of HMP dehydrogenase increase to the category typified by the other two cases already described.

It was well known that the fatty acid composition of liver fatty acids shows a characteristic pattern in animals fed an essential fatty acid deficient diet (12). Characteristically, the livers of such animals contain comparatively large amounts of monoenoic acids, particularly palmitoleic and oleic. Figure 5 shows our confirmation of this fact under the conditions of our experiment in which an increase in HMP dehydrogenase was demonstrated. The fatty acid distribution pattern also shows an increase in stearic acid in the essential fatty acid deficient group and the expected difference in linoleic acid concentration.

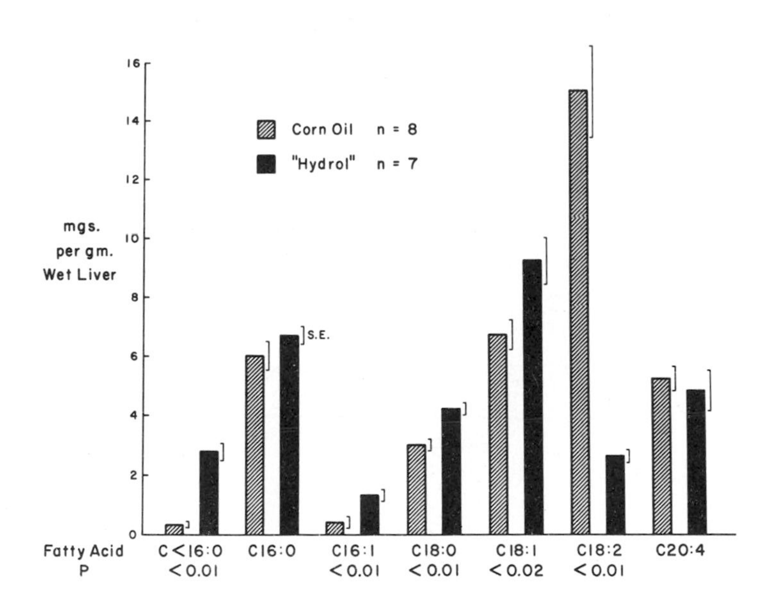

Figure 5. Fatty acid composition of liver slices obtained from rats fed 25 per cent fat diet for two weeks.

Palmitic Acid —(CoA, ATP / Mg^{++})→ Palmityl CoA

Palmityl CoA —(O_2, TPNH)→ (Oxy palmityl CoA)

(Oxy palmityl CoA) ——→ Palmitoleyl CoA

Palmitoleyl CoA —(Thiolase)→ Palmitoleic Acid + CoA

Figure 6. A model fatty acid desaturating system.

This static experiment suggested that a system possibly similar to the one illustrated in Figure 6 may have been more active in the livers of rats fed saturated fat than in those of rats fed isocaloric amounts of corn oil. Therefore, rats were adapted to the two diets for 2 weeks and their liver slices were incubated either with acetate-1-C^{14} or palmitate-1-C^{14}. At the end of the incubation period fatty acids were extracted from the slices, their methyl esters prepared and analyzed by means of a gas-liquid chromatography system that permitted estimation of the radioactivity of each fatty acid peak (13). The results with acetate-1-C^{14} are shown in Table II.

TABLE II

Incorporation of Acetate-1-C^{14} into Individual Fatty Acids by Liver Slices of Corn Oil (C) Fed Rats and Hydrol (H) Fed Rats (25 per cent Fat Diets)

Fatty Acid	Diet (n)	Per Cent Recovered Radioactivity ± S.E.	P	Per Cent
16:0	C8	64.9 ± 2.78	0.01	100
	H7	44.3 ± 1.53		69
16:1	C	4.9 ± 0.73	0.05	100
	H	7.0 ± 0.62		143
18:0	C	9.2 ± 1.03	0.01	100
	H	16.3 ± 1.04		178
18:1	C	3.1 ± 5.1	0.01	100
	H	18.7 ± 0.90		603

More of the label appeared in the C16 and C18 monoenoic acids in the case of the saturated fat diet group. Moreover, stearic acid was also more heavily labelled in the same group. Practically identical results were obtained when a palmitate-1-C^{14}-albumin complex was used as added substrate. The effect of the saturated fat diet on chain lengthening is shown in Figure 7, in which the aggregate 16:0 and 16:1 are plotted on the left and the aggregate 18:0 and 18:1 on the right. Therefore, the livers of the hydrogenated fat diet group must have used more TPNH, not only for introducing double bonds into saturated acids but also for the process of chain lengthening.

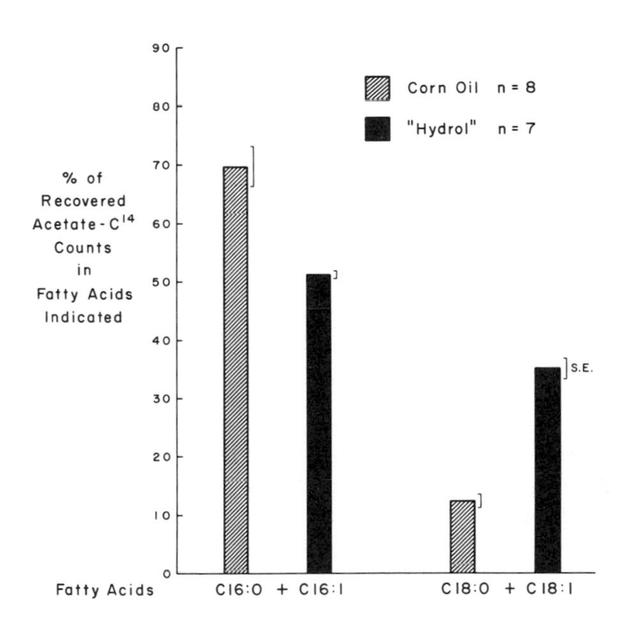

Figure 7. "Chain lengthening" by liver slices of rats fed 25 per cent fat diet.

One rather simple scheme to describe all three of these circumstances is shown in Figure 8. We visualize the increased rate of TPNH oxidation as the primary event. This necessarily results in the production of TPN^+, which first has the effect of "deciding" which reaction sequence a substrate is likely to enter if it can be metabolized by alternate routes. The persistence of this condition over a period of time eventually leads to the accumulation of new apoenzyme.

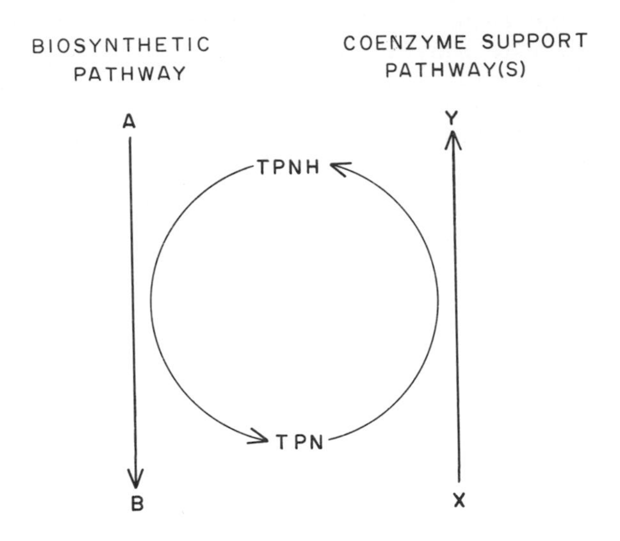

Figure 8. Pathways of TPN reduction and TPNH oxidation.

The mechanism for this increase is not yet known. However, we are attracted by the hypothesis that, in the unstimulated state, the rates of synthesis and degradation of the enzymes in question are balanced to yield a certain concentration of apoenzyme protein. The enzyme may be stabilized by TPN^+, as Kirkman (14) and Marks (15) have shown for erythrocyte G6PD. Chung and Langdon (16) who also worked with the red cell enzyme, described an activation of G6PD by TPN. In a few preliminary experiments we have demonstrated that TPN prevents the destruction of hepatic G6PD which ordinarily occurs in 20,000G supernates of homogenates on incubation at 37° C. Many in this audience will recognize the analogy between this postulated mechanism and that suggested for substrate induced increases in liver tryptophane pyrrolase by Dubnoff and Dimick (17) and neatly proved by Schimke (18). The identification of signals, modulators, and intimate mechanisms of enzyme increase and decrease will no doubt occupy the attention of many of us for a long time. Much of the evidence we deal with will necessarily be inferential and circumstantial, but already the remarkable fact is apparent that increases in enzymes tend to occur when the enzymes are kept busy over a period of time, and that once the enzyme pattern changes, the patterns of substrate disposition tend to become fixed. Thus, changes in enzyme pattern constitute a long-range metabolic control device which is superimposed on other regulatory mechanisms, which operate within a much shorter time scale.

REFERENCES

1. Tepperman, H.M. and Tepperman, J., Am. J. Physiol., 206, 357 (1964).

2. Lee, M., Debro, J.R. and Lucia, S.P., Arch. Biochem. Biophys., 98, 49 (1962).

3. Huggins, C. and Yao, F., J. Exper. Med., 110, 899 (1959).

4. Pette, D., Klingenberg, M. and Bücher, T., Biochem. Biophys. Res. Comm., 7, 425 (1962).

5. Fitch, W.M. and Chaikoff, I.L., J. Biol. Chem., 235, 554 (1960).

6. Pande, S.V., Parvinkhan, R. and Venkitasobramanian, T.A., Biochem. Biophys. Acta, 84, 239 (1964).

7. Wise, E.M., Jr. and Ball, E.G., Proc. Nat. Acad. Sci. (Wash.), 52, 1255 (1964).

8. Young, J.W., Shrago, E. and Lardy, H.A., Biochemistry, 3, 1687 (1964).

9. Bresnick, E. and Yang, H-Y., Biochem. Pharmacol., 13, 497 (1964).

10. Gillette, J.R., Brodie, B.B. and Ladu, B.N., J. Pharmacol. Exp. Therap. 132, 202 (1961).

11. Allman, D.W., Hubbard, D.D. and Gibson, D.M., J. Lipid. Res., 6, 63 (1965).

12. Mohrhauer, H., and Holman, R.T., J. Lipid Res., 4, 151 (1963).

13. Karmen, A., Giuffrida, L. and Bowman, R.L., J. Lipid Res., 3, 44 (1962).

14. Kirkman, H.N., J. Biol. Chem., 237, 2364 (1962).

15. Marks, D.A., Szeinberg, A., and Banks, J., J. Biol. Chem., 236, 10 (1961).

16. Chung, A.E. and Langdon, R.G., J. Biol. Chem., 238, 2317 (1963).

17. Dubnoff, J.W. and Dimick, M., Biochem. et Biophys. Acta, 31, 541 (1959).

18. Schimke, R.T., Sweeny, E.W. and Berlin, C.M., Biochem. Biophys. Res. Comm., 15, 214 (1964).

ADAPTIVE BEHAVIOR OF CITRATE CLEAVAGE ENZYME*

John M. Lowenstein

Graduate Department of Biochemistry
Brandeis University, Waltham, Massachusetts

It is probable that citrate is the main source of carbon for the synthesis of fatty acids in rat and mouse, and possibly in other non-ruminant animals (1-3). Citrate is converted to acetyl CoA by the citrate cleavage enzyme reaction (4):

$$\text{citrate} + \text{CoA} + \text{ATP} \longrightarrow \text{acetyl CoA} + \text{oxaloacetate} + \text{ADP} + \text{orthophosphate} \qquad (I)$$

Citrate cleavage enzyme occurs in the extramitochondrial cell sap. It has been purified and studied by Srere (5). You will note from equation (I) that the reaction involves the cleavage of ATP to ADP and orthophosphate. It is different from the reaction catalyzed by the condensing enzyme, which does not involve these substances.

The activity of citrate cleavage enzyme varies with the nutritional state of the animal. It is suppressed on starvation and restored on re-feeding after starvation. Fig. 1 shows that the increase in enzyme activity that occurs on re-feeding starved animals depends on the diet. In the case of a diet high in fat the increase in enzyme activity is small (curve A). A diet consisting of chow (Wayne Lab-Blox) produces a 12-fold increase in enzyme activity (curve B). A diet high in glucose produces a 30-fold increase (curve C), and a diet high in fructose produces a 50-fold increase (curve E). Lastly, a diet high in glycerol also produces a 30-fold increase (curve D). In each case maximum enzyme activity was reached after three days of feeding the diet. Many other substances, including lactate, pyruvate plus malate, and various members of the citric acid cycle, fail to produce an increase in the activity of citrate cleavage enzyme when they are fed to starved rats. Fructose and glycerol are the

*Supported by NSF GB 3412.

anti-ketogenic substrates par excellence, and it is striking that they are also among the best "inducers" of citrate cleavage enzyme. This, by itself, does not explain why fructose is the most effective substance (Fig. 1). The reason for this may be that part of the fructose is metabolized via the fructokinase reaction. This results in the formation of fructose-1-phosphate, which is cleaved by aldolase to glyceraldehyde and dihydroxyacetone phosphate. Unlike glycolysis, fructolysis does not involve the interconversion of fructose-6-phosphate to fructose-1,6-diphosphate. In other words, fructolysis is not subject to control by phosphofructokinase. In the liver, fructose might therefore be expected to yield 3-carbon compounds more rapidly and more efficiently than glucose. Moreover, glucokinase is repressed by starvation, whereas fructokinase is not.

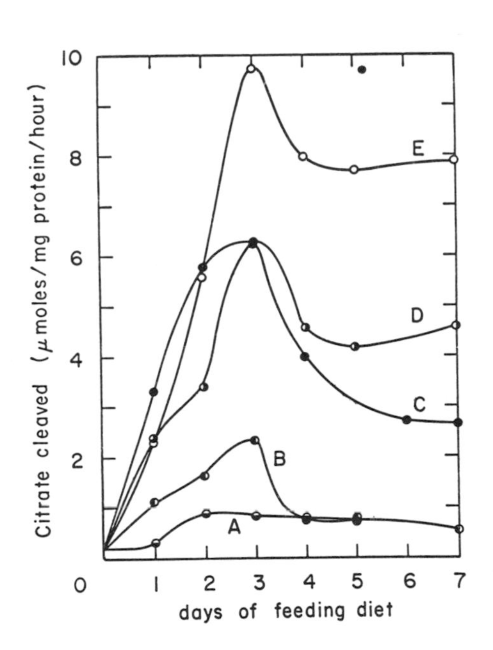

Figure 1. Activity of citrate cleavage enzyme in liver of rat. Effect of re-feeding animals that have been starved for two days with various diets. A, high fat diet; B, normal diet (laboratory chow); C, high glucose diet; D, high glycerol diet; E, high fructose diet. Each point represents the average activity of three to six animals. (Curves A, B and C are taken from ref. 6; curves D and E are unpublished work of Alice F. Spencer).

Diets high in glucose or fructose elevate the activity of citrate cleavage enzyme in normal animals, whereas only the diet high in fructose does so in diabetic animals (Fig. 2). In the case of normal animals the effect of fructose is more rapid and is larger than the effect of glucose. Again, the reason can probably be found in the circumvention by fructolysis of the phosphofructokinase control point. In the case of diabetic animals glucose has no effect. This is not surprising in view of the repression of glucokinase in such animals, although it raises the question of what hexokinase of liver is doing under these conditions. Fructose, on the other hand, causes a large increase in the activity of citrate cleavage enzyme even in diabetic animals. Apparently fructokinase shows no repression in diabetes.

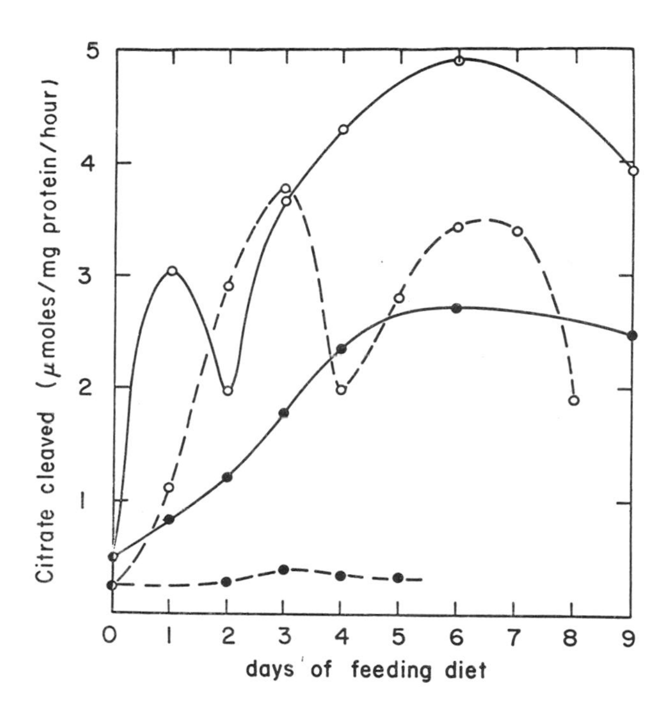

Figure 2. Activity of citrate cleavage enzyme in liver of rat. Effect of transferring animals on normal diet (laboratory chow) to diet high in glucose (●) or high in fructose (o). Solid lines show results obtained with normal animals; broken lines show results obtained with diabetic animals. Each point represents the average activity of three or four animals. (Results taken from M.S. Kornacker and J.M. Lowenstein, in press).

We have tried to relate these results to citrate concentrations in livers of rats in different metabolic states (Table I). The results show that citrate concentrations, expressed in μmoles per g fresh weight of liver, are the same regardless of whether the animals have been fed regularly, starved one, two or three days, or starved two days and then re-fed with a balanced diet, or a diet high in carbohydrate, or a diet high in fat. The measurements do not tell us where the citrate is located in the cell. As was pointed out by Dr. Estabrook this morning, the determination of metabolite concentrations of whole tissues may not be very informative. Perhaps in the livers of animals re-fed with a diet high in carbohydrate, citrate is largely extra-mitochondrial, while in the case of animals re-fed with a diet high in fat, citrate is largely intra-mitochondrial. Our results say nothing about this, but I think that we should continue to measure metabolite concentrations in whole tissues, until we learn how to measure them in individual compartments of the cell. Sometimes one is lucky and observes large changes in the whole tissue concentration. For example, changes in nutritional or hormonal conditions cause large changes in the total concentration of citrate in rat heart. As is discussed elsewhere in this symposium, these changes probably play a role in the regulation of phosphofructokinase.

TABLE I

Citrate in Rat Liver

Diet	[citrate] μmoles/g. fresh wt.
Normal	0.31
Starved 1 day	0.33
Starved 2 days	0.30
Starved 3 days	0.32
Starved 2 days, then re-fed for 3 days with	
balanced diet	0.34
high CHO diet	0.32
high fat diet	0.29

Normal = 10 rats, all others = 5 rats each. Maximum S.D. = ± 0.05. (Unpublished results of A.F. Spencer and J.M. Lowenstein).

REFERENCES

1. Spencer, A.F., and Lowenstein, J.M., J. Biol. Chem., 237, 3640 (1962).

2. Bhaduri, A., and Srere, P.A., Biochim. Biophys. Acta, 70, 221 (1963).

3. Spencer, A.F., Corman, L., and Lowenstein, J.M., Biochem. J., 93, 378 (1964).

4. Srere, P.A., and Lipmann, F., J. Amer. Chem. Soc., 75, 4874 (1953).

5. Srere, P.A., J. Biol. Chem., 234, 2544 (1959); 236, 50 (1961).

6. Kornacker, M.S., and Lowenstein, J.M., Biochem. J., 94, 209 (1965).

SOME ASPECTS OF METABOLIC CONTROL IN THE FERTILIZATION TRANSITION OF SEA URCHIN EGGS*

David Epel

Hopkins Marine Station,
Pacific Grove, California

and Ray M. Iverson

Department of Zoology, University of Miami,
Coral Gables, Florida

Fertilization activates synthetic activities leading to fusion of sperm and egg nucleus, cell division, and differentiation. Many of these changes result from activation of enzymes already present in the unfertilized egg, as indicated by the insensitivity of the eggs to puromycin (1) and actinomycin-D (2) during early development. We present data on some of the enzymes activated, their role in supplying coenzymes and substrates, and the presently available information on the mechanisms by which these enzymes might be activated by fertilization.

Materials and Methods

Gametes of the sea urchins *Strongylocentrotus purpuratus* and *Lytechinus variegatus* were used for these experiments. Temperatures were constant at 17.0° C and 30.8° C., respectively. Perchloric acid was used for extracting oxidized pyridine nucleotides, adenine nucleotides, and glucose-6-phosphate, whereas no alkali extraction was used for the reduced pyridine nucleotides. Recoveries were determined for all compounds, and were 95-100 per cent, except for TPNH and DPNH, which were as low as 50 per cent. Analyses were done enzymatically, using the fluorometric procedures of Estabrook and Maitra (3). DPN kinase was assayed by modifications of the Kaplan-Wang procedure (4). Other techniques are indicated in the text.

Results and Discussion

A rapid and early enzymatic change is the activation of DPN kinase to form TPN and TPNH from DPN and ATP. This is indicated by the balance sheet of pyridine nucleotides in unfertil-

* Supported by PHS 5T1 GM2G277, NSF-6B-2891, and NIH-GM-11156.

TABLE I

Pyridine Nucleotide Content of Strongylocentrotus purpuratus Eggs

	Unfertilized $\times 10^{-10}$ moles/10^5 cells	Fertilized $\times 10^{-10}$ moles/10^5 cells
DPN	66.8 ± 0.9	41.6 ± 1.8
DPNH	5.6 ± 2.6	10.6 ± 2.1
TPN	6.6 ± 0.5	13.9 ± 0.7
TPNH	6.6 ± 2.2	20.5 ± 0.1
Total	85.6	86.6
o/o DPN + DPNH	84.5	60.3
o/o TPN + TPNH	15.5	39.7

ized and fertilized eggs of Strongylocentrotus purpuratus shown in Table I. The data indicate that an interconversion of pyridine nucleotide follows fertilization, since total nucleotide content is unchanged by fertilization, but DPN has decreased from 85 per cent to 60 per cent whilst total TPN has increased from 15 per cent to 40 per cent.

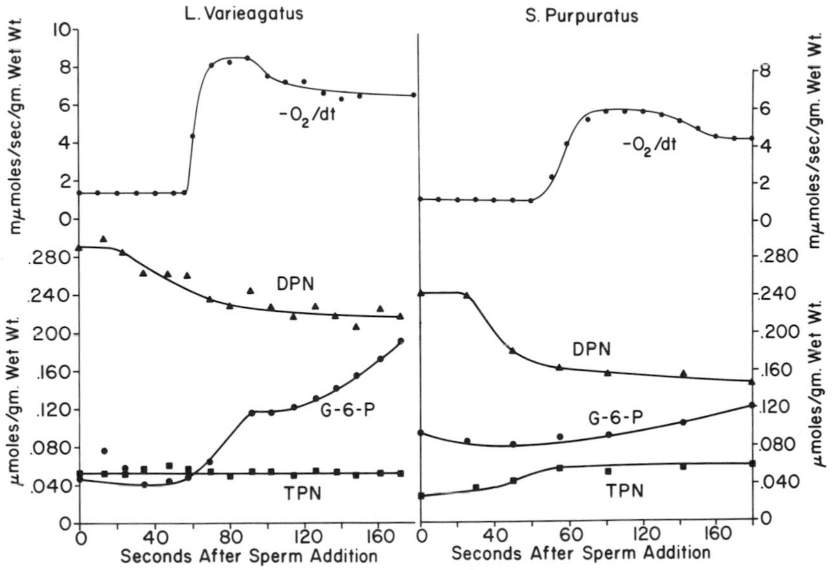

Figure 1. Respiration rate, oxidized pyridine nucleotides, and glucose-6-phosphate levels following fertilization. Respiration was measured polarographically, metabolites by specific enzymatic procedures. The original data was calculated on a per cell basis, and converted to gm wet weight assuming 4×10^6 cells/gm for S. purpuratus and 1.7×10^6 cells/gm for L. varieagatus.

The kinetics of this reaction can be monitored *in vivo* by fluorometry (5) or *in vitro* by analysis of pyridine nucleotides in extracts prepared from eggs at various times after fertilization. Some results obtained with the latter method are given in Figure 1, which shows the kinetics of several parameters in the eggs of two different species of sea urchin. The decrease in DPN content begins about 20 seconds after fertilization in *L. variegatus*, and after 35-45 seconds in *S. purpuratus*. In both species the DPN decrease is mirrored by a TPNH increase (not shown). Conversely, the TPN changes vary. It increases in *S. purpuratus*, but remains constant in *L. variegatus*. The data also show that the pyridine nucleotide changes precede the activation of respiration in both species.

The above pyridine nucleotide conversion is catalyzed by DPN kinase. Although the *in vivo* results demonstrate that this enzyme is active only after fertilization, *in vitro* assays of enzyme activity in homogenates show that the enzyme is present in equal activity in both unfertilized and fertilized eggs. This indicates that DPN kinase is somehow activated *in vivo* by fertilization and possibly following cell breakage *in vitro*.

Experiments aimed at defining the activation mechanism of DPN kinase indicate that activation does not appear to involve (1) changes in subcellular location of the enzyme, (2) changes in subcellular location of substrates, or (3) removal of a soluble inhibitor by fertilization. Evidence for these three points is: (1) the enzyme is found only in the 100,000 x G supernatant fraction of both unfertilized and fertilized eggs, (2) 89 per cent of the ATP and 75 per cent of the DPN is in the extra-mitochondrial and extranuclear space, as determined by metabolite analyses of cell fractions, (3) the plot of enzyme activity versus total homogenate is similar for both unfertilized and fertilized eggs.

Another activation occurring after fertilization (Figure 1) is a 5-fold increase in respiration rate. The controlling factor for this increase does not appear to be ADP, since ATP, ADP, and AMP do not change significantly at the time of maximum respiration. Data of Aketa *et al.* (6) showing a 5-fold increase in various glycolytic esters 5 minutes after fertilization, suggests that respiration of the unfertilized egg is limited by the substrate (State 2, State 3 transition, ref. 7). This possibility is further substantiated by the similar kinetics of increase in G-6-P levels and increased respiration in eggs of *L. variegatus* (Figure 1). However, similar analyses on eggs of *S. purpuratus*, also shown in Figure 1, do not indicate such an obvious correlation. This could mean that different substrates are utilized in these two species, or that levels of the glycolytic esters are better controlled in S. purpuratus. This latter situation would thus be analogous to the content of glycolytic esters in skeletal muscle, which remains constant in the face of an increased glycolytic flux (Helmreich, this volume, p. 299).

TABLE II

Effect of Coenzymes on Leucine-C^{14} Incorporation in a 12,000 g Supernatant of L. variegatus Eggs

Conditions	Unfertilized cpm	Fertilized, 30' cpm
No additions	2	2
10^{3} M ATP, 10^{-2} M PEP	5	47
" , " , 10^{-4} M GTP	9	86
" , " , " , $+10^{-4}$ M DPNH	12	101
" , " , " , $+10^{-4}$ M TPNH	8	81
" , " , " , $+10^{-4}$ M DPN	9	90
" , " , " , $+10^{-4}$ M TPN	7	72

12,000 g supernatant prepared as described by Hultin (13). Besides the noted additions, each sample contained 0.1 ml supernatnat (1.5-1.85 mg protein), 0.1 ml uniformly-labelled C^{14}-leucine and 0.1 ml of a solution of 19 amino acids. Protein was separated in the presence of carrier albumin by three cold trichloracetic acid washes and one hot TCA extraction, followed by washing in isopropanol and acetone. The acetone precipitate was dissolved in formic acid and counted on a gas-flow counter.

At this time a casual relationship between the increase in TPNH and activation of other synthesis in the sea urchin egg is not established. However, as TPNH is the specific reductant in many biosynthetic reactions, it is possible that reductive biosynthesis is limited in the unfertilized egg by both the low TPNH level and the low ratio of TPNH/TPN (See Table I and ref. 6). The increase in these two parameters, especially the change in the redox couple of TPNH/TPN, might be the critical factor in initiating TPNH-dependent reactions essential for early development, such as deoxyribose formation (9), protein disulfide reduction (10), lipid synthesis (11), and thymidine synthesis via the TPNH-specific dihydrofolic reductase (12).

The role of TPNH in the post-fertilization activation of protein synthesis due to the formation of polysomes (13) is difficult to envisage. A possible role for TPNH in this activation, suggested by the effects of pyridine nucleotides on microsomal structures (14), was therefore tested in a cell-free protein synthesizing system. Effects of varying concentrations of all four pyridine nucleotides (10^{-6} to 10^{-3} M) and of 3'5'-cyclic AMP (10^{-7} to 10^{-4} M) on protein synthesis were determined. Some of the representative data (Table II) show the ineffectiveness of these in stimulating incorporation of amino acid into either the unfertilized or fertilized egg proteins. Although these findings do not indicate a direct role for these co-factors in the activation of m-RNA-dependent protein synthesis, an indirect role for them is possible. One such function could be in a cascade-reaction-type system, where a TPNH-limited product is necessary for the activation of amino acid incorporation. The alternative hypothesis is that fertilization initiates parallel activation of enzymes through a common intermediate.

In summary, increases in co-enzymes and substrates important for synthetic activity occur upon fertilization of the sea urchin egg. Whether these are the casual factors in initiating post-fertilization synthesis and development is still unknown, but should become clearer with future research.

References

1. Hultin, T., Experentia, 17, 410 (1961).

2. Gross, P. R., Malkin, L. I., and Moyer, W. A., Proc. Nat. Acad. Sci., 51, 407 (1964).

3. Estabrook, R.W., and Maitra, P. K., Anal. Biochem., 3, 369 (1963).

4. Wang, T. P., and Kaplan, N. O., J. Biol. Chem., 206, 311 (1954).

5. Epel, D., Biochem. Biophys. Res. Commun., 17, 62 (1964).

6. Aketa, K., Bianchetti, R., Marre, E., and Monroy, A., Biochem. Biophys. Acta, 86, 211 (1964).

7. Chance, B., and Williams, G. R., Adv. Enzymol., 17, 65 (1956).

8. Klingenberg, M., and Bücher, Th., Ann. Rev. Biochem., 29, 669 (1960).

9. Laurent, T. C., Moore, E. C., and Reichard, P., J. Biol.

Chem., 239, 3436 (1964).

10. Asaki, T., Bandurski, R. S., and Wilson, L. G., J. Biol. Chem., 236, 1830 (1961).

11. Wakil, S. J., Ann. Rev. Biochem., 31, 369 (1962).

12. Matthews, C. K., and Huennekens, F. M., J. Biol. Chem., 238, 3436 (1963).

13. Stafford, D. W., Sofer, W. H., and Iverson, R. M., Proc. Nat. Acad. Sci., 52, 313 (1964).

14. Lindall, A. W., Exp. Cell Res., 37, 399 (1965).

15. Hultin, T., Exp. Cell Res., 25, 405 (1961).

DISCUSSION

Bücher: I have only one short remark for Dr. Tepperman: we believe that 90 percent of the TPN system of the liver is mitochondria; therefore, if you try to find some relationships between the G-6-P, which is extramitochondrial, and the state of reduction of TPN, you cannot rely on the contents of the liver. Results from this tissue mostly represent the relationships of mitochondrial compartments.

H. Krebs: I would like to raise a question arising from the earlier remarks of Dr. Tepperman that, when reducing power is needed in the liver for fatty acid synthesis, then the enzymes generating reduced TPN, namely the pentose phosphate cycle enzymes and the malic enzyme, increase greatly in activity. Dr. Tepperman rightly pointed out that this is a well-established fact. I think it is appropriate to raise the question of the extent to which the equally well-established reversibility of oxidative phosphorylation has any significance in relation to the generation of reducing power required for physiological processes. If one examines the various physiological reductions, there can be no doubt that fatty acid synthesis from carbohydrate is the main process requiring reducing power in terms of pyridine nucleotide. My own view is that this reducing power comes mainly from the pentose-phosphate cycle and the malic enzyme reactions. There is so much evidence for the parallelism between fatty acid synthesis, the pentose-phosphate cycle, and the increase in the malic enzyme activity, that I am convinced that these provide the reducing power.

At the same time, I have no doubt, on the basis of the work carried out by Dr. Chance and by Dr. Klingenberg and others, that reducing power can be generated by the reversal of oxidative phosphorylation. Therefore, I would ask, what is the physiological significance of this reversibility? I think it has one, but I do not think it is the reduction of bulk quantities of pyridine nucleotide needed for biosynthesis. Ready reversibility may be important to the thermodynamic efficiency of oxidative phosphorylation. In a readily reversible system the efficiency may be 100 percent. And in a micro-organism which can obtain all its energy from the oxidation of a substrate with a rather positive redox potential, for example Fe^{++} to Fe^{+++}, and all its carbon requirements from CO_2(like Ferrobacillus ferrooxidans), ATP and a reversal of oxidative phosphorylation seem essential for the generation of highly reduced carbon compounds like $DPNH_2$ and $TPNH_2$ (Elsden, S.R. in The Bacteria, vol. 3, p. 33., Gunsalus, I.C. and Stanier, R.Y., eds., Academic Press Inc., New York (1962) and Blaylock, B.A. and Nason, A., J. Biol. Chem., 238, 3453 (1964)).

Chance: I would like to respond to the general question raised by Prof. Krebs concerning the relation of the energy-linked reduction of pyridine nucleotide to the problem of generation of reducing power required for physiological processes. While we generally agree that this process is one of high activity in isolated mitochondria, a number of us are interested in the extent to which it contributes to the reduced pyridine nucleotide pool in tissues. Until now it has only been possible to speculate upon this, since total tissue analysis does not distinguish between that which was reduced directly by dehydrogenases or by the energy-linked reversal reaction.

Very recently, we have been fortunate enough to find a reagent which we have found to be a specific inhibitor of the pathway of energy-linked reduction under the conditions of our experiments. The reagent is simply high pressure, or hyperbaric oxygen (Chance, B., et al., Nature, 206, 257 (1965)). Pressurization of the anesthetized rat at several atmospheres for 10 to 20 seconds causes a decrease of fluorescence of the kidney and liver. Under other conditions analytical data show a fluorometric decrease to be correlated with the oxidation of reduced pyridine nucleotide in experiments with rat liver (Chance, B., et al., Biochem. Z., 341, 325 (1965)). and the isolated perfused heart (Chance, B., et al., Biochem. Z., 341, 357 (1965)). In Table I, the column labelled "Decrease at 10 Atm" indicates the percentage decrease of the total fluorescence that is observed after pressurization at 10 atm for a few minutes. It should be noted that this time is much too short to evoke the inhibition of dehydrogenase activity that occurs in longer time intervals (Chance, B., et al., Nature, 206, 257 (1965)). If now this percentage decrease in fluorescence is compared with the oxidized-reduced change when the animal is breathing air at atmospheric pressure, we find the decreases to be 26, 20 and 72 percent for brain, kidney and liver, respectively. The last column gives the approximate value of pressure in atmospheres for half-maximal effect. These experimental data, interpreted according to our data on isolated mitochondria and submitochondrial particles to represent the effect of inhibition of the energy-linked pathway upon the

Table I
EFFECTS OF OXYGEN ON THE REDUCED PYRIDINE NUCLEOTIDE LEVELS OBSERVED IN RAT ORGAN IN VIVO BY FLUORESCENCE MICROSCOPY
366 mμ Excitation, 450 mμ Emission
Anaesthesia 1.0 gr/kg Urethane (i.p.)

Expt.	Organ	Oxidized-Reduced Increase*	Decrease at 10 Atmos.*	Percent of Oxidized-Reduced Change	Pressure for Half Maximal Effect (Atmospheres)
B 40	Brain	15	4	26	3
B 34	Kidney	30	6	20	2
B 31	Liver	25	18	72	4 (or greater)

*Calculated as a percentage of the aerobic fluorescence level (but including a fixed fluorescence in the pressure tank window).

concentration of reduced pyridine nucleotide, suggests that 26, 20 and 72 per cent of the pyridine nucleotide of brain, kidney and liver, respectively, is reduced by the energy-linked pathway. It seems, therefore that we have here a partial answer to Professor Krebs' question as to whether the reversibility of oxidative phosphorylation causes the energy-linked reduction of DPN *in vivo*. I think the facts speak for themselves.

Metabolite assays under hyperbaric conditions were not possible in these experiments, since the time for opening the pressure tank was sufficiently long that the DPNH levels had returned to normal values by the time the access door to the chamber could be opened. We hope, however, to remedy this situation in future experiments, and to determine by metabolite assays the effect of the inhibition of the energy-linked pathway upon the metabolite pattern under various conditions. These results appear to establish the pool size due to the energy-linked pathway, but they do not establish the physiological role of reversed electron transport *in vivo*.

Klingenberg: The physiological role of the reversibility of oxidative phosphorylation can be discussed under two aspects: (1) a net reversed hydrogen transfer from flavin-linked substrate to DPN and DPN-linked substrates, (2) a control of the hydrogen and electron transfer in the respiratory chain by approaching the energy-linked redox equilibrium.

It appears improbable that a net energy-linked hydrogen transfer (case 1) is of physiological importance. A generation of reducing power in the mitochondrial DPN system appears not to be useful except when hydrogen is transferred further to the TPN. The energy-linked transhydrogenation from the DPN to the TPN system appears to be very efficient in mitochondria (Klingenberg, M. and Slenczka, W., Biochem. Z., 331, 486 (1959)). However, there are also other sources for the reduction of TPN such as the TPN-linked isocitrate dehydrogenation in mitochondria. It is not certain how much hydrogen is transferred through the TPN system, since even the function of the TPN system in mitochondria is not known.

It has been proposed that TPNH serves as a hydrogen donor for the glutamate formation by glutamate dehydrogenase, since both the TPN and the glutamate dehydrogenase are found in larger amounts only in liver mitochondria (Klingenberg, M. and Pette, D., Biochem. Biophys. Res. Comm., 7, 430 (1962)). The physiological role of this process may be its participation in the urea cycle. Here NH_3 can be incorporated first to glutamate, transaminated to aspartate and then into the urea cycle.

It appears possible that *in vivo* succinate plays a secondary role, and other flavin-linked substrates, such as fatty acids, are responsible for the energy-linked reduction of DPN from the flavin region.

Of greater physiological importance appears to be the role of the reversibility of oxidative phosphorylation in the control of respiration (case 2) (Klingenberg, M., Angew. Chem., 75, 900 (1963); Angew. Chem. Int. Ed., 3, 54 (1964)). In this case the ratio ATP/ADP would influence the hydrogen and electron transfer in the respiratory chain with an increasing approach to an energy-linked redox equilibrium. Under these circumstances a high degree of reduction in the DPN as well as in the ubiquinone may be built up. It is irrelevant and not distinguishable whether, in the equilibrium, the hydrogen comes from the succinate or from DPN-linked substrates. In fact, it was recently demonstrated (Kröger, A., unpublished) that in heart mitochondria under optimum coupling conditions, with malate and in the presence of substrates which remove oxaloacetate, a high degree of reduction of DPN and ubiquinone can be obtained even when the oxidation of eventually formed succinate is prevented in the presence of malonate.

The energy-linked transhydrogenation may also be discussed in this context. In the TPN system, under the influence of the phosphorylation potential, hydrogen accumulates to an even larger degree than in the DPN system. The hydrogen may come from the DPNH or from isocitrate. A major function of the energy-linked transhydrogenation is to maintain the hydrogen in the TPN system at a relatively negative redox potential, whether it comes directly from a TPN-linked substrate, from isocitrate, or from DPNH by transhydrogenation.

Bücher: We are able to measure the redox state of intracellular DPNH in the hemoglobin-free liver preparation by combined fluorescence and spectrophotometric methods. It turns out that the DPNH in the mitochondria is at a very low percentage level of reduction; between 12 - 20 percent in the steady state level, while the liver is in a continuous state of tremendous activity which uses up considerable quantities of ATP. I believe there cannot be any contribution from mitochondrial DPNH to the fatty acid synthesis.

However, I do think that one of the main sources of reducing power is to be found in the Krebs cycle, because there are two isocitrate dehydrogenases: the TPN-specific isocitrate dehydrogenase, which we know today is not the main Krebs cycle enzyme of oxidative function, and the DPN-specific IDH, which is modified by ADP and is the constant-proportion enzyme of the Krebs cycle in all mitochondria, while the TPN-specific enzyme shows motions over two orders of magnitude. Only tissues with biosynthetic function have these TPN-specific enzymes. Also, there is a constant proportion between the TPN and TPNH concentrations in most mitochondria.

Lardy: In response to Professor Krebs' comments, one source of TPNH for fatty acid synthesis and other reductions is the malic enzyme. In both liver and adipose tissue, malic enzyme is found in the soluble fraction of the cell. In this compartment, the Srere enzyme cleaves citrate to acetyl-Co-A and oxaloacetate. The malic enzyme, together with malic dehydrogenase and oxaloacetate comprises a transhydrogenase system from DPNH and TPN to form TPNH (cf. Fig. 1).

Evidence for such a system in the soluble fraction of rat liver is shown in Figure 2. The supernatant fraction from rat liver homogenate, together with DPNH, oxaloacetate, cytochrome c, and a highly purified cytochrome c reductase, shows no activity until TPN is added; then, after a slight lag, cytochrome c is reduced. If either oxaloacetate or DPNH are omitted, the rate is nil. Plotting only the linear portion of the curve and using the same amount of supernatant from normal, fasted, and fasted-refed animals, the rate of the transhydrogenation is much enhanced in the refed animal, where malic enzyme is high, and it is down in the fasted animal where malic enzyme is low. As you know, it has been shown (Katz, J., and Landau, B., Fed. Proc., 23, 171 (1964)) that TPNH generated by G-6-P dehydrogenase and 6-phosphogluconic dehydrogenase is not sufficient to account for the hydrogen needed for fat synthesis (Flatt, J., and Ball, E., J. Biol. Chem., 239, 675 (1964)). Very likely the malic enzyme also contributes to that task.

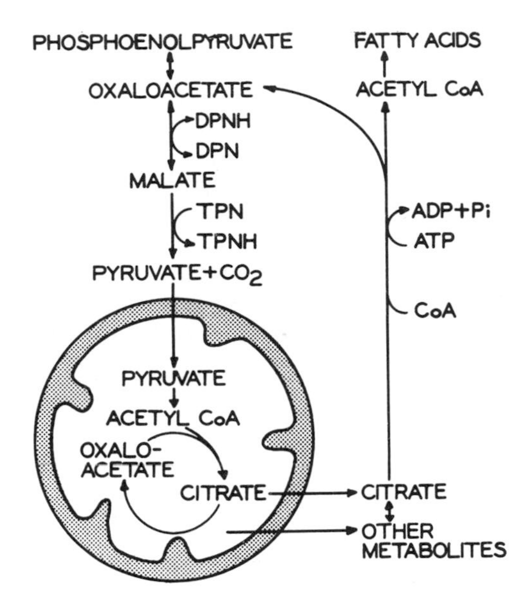

Fig. 1. Reactions in Lipogenesis. Reactions occurring in the mitochondria are shown in the enclosure. The other reactions occur in the cytosol. (Young, J., Shrago, E., and Lardy, H. A., Biochem., 3, 1691 (1964)).

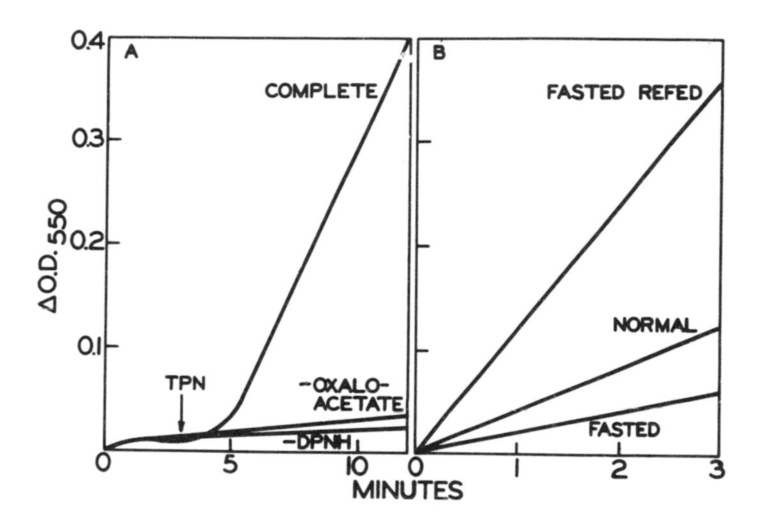

Fig. 2. Transhydrogenase in liver cytosol. The reaction mixture contained 75 µmoles glycylglycine buffer, pH 7.4, 0.76 µmole oxaloacetate neutralized to pH 7.4 with 2 N KOH, 0.2 µmole DPNH, 0.1 µmole TPN^+, 0.15 µmole cytochrome c, 0.03 µmole FMN, 3 µmoles $MnCl_2$, 5 units purified yeast, TPNH-cytochrome c reductase (1 unit = 1 µmole cytochrome c reduced/min), and 0.1 ml enzyme (high-speed supernatant fraction of rat liver homogenate). The reaction was carried out in a volume of 3.0 ml at 25°. The reduction of cytochrome c was followed at 550 mλ. In (B), only the linear part of the reaction curves are plotted. The supernatant fractions were obtained from rats that were fasted 96 hours and refed with commercial chow diet for 96 hours, normal, and fasted 96 hours (Young, J., Shrago, E., and Lardy, H. A., Biochem., 3, 1690 (1964)).

CONTROL OF METABOLISM IN INTACT TISSUES

CHAIRMAN'S INTRODUCTION

Cori: The next two papers deal with muscle, and I feel that I should make some very brief remarks about the pecularities of this tissue. Muscle is a machine which can regulate the flow of chemical energy in relation to the rate and the amount of work performed. This property must lie in the enzymatic system which is idling at rest and can then increase its activity stepwise over a wide range of rates. It can also cut off very rapidly and return to the resting condition. Maximally, this enzyme system is capable of tremendous acceleration; the rate from glycogen to lactate can go up 600-fold or more.

One wonders what kind of regulation is required to accomplish such a speed-up in a multi-enzyme system. I mentioned glycogen as the immediate source of energy because glucose would not be fast enough since it has to pass through a permeability barrier, and hexokinase activity is low in relation to phosphorylase activity. The dark granules visulalized are glycogen; they lie in the narrow spaces between the myofibrils, the same spaces where the mitochondria occur. The sarcotubular system is not very clearly shown in this section but as you know it is a system of channels which runs parallel with the fibrils and also horizontally. It is free of glycogen, as are the mitochondria. Phosphorylase occurs in muscle in a concentration of about 1 mg/ml, but if it were confined to these narrow spaces (as you would expect because one would think that phosphorylase would be near the glycogen on which it acts), then instead of having 1 mg/ml, you might have a much higher concentration.

These facts are mentioned to indicate that kinetics, under conditions where there is a high concentration of phosphorylase perhaps absorbed on the glycogen, might be quite different from the kinetics that we study _in vitro_ where we are forced to use very dilute solutions. What applies to phosphorylase could apply to other glycolytic enzymes if they are organized as a separate structural unit similar to that of the oxidative enzymes in mitochondria. So one should not expect the kinetics _in vivo_ and _in vitro_ to be necessarily the same.

The last point has to do with the compartmentation of cells. It has one consequence: if you have a very small pool in contact with the enzyme, you might have very large concentration changes in that small pool which would not be reflected in another pool of the same substrate if they were separated by a permeability barrier. Therefore, I raise the question, to what extent can one say that the total concentration of any intermediate that one measures in the cell is a reflection of the concentration of the same material at the point of action of the enzyme. I know it is psychologically very difficult to accept the notion that the total concentration may not tell you very much, but I wonder, for example, whether in the cases mentioned today where certain rapidly acting enzymes are not at equilibrium, whether this is not in itself an indication of different pool sizes. I will now call on Dr. Danforth to present his paper.

VIII

Regulation of Glycolytic Activity in Smooth and Skeletal Muscles

ACTIVATION OF GLYCOLYTIC PATHWAY IN MUSCLE*

William H. Danforth

Department of Internal Medicine, Washington University, School of Medicine, St. Louis, Missouri 63110

I believe it is evident to those of us concerned with regulation of the enzyme action in living systems that the search for the single regulator of an important pathway is often in vain. Certainly the rate of flow over a multienzyme pathway may be controlled by the cooperative action of more than one enzyme and perhaps multiple activators and inhibitors, the importance of each varying with the physiologic circumstance. Consider the glycolytic system of frog sartorius muscle. When resting muscle is stimulated repetitively, flow through the glycolytic system may increase many hundred times. The activity of the pathway is increased by the activation of at least two enzymes, the phosphorylase system (1) involving in part the conversion of phosphorylase b to phosphorylase a (2,3) and by the activation of phosphofructokinase (1).

Today, I should first like to consider the effects of changes in muscle pH on these two important control points of glycolysis. When muscle is stimulated repetitively, it becomes briefly acid and then alkaline early in the course of stimulation. It then later becomes acid (4). The evidence suggests that the alkaline phase results from the net reaction:

$$\underset{(pK_2\ 4.58)}{\text{Phosphocreatine}} \longrightarrow \underset{(pK_2\ 7.21)}{\text{Creatine} + P_i}$$

This reaction results in the loss of H^+ because of the differences in pK's. The later acid phase results from the formation of lactic acid.

The time course and magnitude of these reactions in isolated frog sartorii, stimulated rapidly, are shown in Figure 1. Note that large amounts of phosphocreatine break down early in the course of stimulation. Only after 20 seconds does lactate

* This investigation was supported in part by Grant AM-07990 from the United States Public Health Service.

begin to form. It is in this first 20 second period that phosphorylase b is converted to phosphorylase a (5). For this reason and for others we wondered if the conversion of phosphorylase b → a might be influenced by the rise of intracellular pH resulting from the hydrolysis of phosphocreatine, an idea suggested by C. F. Cori in 1956 (6). Unfortunately the measurement of intracellular pH by microelectrodes is difficult (7,8) and other methods are open to possible errors (9); therefore we have studied this problem in indirect ways.

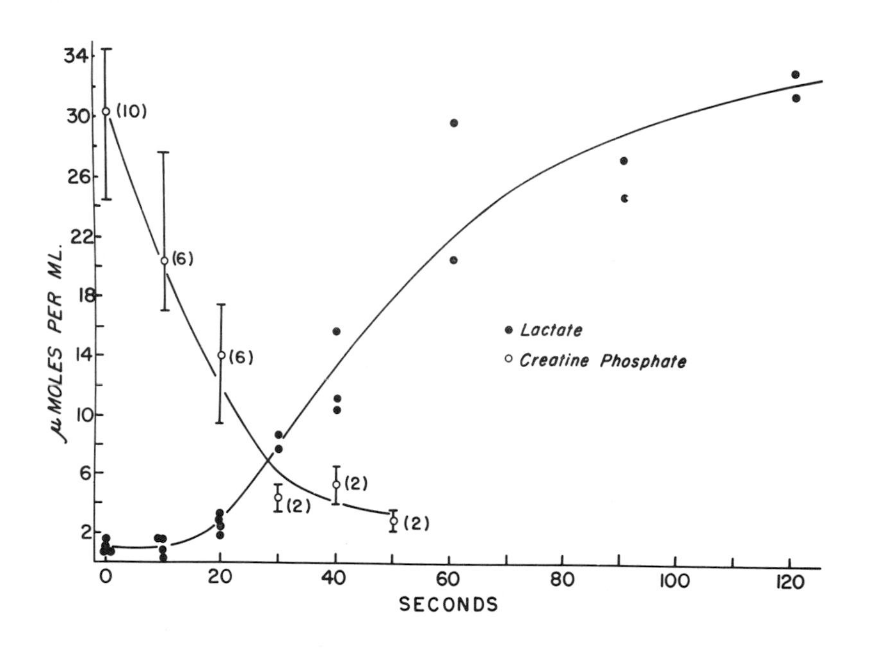

Figure 1. Time course of disappearance of phosphocreatine and appearance of lactate. Isolated frog sartorii were stimulated in the presence of 5 per cent CO_2 - 95 per cent argon at the rate of 6 per second at 20°. The arrangement used has been previously described (5). At the times indicated muscles were frozen in isopentane chilled to near its freezing point. Perchloric acid extracts were neutralized and assayed enzymatically for phosphocreatine and lactate. (O), mean values for phosphocreatine concentrations. Vertical bars extend from the highest to the lowest values measured. The numbers in parentheses are the number of muscles analyzed. (●), lactate concentration of individual muscles. The ordinate numbers represent μmoles per ml intracellular water.

We first used the classical method for varying intracellular pH, that is to alter the CO_2 in the gas phase of the frog Ringer's bicarbonate. In Figure 2 it can be seen that as the CO_2 in the gas phase is increased from the usual 5 per cent, the lag period before the appearance of phosphorylase a becomes longer and longer. At 60 per cent CO_2 the maximum amount of phosphorylase a attained is decreased also.

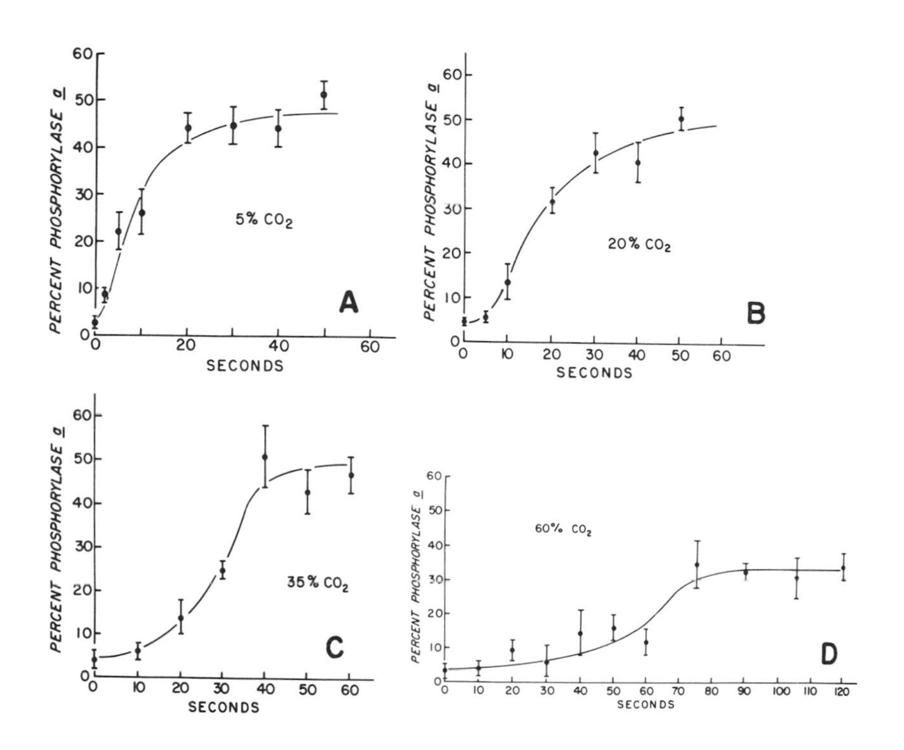

Figure 2. Time course of appearance of phosphorylase a in response to muscle stimulation in varying concentrations of CO_2. The frog sartorii were mounted, stimulated and frozen as described in Figure 1. Tissue extraction and phosphorylase assay have been described previously (2). Phosphorylase a activity is expressed as per cent of total phosphorylase activity. Each point represents the mean of at least 5 muscles. The vertical bars represent the standard error of the mean.

Another way to make a muscle acid is to fatigue it and to allow a short recovery period (4). The time course of the conversion of phosphorylase b to a in fatigued muscles is shown in Figure 3. This figure should be compared with the data on non-fatigued muscles stimulated in 5 per cent CO_2 shown in Figure 2. The long lag period before the appearance of phosphorylase a is similar to that seen when muscles contract in high concentrations of CO_2.

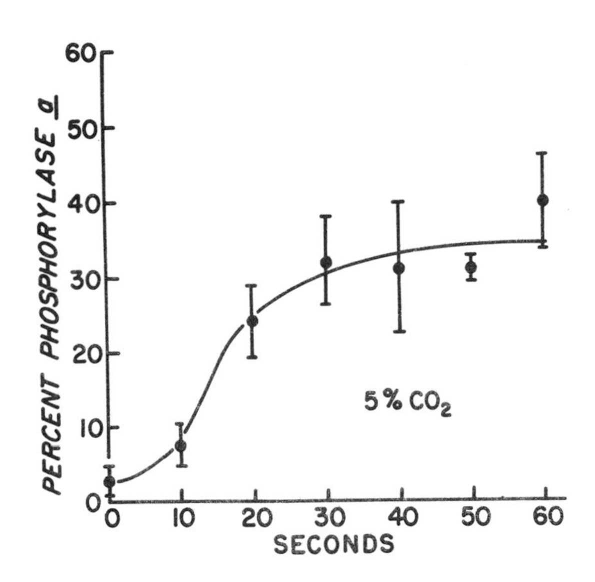

Figure 3. Time course of appearance of phosphorylase a in fatigued muscles in response to stimulation. These muscles were stimulated at the rate of 6 per second for 20 seconds and then allowed to rest for 5 minutes in the presence of 95 per cent argon - 5 per cent CO_2. The second stimulation was then carried out again at the rate of 6 per second for the time indicated on the abscissa. Vertical bars indicate the standard error of the mean of 5 or more experiments.

To examine the effect of making the muscles less rather than more acid we stimulated the isolated frog sartorii at 2 per second rather than at 6 per second. In 5 per cent CO_2 the lag period before the appearance of significant amounts of phosphorylase a is 20 to 30 seconds (Figure 4 top). In 2 per cent CO_2 the lag period is shortened considerably (Figure 4 bottom).

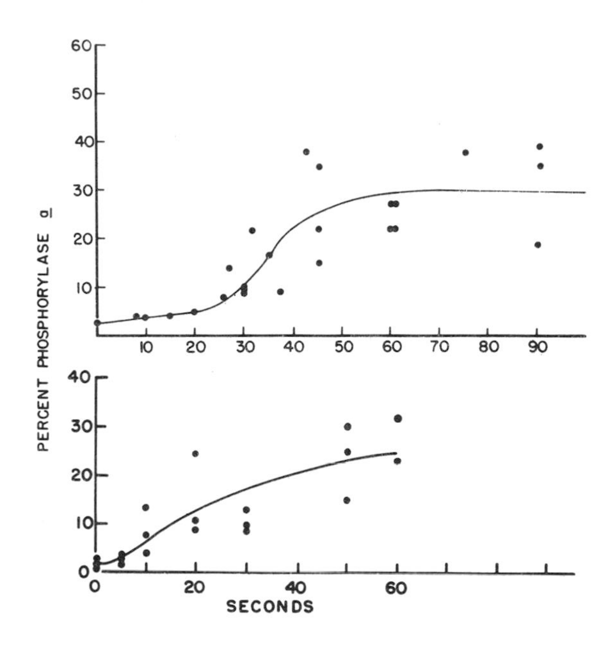

Figure 4. The effect of concentration of CO_2 in the gas phase on the appearance of phosphorylase a in response to stimulation. The muscles were stimulated at the rate of 2 per second. The top panel represents muscles in 95 per cent argon - 2 per cent CO_2. The muscles were handled as described in Figure 2. Each point represents a single muscle.

The situation in intact muscle is quite complex; however, the conclusions are compatible with data obtained in vitro. Krebs and co-workers have shown in a purified system that both the conversion of phosphorylase b to phosphorylase a by phosphorylase b kinase and the activation of phosphorylase b kinase are speeded up by elevation of the pH (10,11). It now seems likely that at least under certain conditions pH may be important in vivo also.

Next, consider the effects of epinephrine on this system. Figure 5 shows the phosphorylase b → a conversion in response to a standard stimulus in the presence of different concentrations of CO_2. The higher the concentration of CO_2, the less phosphorylase a was formed. In the presence of epinephrine, the curve is shifted into the higher CO_2 (or lower pH) range. Similar curves have been obtained in fatigued muscles (5). These curves are similar to the pH curves for phosphorylase b kinase activation and for phosphorylase b → a conversion obtained in vitro by Krebs and co-workers, in the presence and

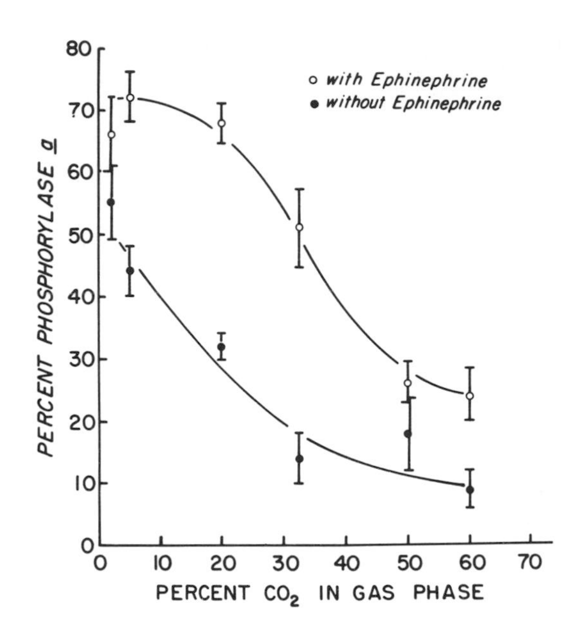

Figure 5. The interaction of epinephrine and of varying concentrations of CO_2 on the phosphorylase a present after a standard stimulus. Each muscle was stimulated for 20 seconds at the rate of 6 per second and then quick frozen. (O-O), muscles presoaked in 1.1 x 10^{-6} M epinephrine for 15 minutes before stimulation; (●-●), no epinephrine added.

in the absence of 3', 5'-cyclic AMP (10,11). Since it appears likely that changes in phosphorylase b kinase activity are essential for changes of the phosphorylase system in vivo, epinephrine action may be thought of as shifting the activity curve of phosphorylase b kinase so that the enzyme becomes more active at acid pH.

Phosphofructokinase. There is already evidence 32 years old that high concentrations of CO_2 in the gas phase of Ringer's solution inhibits the conversion of hexosemonophosphate to lactate (12). Since phosphofructokinase is a likely control point, we looked at the pH effect on the enzyme in vitro. It turns out that the ATP inhibition of phosphofructokinase in extracts of frog skeletal muscle is critically dependent on pH (Figures 6 and 7). Relatively small changes in pH have profound effects on ATP inhibition. Thus it is suggested that changes in pH in the range that may well occur within muscle cells have important effects on two major regulatory enzymes of glycolysis, phosphorylase b kinase and phosphofructokinase.

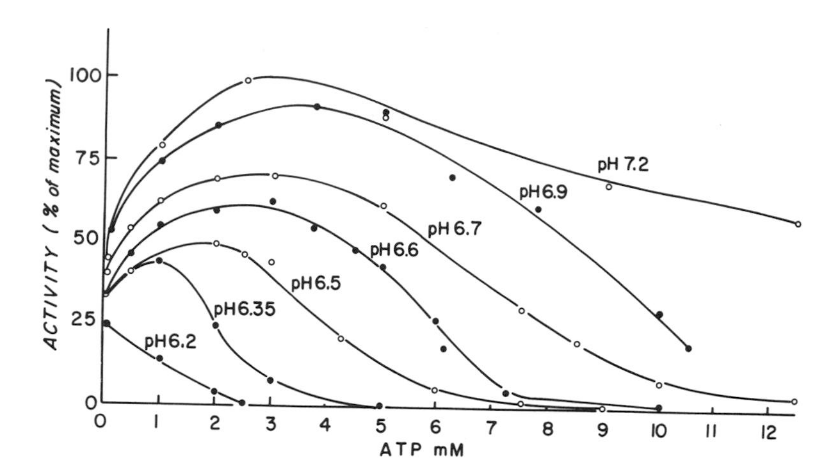

Figure 6. Effect of pH on the ATP inhibition of phosphofructokinase. Phosphofructokinase activity was assayed by the method of Passonneau and Lowry in a 1:10,000 dilution of extract from frog skeletal muscle (16). Fructose-6-phosphate concentration was 2.2 mM and Mg^{++} concentration 5 mM in all cases. The highest point on the graph was arbitrarily chosen as 100 per cent activity. The complete ascending curves are not plotted.

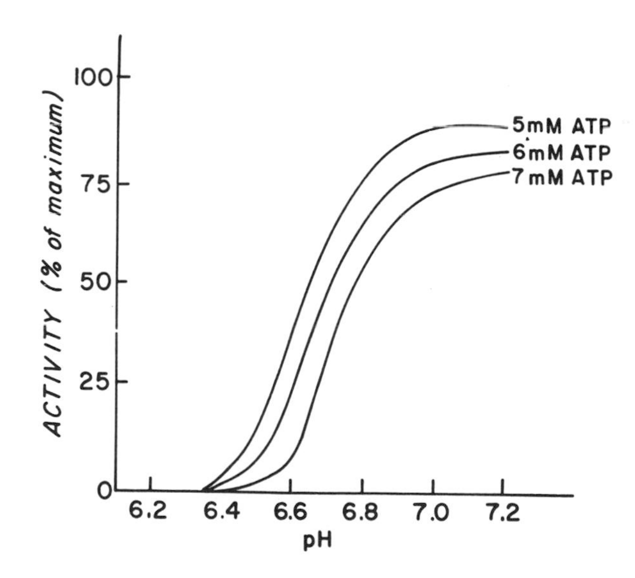

Figure 7. Effect of pH on phosphofructokinase activity at three concentrations of ATP. The figure is drawn from the information in Figure 6.

In each case the higher pH's activate; lower pH's inhibit.

One might now question the role of the various activators of phosphofructokinase. It is already known that muscle work may be associated with four changes that might serve to activate phosphofructokinase. At rapid rates of stimulation inorganic phosphate, AMP, and fructose-6-phosphate may rise (1,13) and all have been shown to be activators of phosphofructokinase by Passonneau and Lowry (14). ATP may fall (13), an event that should serve to release inhibition of phosphofructokinase (14,15). Also, early in the course of muscle contraction pH rises (4). Thus, during the early phase of a series of contractions phosphofructokinase is undoubtedly subjected to the combined effects of multiple activators. As a consequence of phosphofructokinase activation fructose-1,6-diphosphate, another potent activator of phosphofructokinase (14), may be expected to increase in concentration and to perpetuate and further an activation already accomplished. Activation by fructose-1,6-diphosphate might be especially important during the late acid phase of contraction.

The question now arises as to whether there is a selective advantage to having many activators which arise from a single event (muscle contraction) and which act on the same enzyme (phosphofructokinase). There seem to be three advantages. First, several activators appearing simultaneously and acting independently allow great flexibility in enzyme action with minimal changes in the concentrations of activators or inhibitors. For example, assume that an enzyme must increase its activity 100 times. The system may be greatly oversimplified as follows. If a single activator behaves according to first order kinetics, the activator must increase in concentration 100 fold in order to increase enzyme activity by a like amount. If not one but two independent activators increase simultaneously, the necessary rise in concentration of each might be visualized to be 50 (one half of 100) or 10 (the square root of 100) depending on whether the effects add to each other or multiply each other. In a like manner, a simultaneous increase in 4 activators by 25 fold or 3.2 fold might stimulate the reaction 100 fold. If, on the other hand, the activation curve is sigmoid shaped, as in the case with many regulatory or "allosteric" enzymes, including phosphofructokinase (14), we may assume that smaller increases of a single activator are necessary for the same effect, perhaps only a 10 fold rise for a 100 fold increase in activity. In this case an increase in the number of activators to four decreases the necessary rise of each so that a 100 fold increase in activity might be visualized with only a 1.8 to 2.5 fold concentration rise provided these concentrations were in the range that acted upon the steep part of a sigmoid curve. A second advantage of multiple activators of a single enzyme is that such an arrangement allows for flexibility under a variety of physiologic circumstances. Any three or four of five activators could produce a drastic change in enzyme activity without large changes in tissue concentration. A third advantage of such a system is that it allows for a tight coupling of glycolysis to muscle work. Most of the activators mentioned above are returned toward normal by flow through the glycolytic system so that any overshoot or undershoot would tend to be immediately self-correcting.

The above discussion has centered on phosphofructokinase, a single enzyme in the glycolytic pathway. In order to speed flow over the total pathway it is also necessary to activate glycogen phosphorylase (1,3) and perhaps other enzymes as well in a coordinated fashion. pH, of course, is not the only regulator of either system.

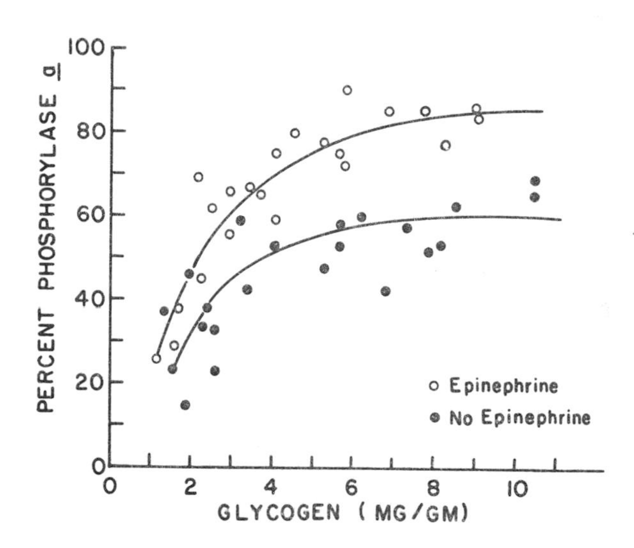

Figure 8. Relation between the glycogen content of muscle and the phosphorylase b → a conversion. Paired frog sartorii were removed. In some cases glycogen was lowered by stimulation. All muscles were then allowed to recover at 20° for 4 hours in oxygenated Ringer's solution. At the end of this period lactate and glucose-6-phosphate concentrations were always quite low. One muscle from each pair was then stimulated at 6 per second and then frozen and assayed for phosphorylase. The mate was frozen and assayed for glycogen (18).

The relationship between muscle glycogen content and phosphorylase b → a conversion is shown in Figure 8. It is evident that the more glycogen present in the muscle, the greater the amount of phosphorylase a formed. Epinephrine alters the position of the curve, but does not abolish the relationship. These experiments fit well with the *in vitro* stimulation of phosphorylase b kinase by glycogen described by Krebs and co-workers (11). The data are also reminiscent of the effect of glycogen on the interconversion of glycogen synthetase in skeletal muscle (17), and suggest a mechanism for glycogen to control its own breakdown as well as its synthesis.

In summary, a few of the complexities of the regulation of glycolysis have been dealt with. Undoubtedly future research will uncover other factors not now considered.

ACKNOWLEDGEMENT

The author wishes to express appreciation to Mr. Preston Harvey, Mrs. Ann Mitchell, and Miss Sandra Ball for obtaining the data presented in this paper.

REFERENCES

1. Karpatkin, S., Helmreich, E., and Cori, C. F., J. Biol. Chem., 239, 3139 (1964).

2. Danforth, W. H., Helmreich, E., and Cori, C. F., Proc. Natl. Acad. Sci., 48, 1191 (1962).

3. Danforth, W. H., and Lyon, J. B., Jr., J. Biol. Chem., 239, 4047 (1964).

4. Dubuisson, M., Ann. Physiol. Physiochem. Biol., 15, 443 (1939).

5. Danforth, W. H., and Helmreich, E., J. Biol. Chem., 239, 3133 (1964).

6. Cori, C. F., in O. H. Gaebler (Editor), *Enzymes, Units of Biological Structure and Function*, Academic Press, Inc., New York, 1956, p. 573.

7. Caldwell, P. C., J. Physiol., 142, 22 (1958).

8. Kostyuk, P. G., and Sorokina, Z. A., in A. Kleinzeller and A. Kotyk, (Editors), *Symposium on Membrane Transport and Metabolism*, Academic Press, Inc., New York, 1961 p. 193.

9. Caldwell, P. C., Int. Rev. Cytology, 5, 229 (1956).

10. Krebs, E. G., Graves, D. J., and Fischer, E. H., J. Biol. Chem., 234, 2867 (1959).

11. Krebs, E. G., Love, D. S., Bratvold, G. E., Trayser, K. A., Meyer, W. L., and Fischer, E. H., Biochemistry, 3, 1022 (1964).

12. Ronzoni, E., and Kerly, M., J. Biol. Chem., 103, 175 (1933).

13. Helmreich, E., and Cori, C. F., in G. Weber (Editor) Advances in Enzyme Regulation, III, Pergamon Press, Oxford, 1965, p. 91.

14. Passonneau, J. V., and Lowry, O. H., Biochem. and Biophys. Res. Comm., 7, 10 (1962).

15. Lardy, H. A., and Parker, R. E., Jr., in O. H. Gaebler (Editor), Enzymes, Units of Biological Structure and Function, Academic Press, New York, 1956, p. 584.

16. Lowry, O. H., and Passonneau, J. V., J. Biol. Chem., 239, 31 (1964).

17. Danforth, W. H., J. Biol. Chem., 240, 588 (1965).

18. Pfleiderer, G., in H. U. Bergmeyer (Editor), Methods of Enzymatic Analysis, Academic Press, New York, 1963, p. 59.

THE RESPONSE OF THE GLYCOLYTIC SYSTEM OF ANAEROBIC FROG SARTORIUS MUSCLE TO ELECTRICAL STIMULATION*

Ernst Helmreich, William H. Danforth**, Simon Karpatkin*** and Carl F. Cori

From the Department of Biological Chemistry
Washington University School of Medicine
St. Louis, Missouri 63110

Introduction and Methods

The problem which will be discussed relates to the link between metabolism and function in muscle. Frog sartorius stimulated electrically without external load while immersed in anaerobic frog Ringer's-bicarbonate solution at 20° without the addition of glucose. In order to avoid transition effects, stimulation was preceded by an anaerobic incubation for 25 minutes at rest. Rates of isotonic contraction from 3 to 48 minutes were used for a period of up to 30 minutes (1). For the study of the phosphorylase $\underline{b} \rightleftharpoons \underline{a}$ interconversion the muscles were mounted in a moist chamber and were stimulated against a 2 g load at higher frequencies for a shorter period of time (2). In both groups of experiments the stimulation period was terminated by plunging the still contracting muscles into isopentane cooled to -170°. The unstimulated control muscles were treated alike. Analyses for lactate, glucose-6-P, fructose-1, 6-di P, α-glycero-P, ATP, ADP, and 5'-AMP were carried out on the same muscle either spectrophotometrically or fluorometrically using routine enzymatic test procedures based on the measurements of extracellular space and of total tissue water, and values are expressed in terms of μmoles/ml of intracellular water. Methods

* This work was supported in part by research grants AI-03765, AM-6830 and AM-9242 from the National Institutes of Health, United States Public Health Service, and by a grant of the American Cancer Society to Washington University, St. Louis, Missouri.

** Present address: Department of Medicine, Washington University, St. Louis, Missouri.

*** Present adress: Department of Medicine, New York University, New York, New York.

for extraction of phosphorylase from frozen frog muscles at temperatures below 0° C and methods for the determination of phosphorylase a and b activity have been published (3). For a study of the effects of stimulation on sugar penetration and phosphorylation, the muscles were incubated in 10 mM tritiated 2-deoxyglucose (4). These experiments will be described in a forthcoming publication.

Results

The response of the glycolytic system of frog muscle to stimulation. Under the experimental conditions described above, the glycolytic response is related directly to the frequency of stimulation over an 80-fold increase in rate. This is illustrate in Figure 1. Even at 3 S. P. M.* -- the lowest rate of stimulation used -- more lactate was formed than at the resting rate, referred to as control in Figure 1. In a true steady state a linear rate of lactate formation would be expected. Actually, the rate of lactate formation declined with time. Thus at 24 S. P. M., the rate between 20 and 30 minutes was 30 per cent lower than between 10 and 20 minutes. The reason for this decline in rate has not been determined, but could be related to a change in pH as a result of accumulation of considerable amounts of lactate.

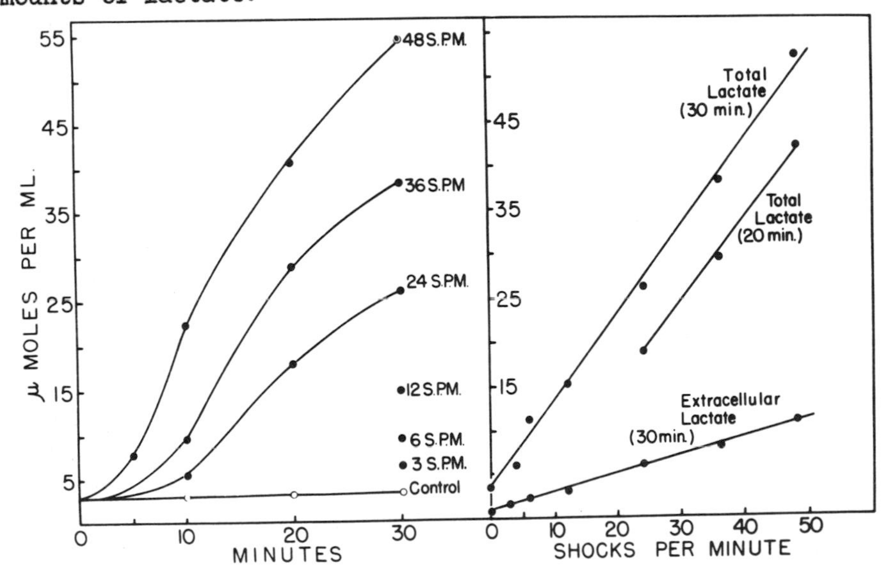

Figure 1. Lactate formation in stimulated frog sartorius muscle. (Reprinted by permission from J. Biol. Chem. (1)).

* S. P. M. = shocks per minute

The increase in flow rate over the glycolytic system was preceded by a lag period (see Figure 1). Increasing the rate of contraction shortened the lag period. Since the glycolytic system consists of a series of consecutive reactions, a lag period is to be expected as the system undergoes transition from one steady state to another.

The activity of at least two enzymes, phosphorylase and phosphofructokinase, appears to be geared closely in stimulated frog muscle. This can be deduced from the finding that up to 18 S. P. M. when the flow rate had increased about 30-fold, there was little change in the concentration of G-6-P (1). This would seem to require nearly simultaneous and proportional activation of these two enzymes. At higher frequencies of stimulation, G-6-P increases progressively (1). The enzymatic reactions below PFK, judging from the concentrations of fructose-1,6-di P, seemed also to be in step with the increased flow rates produced by a single shock stimulation up to 36 S. P. M. (5). Only when there was maximal stimulation as in a 10 second tetanus was there an appreciable accumulation of fructose-1,6-di P in frog sartorius muscle, amounting to 0.36 μmoles/ml or more (6). During a tetanus the rate of glycolysis increases several hundred fold (7,8).

The increase in α-glycero-P during stimulation is likewise proportional to the rate of stimulation. Anaerobically the glycero-P shuttle is not operative, hence there is no mechanism for the rapid removal of α-glycero-P, once it has been formed. Thus, under these conditions, α-glycero-P is an end product of glycolysis as is lactate. These results are shown in Table III, as will be seen later.

Return to rest. Muscle can not only turn on energy yielding reactions very quickly during activity, but it can also turn these reactions off rapidly at the cessation of activity. The "off" effect is shown in Table I. There was a decline in the rate of lactate formation, during the first 5 minutes of rest to about 7 per cent of the rate during the preceding period of stimulation. During the following 5 to 25 minutes, lactate formation proceeded at the resting rate for this batch of frog muscles. The concentration of G-6-P did not fall after cessation of stimulation, which suggests that both phosphorylase and PFK are deactivated simulataneously (1).

After having described some of the properties of the glycolytic system in a working muscle, the activation of individual enzymes in response to stimulation will now be considered.

TABLE I

Return to rest after stimulation

Experimental conditions	Rate of lactate formation
	μmoles/ml/min.
Stimulation at 24 shocks per min. (10 minute period)	1.3
Rest, 0-5 min.	0.09
Rest, 5-25 min.	0.02

Activation of phosphorylase. The first reaction in the conversion of glycogen to lactate is catalyzed by the phosphorylase system. The results presented in the preceding section have shown a rapid "on" and "off" effect of the activity in response to stimulation. One mechanism of activation of phosphorylase which could satisfy this requirement involves the conversion of phosphorylase *b* to phosphorylase *a* by phosphorylase *b* kinase in the presence of ATP and Mg^{++}. In the tetanized frog sartorius at 30° phosphorylase *a* rises to nearly 100 per cent of total with a half-time of 0.7 seconds. The rate of fall following stimulation is determined by phosphorylase phosphatase and has a half-time of 12 seconds (3). From kinetic evidence it was deduced that the activation of phosphorylase *b* kinase is responsible for the rise in phosphorylase *a* rather than a change in the activity of phosphorylase phosphatase (3). Stimulation of frog sartorii with single shocks showed that the rise of phosphorylase *a* is preceded by a lag period (2). Increasing the frequency of stimulation shortened the lag period in the rise of phosphorylase *a*. Studies with a partially purified preparation of phosphorylase *b* kinase indicated that there was also a lag period in the spontaneous activation of this enzyme *in vitro* in the presence of Mg^{++} ions and ATP (2). It is noteworthy also, that energy turnover in intact muscle does not seem to be an important factor in the activation of phosphorylase *b* kinase since increasing the external work load of the muscles had no effect on rate or extent of phosphorylase *a* formation (2). However, the rate of contraction had a pronounced effect, since the steady state level of phosphorylase *a* increased with the frequency of stimulation. In Figure 2 the relationship of the rate of stimulation to the ratio of the velocity constants for the forward and backward reaction in the

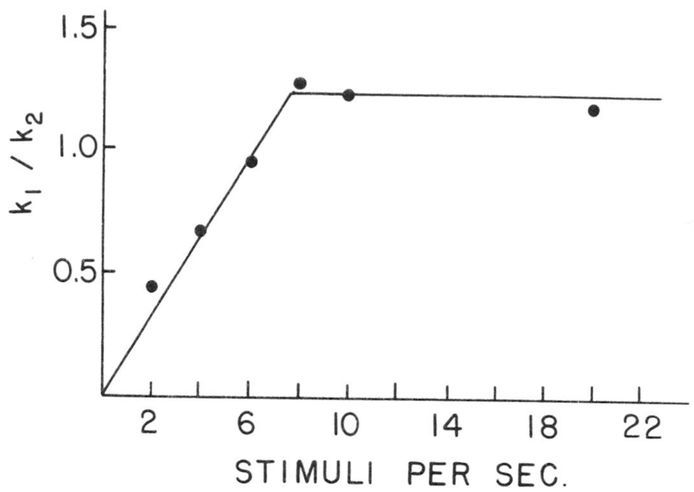

Figure 2. Ratio of the velocity constants for the forward and backward reaction in the phosphorylase $\underline{b} \rightleftharpoons \underline{a}$ interconversion as a function of the frequency of stimulation. (Reprinted by permission from J. Biol. Chem. (2)).

phosphorylase $\underline{b} \rightleftharpoons \underline{a}$ interconversion is shown. These data were obtained from the steady state equation: $k_1/k_2 = a/b$. The data in Figure 2 show that the increase in phosphorylase b kinase activity is proportional to the rate of contraction in the range from 2 to 8 stimuli/second. These and other data support the view that the activation of phosphorylase b kinase can be rapidly turned "on" and "off" that the activity of this enzyme responds in a graded fashion to electrical stimulation (2). Since the a form in contrast to the b form is active in the absence of 5'-AMP a graded response of the glycolytic system involving the $\underline{b} \rightleftharpoons \underline{a}$ interconversion seems possible. This then raises the question: What might trigger the activation of phosphorylase b kinase in stimulated muscle?

Electrical impulses are propagated through ion fluxes in muscle. An effective electrical stimulus is accompanied by a rapid fall in the potential across the cell membrane. This drop in potential is then followed by the mechanical response of the muscle which is initiated by the release of ionized Ca^{++} in the order of 0.1 µmole/gm of muscle (9). Relaxation follows the removal of this amount of Ca^{++} from the myofibrils presumably by means of the Ca^{++} pump in the sarcotubular vesicles (10,11). In frog sartorius, as in many other muscles, the transmembrane potential varies with the logarithm of the ratio of K^+ inside and outside the muscle (or since the concentration of K^+ remains practically constant with changes in the external K^+ concentration, the transmembrane potential also

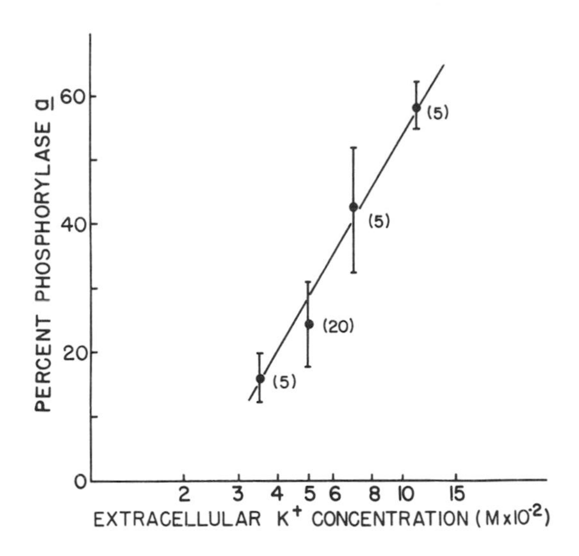

Figure 3. Increase in phosphorylase a content of frog muscle with increasing extracellular K^+ concentrations. (Reprinted by permission from J. Biol. Chem. (2)).

varies with the logarithm of the external concentration of K^+). In Figure 3, it is shown that when the external concentration was increased from 0.035 to 0.115 M, the percentage of phosphorylase a was likewise related to the logarithm of K^+ concentration in the medium.

These experiments suggested that events associated with the excitation-contraction sequence may be related to the increase in phosphorylase a. Krebs, Graves, and Fischer proposed some years ago that Ca^{++} ions might be involved in the activation of phosphorylase b kinase, since they observed an activation *in vitro* (12, 13).

In the following experiments an attempt was made to study the role of Ca^{++} in the interconversion of phosphorylase b ⇌ a in the intact frog sartorius muscle.

Herz and Weber (14) have recently reported that 0.01 M caffeine causes the release of enough Ca^{++} from the sarcoplasmic reticulum to account for the contracture of frog muscle in the presence of this agent. It is of interest that exposure of frog sartorii to the same concentration of caffeine results in an increase in phosphorylase a (See Table II).

TABLE II

Effect of Caffeine on Phosphorylase a Content of Frog Sartorius

Phosphorylase a in percent of total phosphorylase after addition of 0.01 M caffeine	
0 seconds	30 seconds
1.6 ± 0.7 % (5)	19 ± 3 % (6)

Caffeine seems to increase the concentration of ionized Ca^{++} in muscle through inhibition of the sarcotubular Ca^{++} pump (14). According to Karsten and Mommaerts (15) oligomycin is another agent which inhibits Ca^{++} uptake by an isolated sarcotubular vesicle preparation of rabbit skeletal muscle. It thus seemed of interest to study the effect of oligomycin on the phosphorylase b⇌a interconversion in frog muscle*. Neither the rise or fall of phosphorylase a during and following electrical stimulation was affected in muscles treated with oligomycin. There was also no change in tension development or in relaxation. Moreover, unstimulated muscles treated with oligomycin did not develop a contracture. Since this substance has only been tested on isolated mitochondria and sarcotubular vesicles, the negative results could mean that the inhibitor does not have access to the Ca^{++} pump in intact frog sartorii. Clearly more evidence is required before the role of Ca^{++} in the activation of phosphorylase b kinase *in vivo* can be discussed in more definitive terms.

An analysis of the physiological importance of the phosphorylase b⇌a transformation for glycolysis in stimulated muscle was made possible through the work of Drs. Danforth and Lyon with a strain of mice (Strain I_{FnLn}) which apparently lacks phosphorylase b kinase in muscle (8,16). Their work showed that in muscles of the I strain mice, no significant rise in the level of phosphorylase a could be demonstrated after a 10 second tetanus, whereas in the normal muscle (C_{57} strain) the phosphorylase a content rose to 70 per cent of the total. On comparing the changes in the concentration of G-6-P and lactate in the muscles of C_{57} mice with muscles of the I mice it became apparent that the muscles producing phosphorylase a formed G-6-P and lactate twice as fast as the muscles without phosphorylase a.

*These experiments were made possible by a generous gift of oligomycin from Dr. H. A. Lardy.

Although these experiments did show that the b⇌a transformation plays a role in the rapid activation of the glycolytic chain at high frequencies of stimulation, they also indicated that this transformation *per se* is not essential for increased lactate formation. In order to see whether this transformation played a role shown by the experiments of Figure 1, in which the rate of stimulation was slower but lasted longer, muscles were stimulated at 36 S. P. M. for 30 minutes. These muscles contained from 3.1 to 6 (an average of 5.4) per cent phosphorylase *a* as compared to less than 5 per cent for the resting control muscles. This does not exclude formation of phosphorylase *a* during each contraction which lasts only about 100 mseconds and its disappearance during the pauses between contractions which last about 1.5 second at this rate of contraction.

Since inorganic P is a substrate, its concentration could control phosphorylase activity in the manner of a substrate saturation curve. The same applies to glycogen. This would require a progressive increase in concentration of inorganic P with increasing frequency of stimulation. The data presented in Table III do not show such a correlation. Up to 24 S. P. M. there was little change in the concentration of inorganic P whereas lactate formation had increased 40-fold. Another possibility for a stepwise activation of phosphorylase *b* is afforded by an increase in 5'-AMP concentration. However, as shown in Table III, concentrations of 5'-AMP remain virtually unchanged at slow frequencies of stimulation. Only at 36 S. P. M. was there a 2-fold increase in 5'-AMP concentration.

The effects of 5'-AMP on the kinetics of phosphorylase have been studied in some detail in this laboratory. The dependence of rabbit skeletal muscle phosphorylase *b* on 5'-AMP for activity has been explained on the basis of a conformational change of the enzyme, which expresses itself kinetically in large decreases of the K_m values for inorganic P and for glycogen with no change in V_{max} (17). This interaction is reciprocal since increasing the substrate concentration decreases the K_m for 5'-AMP. Basically similar interactions occur between 5'-AMP and phosphorylase *a* (17,18). Additional factors which influence the K_m values for substrate are pH and temperature (18).

In recent experiments with Dr. Maria Michaelides, the binding of 5'-AMP to phosphorylase *a* has been reinvestigated by equilibrium dialysis (19). It has been found that addition of substrates increases the association constant of 5'-AMP for the enzyme. These results thus provide direct evidence that the interaction between substrate and activator binding sites results in tighter binding of 5'-AMP to the enzyme.

TABLE III

Formation of End Products and Concentration of Inorganic P and Adenine Nucleotides in Stimulated Frog Muscle

Stimuli per min	P_i	AMP	ADP	ATP	Increase over basal rate α-glycero-P	Lactate
		µmoles/ml				
0	4.1	0.4	2.3	7.2	1.0	1.0
3						8.3
6	4.2	0.5	3.1	6.7	2.2	13.5
12		0.4	3.7	6.2	3.7	22.0
18		0.5	4.6	5.9	7.2	31.5
24	4.4					41.0
36	8.2	0.8	5.1	4.8	10.8	60.0
48	9.6					85.0

These findings rule out other possible explanations for the kinetic effects.

Morgan and Parmeggiani have proposed that the inhibition of phosphorylase b by ATP may play an important regulatory role (20,21). These authors have shown that the ATP inhibition of phosphorylase b is competitive for 5'-AMP. As can be seen from Table III, there is a slow but continuous fall in the ATP concentration over the whole range of stimulation and a concomitant rise in ADP. Recent in vitro experiments revealed that ADP also inhibits phosphorylase b presumably by competition with 5'-AMP. Equimolar concentrations of ADP and ATP inhibited the enzyme to about the same extent (22). The inhibition by ADP may have escaped detection because of the presence of considerable amounts of 5'-AMP in some commercially available ADP preparations. It is therefore difficult to see how the slow decrease in ATP can result in an increase of phosphorylase b activity, since the ratio of the total concentration of inhibitor and activator, i.e., (ATP + ADP)/(AMP) does not change in the frog sartorius up to a rate of contraction of 36 S. P. M.

Conformational changes of a catalyst may change the substrate saturation curve from a hyperbolic to a sigmoidal curve. Such kinetic changes are interpreted as an expression of cooperative interaction between several binding sites (23). Rate effects could thus be magnified by small changes in the concentrations of the various reactants in contact with the enzyme. The results obtained with the stimulated frog muscle show how difficult it is to correlate changes in enzymatic rates with changes in the concentrations of reactants if only their total concentration in the intracellular water is known.

Activation of hexokinase. In the above experiments the activation of the glycolytic system in response to stimulation was studied in the absence of glucose and oxygen. Under these conditions glycogen serves as main energy source. It was therefore of interest to see if similar mechanisms of activation exist in muscle for the phosphorylation of glucose. Anaerobiosis, treatment with insulin and electrical stimulation cause increased permeability of frog muscle to sugars. Utilization of sugar is enhanced also under these conditions, but this could result from the increase in permeability (24,25,26,27). An alternative is an increase in hexokinase activity independent of any effect these conditions may have on the rate of sugar transport. We have recently made an attempt to distinguish between these possibilities (4). For this purpose rates of penetration and of phosphorylation of 2-deoxyglucose were compared and related to the concentration of free sugar in the intracellular water of frog sartorius muscle. In the experiments shown in Figure 4 it took 30 minutes at a rate of

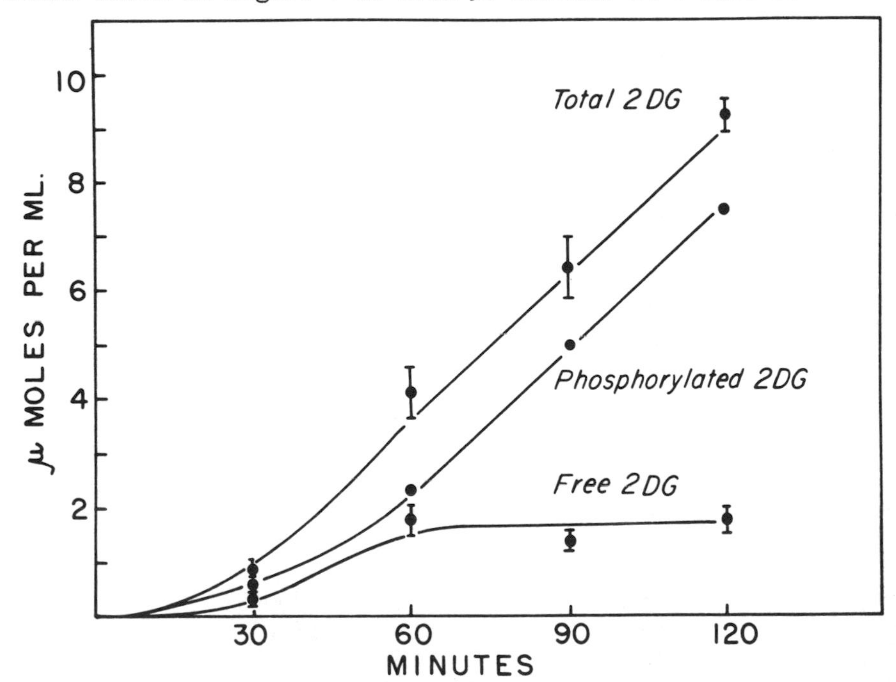

Figure 4. Penetration and phosphorylation of 2-deoxyglucose in stimulated frog muscle. (See text).

stimulation of 48 S. P. M. until a constant rate of uptake of 2-deoxyglucose was reached. In the steady state $K\ (a-x) = V_h$; where K is a first order rate constant, (a-x) is the concentration difference of sugar across the cell membrane and V_h is the rate of phosphorylation per hour. The relative effect of stimulation on sugar utilization and penetration can be expressed by the ratio of V_h/K in the above equation. This ratio was 8.3 in the case of stimulation as compared to a ratio of 1.3 in the case of insulin. Thus it follows that stimulation has relatively a much greater effect on phosphorylation than on penetration.

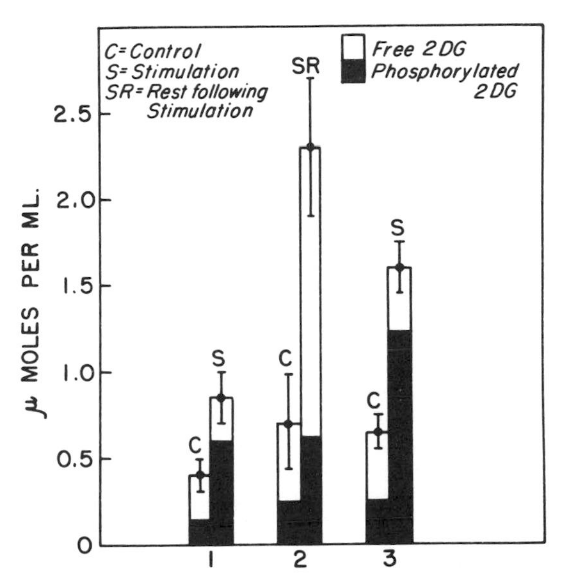

Figure 5. Penetration and phosphorylation of 2-deoxyglucose during and after stimulation. (See text).

The question of how long the effect of stimulation on permeability and on phosphorylation persists after return to rest has been analyzed in the manner shown in Figure 5. The experiment was performed on paired muscles one of which served as control (C) while the other was stimulated (S) at 48 S. P. M. for 30 minutes in the presence of 2-deoxyglucose either aerobically (group 1) or anaerobically (group 3). In group 2, the column marked SR refers to muscles first stimulated for 30 minutes before the uptake of 2-deoxyglucose by the resting muscle was measured for a period of 30 minutes in oxygen. On comparing groups 1 and 2 one finds that prior stimulation results in a large increase in free 2-deoxyglucose without a cooresponding increase in phosphorylation. This may be interpreted to mean that the effect of stimulation on phosphorylation does not persist and that it is not the concentration of substrate *per se* but the degree of activation of hexokinase which determines the rate of phosphorylation. On comparing groups 1 and 3 one finds that stimulation also increases phosphorylation and penetration of sugar in the anaerobic muscle. This would seem to rule out the possibility that insufficient oxygenation is responsible for the increase in phosphorylation and penetration of 2-deoxyglucose in the stimulated aerobic muscle.

It seems that hexokinase in frog muscle stimulated electrically is activated in a manner similar to that described above for phosphorylase and phosphofructokinase, that is, the "on" and "off" effect of enzyme activity during and after contraction applies to hexokinase also.

Discussion and Summary

The conversion of glycogen to lactate in anaerobic frog muscle in response to increasing frequency of stimulation has been investigated. The formation of end products, lactate and α-glycero-P was proportional to the rate of stimulation up to flow rates many times higher than the resting rate. The concentrations of inorganic P, G-6-P and fructose-1,6-diP did not show changes indicative of the increased flow rate. The changes in the concentration of 5'-AMP were minimal except at the highest frequency of stimulation (36 S. P. M.) used in these experiments. The concentration of ATP decreased and that of ADP increased with increasing frequency of stimulation, but their sum remained the same. It has now been found that ADP inhibits phosphorylase *b* to about the same extent as ATP. This makes it unlikely that the changes in the concentration of adenine nucleotides are responsible for the activation of phosphorylase *b* in these experiments. In general, these results show that the glycolytic system in muscle functions as a well integrated unit. It is only at higher frequencies of stimulation (above 36 S. P. M.) or during a tetanus that the enzymatic rates get out of step. Therefore it is tempting to speculate that glycolytic enzymes exist in muscle as a discrete structural unit.

The mechanism which is operative in activation and relaxation of the contractile system involves relocation of Ca^{++} ions between the myofibrilar spaces and the sarcotubular vesicles (see 28). The effect of stimulation on the phosphorylase *b*⇌*a* interconversion could be explained by a similar mechanism involving the activation of phosphorylase *b* kinase by Ca^{++} ions. This system might prove useful for the study of the link between metabolism and function in muscle.

The phosphorylation of 2-deoxyglucose by hexokinase in frog muscle is likewise increased as the result of stimulation. After cessation of stimulation hexokinase activity returns to the resting rate.

References

1. Karpatkin, S., Helmreich, E., and Cori, C. F., J. Biol. Chem., 239, 3139 (1964).
2. Danforth, W. H., and Helmreich, E., J. Biol. Chem., 239, 3133 (1964).
3. Danforth, W. H., Helmreich, E., and Cori, C. F., Proc. Nat. Acad. Sci. (U. S.), 48, 1191 (1962).
4. Karpatkin, S., Helmreich, E., and Cori, C. F., Fed. Proc., 24, 423 (1965).
5. Helmreich, E., and Cori, C. F., in G. Weber (ed.), Advances in Enzyme Regulation, Vol. 3, Pergamon Press, Oxford, 1965, p. 91.
6. Özand, P., and Narahara, H. T., J. Biol. Chem., 239, 3146 (1964).
7. Cori, C. F., in O. H. Gaebler (ed.), Enzymes: Units of Biological Structure and Function, Academic Press, Inc., New York, 1956, p. 573.
8. Danforth, W. H., and Lyon, J. B., Jr., J. Biol. Chem., 239, 4047 (1964).
9. Weber, A., and Herz, R., J. Biol. Chem., 238, 599 (1963).
10. Hasselbach, W., and Makinose, M., Biochem. Z., 333, 518 (1961).
11. Ebashi, S., and Lipmann, F., J. Cell Biology, 14, 389 (1962).
12. Krebs, E. G., Graves, D. J., and Fischer, E. H., J. Biol. Chem., 234, 2867 (1959).
13. Meyer, W. L., Fischer, E. H., and Krebs, E. G., Biochemistry, 3, 1033 (1964).
14. Herz, R., and Weber, A., Fed. Proc., 24, 208 (1965).
15. Karsten, M. E., and Mommaerts, W. F. H. M., J. Gen. Physiol., 48, 183 (1964).
16. Lyon, J. B., Jr., and Porter, J., J. Biol. Chem., 238, 1 (1963).
17. Helmreich, E., and Cori, C. F., Proc. Nat. Acad. Sci. (U. S.), 51, 131 (1964).

18. Helmreich, E., and Cori, C. F., Proc. Nat. Acad. Sci. (U. S.), 52, 647 (1964).

19. Michaelides, M. C., and Helmreich, E., unpublished results.

20. Morgan, H. E., and Parmeggiani, A., J. Biol. Chem., 239, 2435 (1964).

21. Morgan, H. E., and Parmeggiani, A., J. Biol. Chem., 239, 2440 (1964).

22. Michaelides, M. C., and Helmreich, E., unpublished results.

23. Monod, J., Wyman, J., and Changeux, J. P., J. Mol. Biol., in the press (1965). We are indebted to Dr. J. Monod for making this paper available to us prior to publication.

24. Özand, P., Narahara, H. T., and Cori, C. F., J. Biol. Chem., 237, 3037 (1962).

25. Narahara, H. T., Özand, P., and Cori, C. F., J. Biol. Chem., 235, 3370 (1960).

26. Helmreich, E., and Cori, C. F., J. Biol. Chem., 224, 663 (1957).

27. Holloszy, J. O., and Narahara, H. T., J. Biol. Chem., 240, in the press (1965).

28. Davies, R. E., Nature, 199, 1068 (1963).

SOME BIOCHEMICAL PROPERTIES OF INTESTINAL SMOOTH MUSCLE IN RELATION TO THE PHYSIOLOGICAL ACTIONS OF EPINEPHRINE+

Ernest Bueding and Edith Bülbring

Department of Pathobiology, School of Hygiene and Public Health
The Johns Hopkins University, Baltimore, Maryland
and
Department of Pharmacology
University of Oxford, England

Historically, phosphorylase _b_ kinase was the first enzyme which was found to be activated by cyclic 3',5'-AMP (1); since then, many other systems have become known to be susceptible to this nucleotide. These effects are by no means limited to reactions concerned with glycolysis, glycogenolysis, or glycogen synthesis. To mention only a few examples, it has been shown that cyclic 3',5'-AMP activates a lipolytic enzyme (2); there is evidence that cyclic 3',5'-AMP increases the formation of ketone bodies from acetate and that it decreases the incorporation of acetate into fatty acids (3,4,5). There also are reports that it stimulates tryptophane pyrollase (6) as well as the hydroxylation of steroids in the beta 11 position (7). Another action of this nucleotide is an increased permeability of the toad bladder to water (8).

In view of this multiplicity of the known effects of cyclic 3',5'-AMP - suggesting a function in the nature of a coenzyme - and in view of the distinct possibility that this nucleotide may have hitherto unknown actions on other systems, it cannot be taken for granted that, in a given tissue, the physiological effects of epinephrine are accounted for by an activation of phosphorylase or of some other glycolytic reaction. This is illustrated by some observations using intestinal smooth muscle. The preparation used is the _taenia coli_ of the guinea pig, a thin band of intestinal smooth muscle, approximately 1 to 2 mm in diameter, attached longitudinally to the _caecum_. In contrast to most other preparations of smooth muscle, _taenia coli_ is virtually free from contamination by other tissue elements. Intestinal smooth muscle tone is

+This investigation was supported by grants from the National Heart Institute (HE-05268) and the American Heart Association (62-G-21).

maintained by the continuous spontaneous discharge of action potentials. The reduction in tension of _taenia coli_ produced by epinephrine is the result of the cessation of this spontaneous discharge, and this usually is associated with a hyperpolarization of the cell membrane (9,10). There is evidence that this action of epinephrine requires metabolic energy (10,11,12). In an attempt to localize the source of this energy, the effect of epinephrine on phosphorylase activity of _taenia coli_ was determined. It was found that epinephrine produces _no_ activation of phosphorylase during its physiological effect on _taenia coli_ - that is, when it causes relaxation, cessation of spike activity, and membrane hyperpolarization (although it is possible to observe an increase in phosphorylase _a_ activity under certain artifactual conditions which are, however, unrelated to the physiological actions of the neurohormone on intestinal smooth muscle) (13). This lack of activation of phosphorylase is corroborated by the absence of changes in the glycogen and lactic acid levels when the tissue is exposed to physiologically active concentrations of epinephrine. Nor are there any changes in the concentrations of the hexosemono- and diphosphate esters under these conditions. Therefore, it appears that the actions of epinephrine on intestinal smooth muscle are not associated with a stimulation of glycogenolysis or of glycolysis, and the question arises whether the physiological effects of epinephrine on smooth muscle are dependent at all upon carbohydrate metabolism. Information on this problem was obtained by exposure of the tissue, first anaerobically (10 min.) and then aerobically (120 min.), to a substrate-free Krebs-Ringer solution; this results in the complete disappearance of glycogen and a considerable reduction in energy-rich phosphate compounds (ATP and creatine phosphate). Following this treatment, addition of β-hydroxybutyrate, in an atmosphere of 97 per cent O_2 - 3 per cent CO_2, results in immediate increases in tension and in the concentrations of energy-rich phosphate compounds. These levels of ATP and creatine phosphate are maintained for many hours if exposure to β-OH butyrate is continued. Under these conditions, epinephrine produces a further increase in high energy phosphate compounds as well as its usual physiological effects on smooth muscle, i.e. a block of spike discharge, relaxation and hyperpolarization, _despite the complete absence of carbohydrate from the tissue and from the medium._

The elevation in the concentration of energy-rich phosphate compounds following exposure of the tissue to epinephrine could be due either to a stimulation of ATP formation or to a decreased utilization of ATP by the contractile mechanism as a result of the relaxation of the tissue. The latter possibility is considered unlikely because manual reduction of tension of isotonically suspended *taenia coli* does not produce any change in ATP and CP levels. Therefore, a decrease in the tension of the muscle *per se* does not result in increased ATP and creatine phosphate levels. However, the latter are increased when tension is reduced to the same degree following exposure to epinephrine. Furthermore, after brief exposure (10 sec) of *taenia coli* to inorganic P^{32}-labelled phosphate, the specific activity of ATP is significantly higher after epinephrine (14), indicating that epinephrine increases the turnover of phosphate in ATP.

These observations are consistent with the conclusions that the physiological effects of epinephrine have no obligatory requirement for carbohydrate metabolism, but that they are dependent on metabolic processes generating energy-rich phosphate compounds.

REFERENCES

1. Sutherland, E.W. and Rall, T.W., Pharmacol. Rev., 12, 265 (1960).
2. Rizack, M.A., J. Biol. Chem., 239, 392 (1964).
3. Haugaard, E.S. and Stadie, W.C., J. Biol. Chem., 200, 753 (1953).
4. Haugaard, E.S. and Haugaard, W., J. Biol. Chem., 206, 641 (1954).
5. Berthet, J., Proc. 4th Internatl. Cong. Biochem., Vienna, 15, 107 (1960), Pergamon Press, London.
6. Chytyl, F. and Skrivanova, J., Biochim. Biophys. Acta, 67 164 (1963).
7. Creange, J.E. and Roberts, S., Biochem. Biophys. Res. Comm., 19, 73 (1965).
8. Orloff, J. and Handler, J.S., J. Clin. Invest., 41, 702 (1962).
9. Bülbring, E., J. Physiol., 125, 302 (1954).
10. Bülbring, E., Ciba Found. Symp. on Adrenergic Mechanisms, Churchill, London, 1960, p. 275.
11. Axelsson, J., and Bülbring, E., J. Physiol., 156, 344 (1961).
12. Axelsson, J., Bueding, E. and Bülbring, E., J. Physiol., 156, 357 (1961).
13. Bueding, E., Bülbring, E., Kuriyama, H. and Gercken, G., Nature, 196, 944 (1962).
14. Bueding, E., Saz, H.J., and Hawkins, J., unpublished observations.

DISCUSSION

Berry: With reference to Dr. Danforth's observations, I would like to mention some results that Dr. J. Scheer and myself have obtained in Professor Olson's laboratory in Pittsburgh. We have found that in the anesthetized dog, forced hyperventilation raises the blood pH to 7.8 and reduces the pCO_2 to less than 10 mm, bringing about a massive production of lactic acid in the liver. The blood concentration of lactic acid may rise from 1 mM to 7 mM within 30 minutes. These changes are, however, associated with a fall in hepatic blood flow and a marked increase in the lactate:pyruvate ratio, suggesting that there is a hypoxic component to this effect.

However, similar effects can be produced in the isolated perfused rat liver, where a steady flow rate can be maintained. In this system, changing the gas phase from 95 percent O_2 - 5 percent CO_2 to 100 percent O_2 changes the pattern of lactate metabolism from net uptake to net production without alteration of the lactate:pyruvate ratio. Thus, a rise of intracellular pH in the liver cell may produce effects similar to those described by Dr. Danforth for muscle.

Davies: I should like to concentrate on just one point in Dr. Danforth's and Helmreich's presentation which, I believe, has a special significance that they did not bring out, and this was when they got an absence of an effect. Those of us who have been trying to find the energy utilization during the different phases of a single muscle contraction, where the energy may be used for activation, during shortening, during work associated with shortening, during the mechanical relaxation and during the decay of the active state, had exceedingly great difficulties in proving anything happened at all. Early experiments were done in the presence of iodoacetate and 2,4-dinitrophenol which give you a poisoned muscle. Then 2,4-dinitrofluorobenzene was tried and this turned out to be a most important compound. With it we could see the change of ATP during a single muscle contraction. However, this had the disadvantage of its still being a poisoned muscle. The problem is, can we use a completely unpoisoned muscle and still get the same answer?

Once we could prove that ATP really was involved, then we could measure inorganic phosphate production as a measure of the ATP breakdown. The problem then was, did respiration or anaerobic glycolysis vitiate all the results? You remember from Dr. Danforth's paper that even after 10 seconds at one stimulus per second the lactic acid had not increased. We have found that at 0° C you can use the increase of inorganic phosphate as a marker for the breakdown of ADP, for at least 1.5 sec which is the maximum duration of our experiments. ATP in perfectly normal, unpoisoned natural muscle is exactly the same for all these various stages of contraction-relaxation as found with muscles pretreated with dinitrofluorobenzene. So I'm very pleased to have this _ex-post facto_ confirmation that, in fact, the change of inorganic phosphate P_i can be used under these conditions in a single contraction to provide a real measure of the amount of ATP broken down.

IX

Regulation of Metabolism in Brain

THE EFFECTS OF ALTERED BRAIN METABOLISM ON THE LEVELS OF KREBS CYCLE INTERMEDIATES*

Nelson D. Goldberg,** Janet V. Passonneau and Oliver H. Lowry

Washington University School of Medicine, Department of Pharmacology, St. Louis, Missouri

The present investigation is concerned with the level of Krebs cycle intermediates in brains of normal mice and in the brains of mice in which metabolism was altered *in vivo*. In an attempt to determine what steps might be regulatory in oxidative metabolism, the changes in the substrate levels have been measured following ischemia, hyperthermia, the administration of anesthetic agents, insulin and fluoroacetate poisoning.

Experimental Procedure

The mice used were 25 to 30 g white males. The control animals were frozen in Freon 12 at -150° C as previously described (1). To produce different periods of ischemia the heads were frozen at intervals following decapitation. Anesthesia was produced with either phenobarbital (225 mg per kg) amobarbital (135 mg per kg) or ether (4-1/2 volume per cent). Anesthesia was maintained for an hour before freezing. Hyperthermia was produced by placing the mice in a heated chamber until they attained a rectal temperature of 43° to 44°. The fluoroacetate was used at a dosage of 100 mg per kg. The insulin treated animals were given 125 units per kg and frozen at the first indication of convulsions. This occurred about 30 minutes after giving the insulin.

The brains were dissected at -15° and extracted at -10° (1).

* The work reported here was supported by Grants from the American Cancer Society (P-38) and the National Institutes of Health 5 T1 NB 5221 and 1F2-GM-19,735.

** Present address -- Department of Pharmacology, University of Minnesota, Minneapolis, Minnesota.

The analyses were made by measuring fluorometrically the appearance of TPNH or the disappearance of DPNH upon addition of appropriate enzymes. P-creatine, ATP, ADP and AMP were measured as previously outlined (1). Isocitrate was measured with isocitric dehydrogenase and TPN^+, and in the case of citrate the same reaction was coupled with aconitase. α-Ketoglutarate was measured with glutamic dehydrogenase and DPNH. Succinate was measured with succinate thiokinase and guanosine triphosphate. The resulting guanosine diphosphate was measured with pyruvate kinase, lactate dehydrogenase and DPNH. Malate was measured with malic enzyme and TPN^+. The same reaction coupled with fumarase was used to measure fumarate. Oxalacetate was measured with malate dehydrogenase and DPNH. The sensitivity of the fluorometric assays is such that even substrates present in brain at such low levels as isocitrate and oxalacetate can be measured with precision. The reproducibility for replicates in the case of oxalacetate for example, is within 3 per cent. The enzymes were obtained from Boehringer and Sons through California Biochemical Corporation except for the following: Aconitase was prepared from hog heart by a procedure modified from that of Morrison (2). Succinate thiokinase was prepared according to Cha (3). The exact analytical procedures will be described elsewhere (4).

Results

The changes in levels of substrates following decapitation are recorded in Figure 1. Glucose and glucose-6-P fall rapidly, so that by 30 seconds the levels are 9 per cent and 37 per cent respectively, of control values. Pyruvate levels increase to 150 per cent of initial value in 5 seconds and show no further increase at 30 seconds. These changes caused by anoxia reflect the increase in glycolytic flux, which results in great part from facilitation at the phosphofructokinase step (1,5,6).

In the Krebs cycle the sudden anoxia causes changes which seem to be reasonably explained as a transition from a dynamic state of flux to a static state with equilibration wherever possible. Citrate levels fall resulting in a shift in ratio of isocitrate to citrate from 20 to 1 to the equilibrium ratio of 15 to 1. Within 5 seconds α-ketoglutarate levels fall to 35 per cent of the control value. This also appears to be a shift toward equilibrium, resulting from the known increases in ammonia and DPNH which occur in anoxia. Succinate rises slowly to 140 per cent of control levels at 30 seconds. Since α-ketoglutarate levels remain low, this may result from succinate formation via pyruvate carboxylation and a reversal of succinate dehydrogenase. The latter phenomenon has been reported in liver (7). The delayed rise in fumarate, and equili-

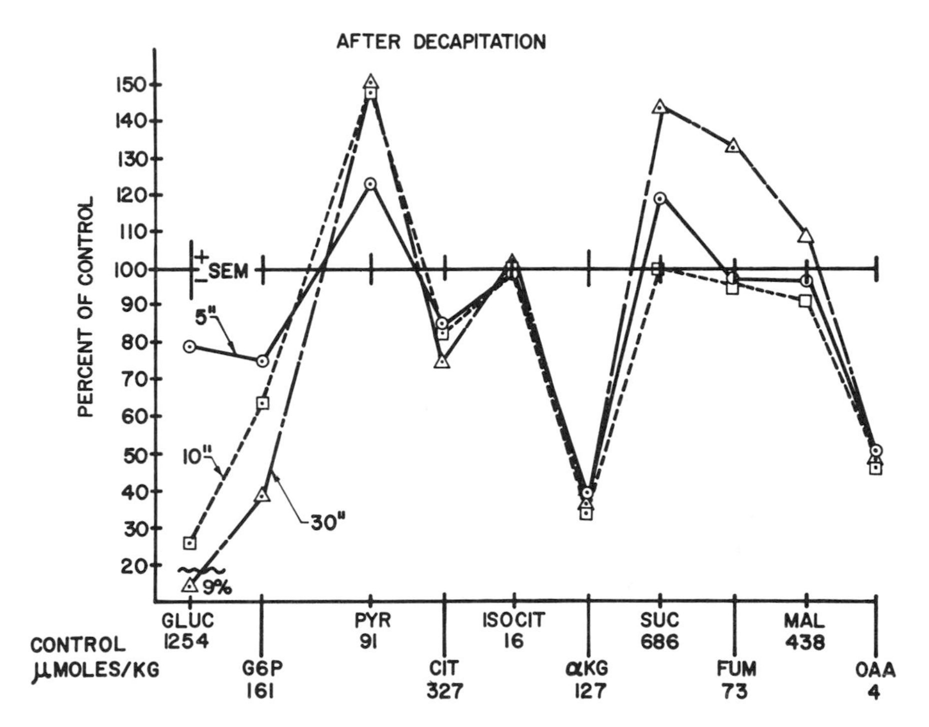

Figure 1. Changes of substrates in the mouse brain after 5, 10, or 30 seconds of ischemia. The abbreviations are Gluc, glucose; G6P, glucose-6-P; Pyr, pyruvate; Cit, citrate; Isocit, isocitrate; αKG, α-ketoglutarate; Suc, succinate; Fum, fumarate; Mal, malate; OAA, oxalacetate. The control levels are given below each substrate in micromoles per kg wet weight. The dotted symbols indicate values significantly different from control values.

bration of fumarase which occurs only after 30 seconds of anoxia might also be explained by this phenomenon.

In order to assess the effects of extreme changes in metabolic rate, a comparison has been made of substrate levels when flux has been decreased by anesthesia, and increased by hyperthermia (Figure 2). In all of the anesthetized animals the levels of P-creatine and ATP are slightly higher and ADP and AMP levels lower than in controls (Table I). The opposite effect is discernible in hyperthermic animals. The substrate changes induced by all of the anesthetic agents are similar, and differ only slightly in degree. As observed previously (1), there are increased levels of glucose and glucose-6-P and lowered levels of pyruvate which indicate a diminished rate of glycolytic flux. This presumably means a decreased flux through

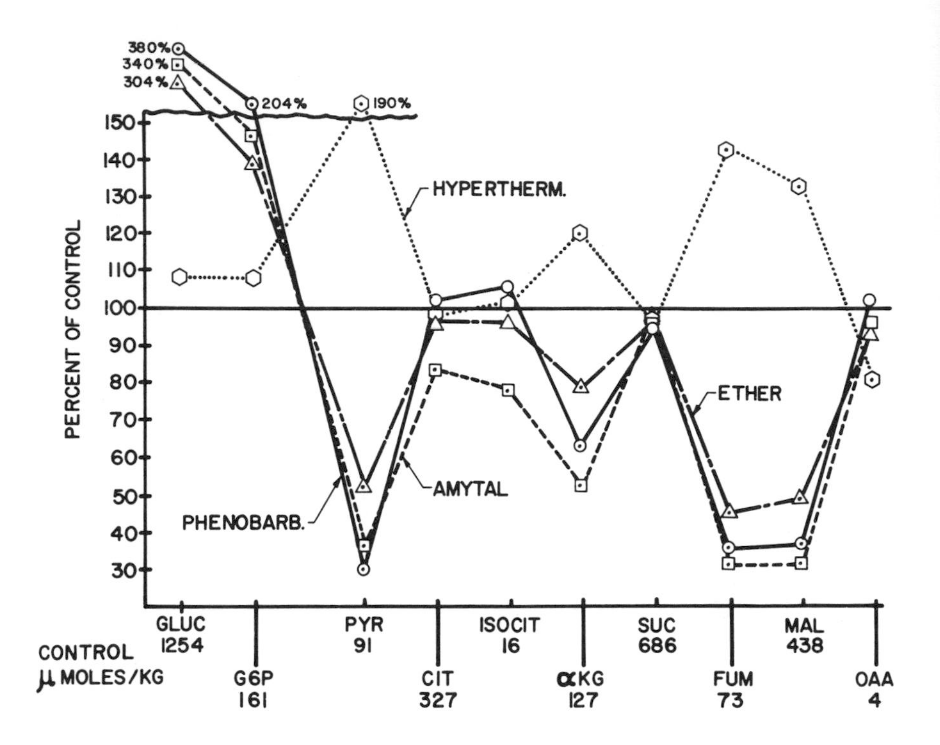

Figure 2. Changes in substrates in mouse brain following hyperthermia or anesthesia with ether, amytal or phenobarbital. The conditions are given in the text. The abbreviations are the same as for Figure 1.

the Krebs cycle as well. Conversely the elevated pyruvate levels in the hyperthermic animals indicate an increase in glycolytic flux. The levels of α-ketoglutarate were diminished by 20 to 40 per cent with the anesthetics, and increased signifcantly by hyperthermia. Succinate levels did not change with either type of treatment, while the fumarate and malate levels were decreased by 30 per cent of control values by anesthesia and increased almost 50 per cent by hyperthermia. Anesthetics had no effect on oxalacetate levels, while hyperthermia resulted in a decrease of 20 per cent. In general, therefore, the substrate changes under conditions of increased or decreased metabolic rates are almost mirror images of each other. The pattern of the changes suggests the presence of coordinated controlling steps in the citric acid cycle at the points of isocitrate and succinate oxidation as well as at some step between pyruvate and citrate. Modifications of the activity at other metabolic steps such as that of glutamic-aspartic transamination, or carbon dioxide fixation may also affect the substrate levels. The alterations in patterns produced by the

TABLE I

Levels of Phosphocreatine and Adenylates in the Brains of Control and Treated Mice

The experimental conditions are given in the text. The values are recorded as millimoles per kg wet weight ± the standard error of the mean.

Treatment	No. of mice	P-creatine	ATP	ADP	AMP
Controls	10	3.63 ± 0.09	2.95 ± 0.04	0.33 ± 0.01	0.05 ± 0.01
30" ischemia	5	0.64 ± 0.04	1.67 ± 0.13	0.65 ± 0.02	---
Phenobarbital	6	5.07 ± 0.18	3.21 ± 0.07	0.27 ± 0.05	0.03 ± 0.004
Amytal	4	4.88 ± 0.07	3.22 ± 0.08	0.20 ± 0.01	0.03 ± 0.003
Ether	6	4.62 ± 0.09	3.18 ± 0.06	0.218 ± 0.004	0.03 ± 0.002
Hyperthermia	5	3.22 ± 0.14	2.77 ± 0.06	0.37 ± 0.01	0.13 ± 0.01
Insulin	6	3.37 ± 0.07	2.61 ± 0.08	0.40 ± 0.02	0.10 ± 0.01
Fluoroacetate-40'	4	4.04 ± 0.18	3.04 ± 0.18	0.39 ± 0.02	0.07 ± 0.01

three anesthetic agents are remarkably similar. This is in spite of the fact that amobarbital is much more inhibitory than phenobarbital to electron transport *in vitro*, and ether is structurally unrelated. These results coupled with the observed fall in levels of pyridine nucleotide-linked substrates, α-ketoglutarate and malate, indicate that inhibition of elecron transport by amobarbital or other anesthetics is not significant *in vivo* in brain.

Following administration of fluoroacetate P-creatine and ATP levels were unchanged or slightly elevated (Table I), i.e., the block was not complete enough to interfere with maintenance of high energy phosphate levels. The block by fluoroacetate at the aconitase step is seen in the increase in the ratio of citrate to isocitrate from 20:1 to 60:1 (Figure 3). The levels of substrates in the subsequent steps of the Krebs cycle are high, indicating that the flux has been maintained, i.e., the increase in citrate concentration has been sufficient to compensate for the aconitase inhibition. Since isocitrate does not fall below control levels, there is no reason to believe that isocitrate dehydrogenase activity has been stimulated by the high citrate levels as described for the DPN enzyme *in vitro* in Neurospora (8) and brain (9). After 40 minutes the significant increase in glucose-6-P and fall in pyruvate indicate that glycolytic flux has decreased. The glycolytic block probably results from the inhibition of phosphofructokinase by the high citrate concentration.

The production of insulin hypoglycemia represents another method of decreasing flux through the Krebs cycle (Figure 3). In the brain glucose is reduced to 9 per cent of normal levels and pyruvate to 40 per cent. In this case the decrease in flux is due to lack of oxidizable substrate rather than a lack of ~P acceptors. Consequently, one would not expect controls within the Krebs cycle itself to be operative. This is borne out by the general lowering of all members of the cycle except oxalacetate, which is in marked contrast to the results when flux was lowered by anesthesia.

Summary

Measurements of substrates of the Krebs cycle in control animals have been compared with anoxic, anesthetized, fluoroacetate-poisoned, hyperthermic and insulin treated animals. The data suggest that there are three control steps in oxidative metabolism. These are at the points of oxidation of isocitrate and succinate and at some step between pyruvate and citrate.

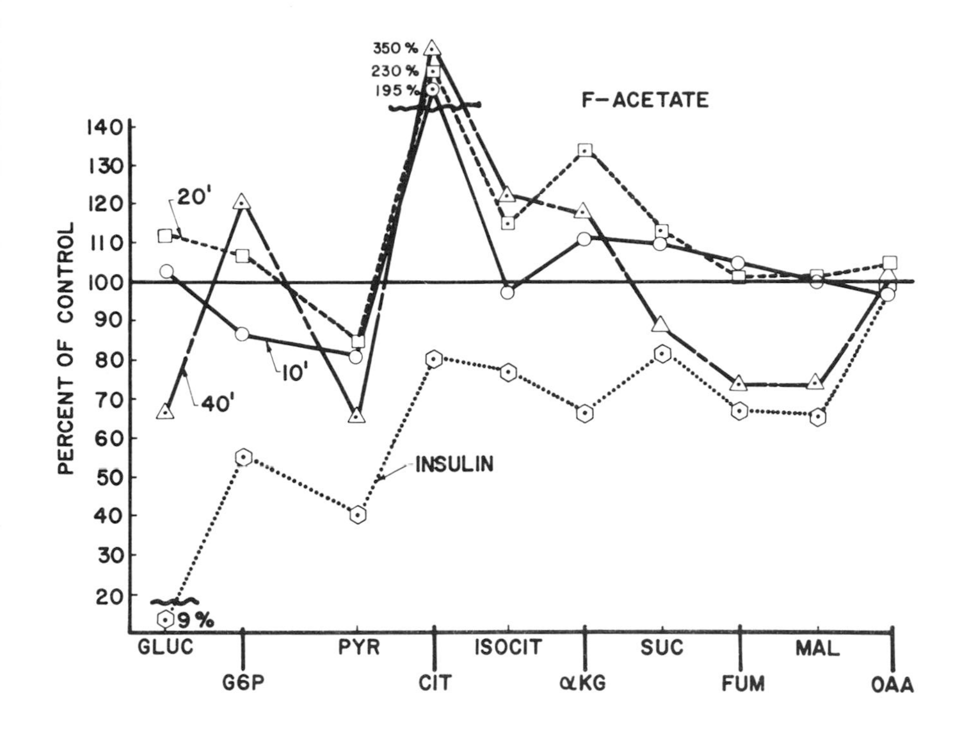

Figure 3. Changes in substrates in mouse brain after administration of fluoroacetate, or insulin as described in the text. The time after fluoroacetate administration is indicated. The control levels are the same as in Figures 1 and 2. The abbreviations are the same as in Figure 1.

References

1. Lowry, O. H., Passonneau, J. V., Hasselberger, F. X., and Schulz, D. W., J. Biol. Chem., 239, 18 (1964).
2. Morrison, J. F., Biochem. J., 56, 99 (1954).
3. Cha, S. and Parks, R. E., Jr., J. Biol. Chem., 239, 1961 (1964).
4. Goldberg, N. D., Passonneau, J. V., and Lowry, O. H., to be published.
5. Passonneau, J. V., and Lowry, O. H., Biochem. and Biophys. Res. Comm., 7, 10 (1962).
6. Lowry, O. H., and Passonneau, J. V., Proc. VI Intern. Congr. Biochem., New York, 1964, p. 705.
7. Hoberman, H. D., Prosky, L., and Arfin, H. W., Fed. Proc., 24, 229 (1965).
8. Sanwal, B. D., and Stachow, C. S., Biochim. and Biophys. Acta, 96, 28 (1965).
9. Holowach, J., and McDougal, D. B., Jr., to be published.

DISCUSSION

H. Krebs: Dr. Passonneau seems to have solved a problem which has concerned many people, namely, the reliable determination of the intermediates of the cycle in a small amount of tissue. I am very impressed by this, having tried myself many times in many different ways. Can you tell us briefly the principle of the methods employed?

Passonneau: They are all enzymatic analyses, and the fluorometric method permits a great deal of sensitivity. We can easily detect a recording on the fluorometer equivalent to 5×10^{-9} M. For isocitrate, we use TPN^+ and ICDH, and measure the formation of TPNH. Citrate was analysed in the same system with the addition of aconitase. Malate was measured with TPN^+ and malic enzyme, and fumarate by the addition of fumarase. Succinate was measured with succinate thiokinase and GTP, and the resulting GDP measured by the formation of pyruvate with the addition of pyruvate kinase and lactate dehydrogenase, watching the disappearance of DPNH. Oxaloacetate was the most difficult, but by keeping our brain extract dilutions low, we were able to get reproducibility within 3 percent, as I have stated. It was measured with DPNH and malate dehydrogenase. Also, there was a fluorescent blank from the tissue extracts which caused some trouble. I am not quite sure what this is due to; perhaps flavins. This fluorescence can be removed by treating brain extracts with Florosil, although it cannot be used for all substrates, since it absorbs some substrates -- phosphorylated intermediates, for example.

Lowenstein: Garland and Randle (Biochem. J., 91, 6C (1964)) have shown that the pyruvic dehydrogenase system is strongly inhibited by one of its products, namely, by acetyl-Co-A. This makes it important to measure acetyl-Co-A concentrations under your conditions. Did you measure succinyl-Co-A concentrations?

Passonneau: We attempted to measure succinyl-Co-A levels and were unable. If the levels had been as high as 4 μM we would have been able to detect it.

Chance: I agree with you that Amytal titrations cause very little increased DPN reduction in the brain of the resting animal, but the stimulated brain is quite different (Chance, B., in *Oxygen in the Animal Organism*, F. Dickens, Ed., Pergamon Press, London, 1964, p. 367). The addition of Amytal to the metrazol-stimulated brain might give some interesting results.

X

Regulation of Glycolytic Activity in Heart Muscle

METABOLIC CONTROL IN THE PERFUSED RAT HEART *

John R. Williamson +

Johnson Research Foundation, University of Pennsylvania
Philadelphia, Pennsylvania 19104

Previous speakers have shown that the activity of purified phosphofructokinase preparations from several species and from several animal organs is markedly affected by changes of the phosphate potential, [ATP]/[ADP][P_i], and the concentration of citrate. In addition, it has been shown that the degree of inhibition of enzymic activity induced by ATP or citrate is very sensitive to the levels of fructose-6-P and fructose-1,6-diP. In this paper, I shall attempt to relate the relative activity of phosphofructokinase, functioning as an individual member in the intact sequence of glycolytic enzymes, to changes in the levels of the known activators and inhibitors. For this purpose, the perfused rat heart preparation has been used, and changes of glycolytic flux have been induced by the addition of iodoacetamide, acetate, epinephrine, or by anoxia.

Hearts were perfused by gravity feed as previously described (1,2), and in some experiments the mechanical performance was monitored by means of a Statham strain gauge. The 480 mμ fluorescence emission signal from the surface of the beating heart, upon excitation with light of wavelength 366 mμ from a mercury arc lamp, was measured with an Ultropak microfluorometer as described elsewhere (3). Perfusion was terminated by rapidly freezing the heart with tongs cooled to the temperature of liquid nitrogen, and metabolic intermediates present in neutralized perchloric acid extracts prepared from the frozen heart powder were assayed by enzymic techniques in an Eppendorf fluorometer (2,4).

Although in this presentation I shall confine my attention principally to control at the phosphofructokinase site, we must consider it within the framework of the entire glycolytic system, since interaction at several sites contributes to the overall metabolite profile pattern.

* Supported by U. S. Public Health Service Grant No. 12202-01.

+ Recipient of a Wellcome Foundation travel grant.

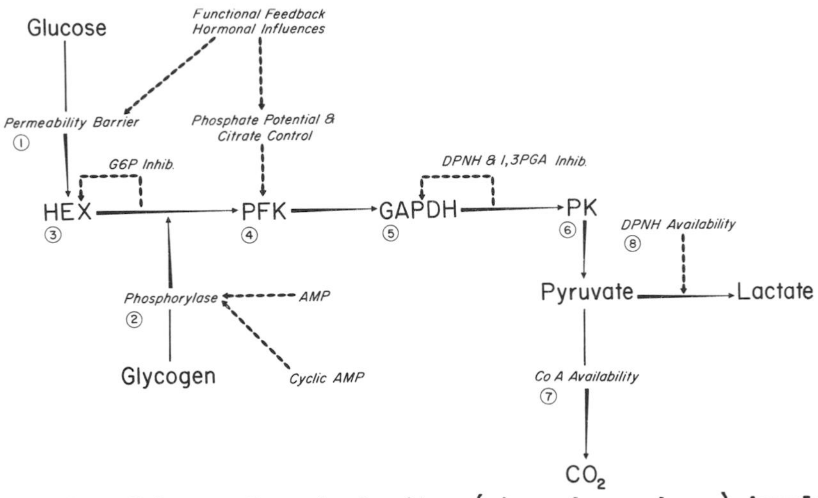

Figure 1. Scheme of control sites (shown by numbers) involved in the metabolism of glucose and glycogen in rat heart.

In Figure 1, I have summarized the major sites which have been experimentally proved, or postulated to be involved in the control of glucose and glycogen degradation. In heart muscle, entry of glucose into the cell is restricted by a permeability barrier, which is relieved wholly or partially by drugs or humoral factors such as insulin (5), epinephrine (1), glucagon (6), ouabain (7), by anoxia (8), or by an increase in the work load on the heart (9). The fact that the state of mechanical activity of the heart affects the glucose transport system, implies some form of functional feedback, as in frog skeletal muscle (10), so that when more glucose is required, more is supplied to the glycolytic enzymes. Other control sites or potential control sites are phosphorylase, hexokinase, phosphofructokinase, glyceraldehyde-P dehydrogenase, pyruvic kinase, and CoA availability or DPNH availability, leading respectively to pyruvate oxidation, or reduction to lactate. Elements contributing to control at these sites, e.g., AMP on phosphorylase activity, and cyclic AMP on the phosphorylase interconversion, are also shown in the figure. The main point I wish to make at the present time is that in studying glycolytic control mechanisms, we are really dealing with a problem of multi-site control interactions. Thus, the rate of substrate flux through the hexokinase and phosphorylase reactions will help determine the level of fructose-6-P in the cell, while the activity of glyceraldehyde-P dehydrogenase helps regulate the level of fructose-1, 6-diP. Both these intermediates are potential determinants of phosphofructokinase activity.

From a study of intermediate profile patterns in rat heart, examples of which are given for the convenience of reference in Table I, it is apparent that certain reactions of the glycolytic sequence are maintained close to equilibrium, even when the flux rate is high, while other reactions are far displaced from equilibrium.

TABLE I

Metabolite Patterns in Perfused Rat Heart

	20 mM Glucose		5 mM Glucose	
	Aerobic	Anoxic (40")	Control	2×10^{-3} units/ml Insulin
	mμmoles/g dry weight			
Intracell. glucose	-	-	-	1980
Glucose-6-P	798	490	630	1605
Fructose-6-P	182	108	154	326
Fructose-1,6-diP	39	384	42	79
Dihydroxyacetone-P	56	364	55	150
Glyceraldehyde-3-P	7	43	13	27
3-P-Glycerate	138	512	119	252
2-P-Glycerate	16	51	14	30
P-enol pyruvate	30	39	19	62
Pyruvate	77	50	88	275
Lactate	2033	7020	1920	9560
α-Glycero-P	276	1460	263	1104
ATP/ADP	8.01	3.25	8.71	12.30
ATP/ADP x P_i (liter $moles^{-1}$)	1070	165	1160	1640
E'h (mV)	-249	-271	-246	-253
DPN/DPNH	731	136	870	550
AMP	223	640	350	150
ADP	2660	5700	2490	1820

Table 1. Metabolite profile patterns in rat hearts perfused with glucose under aerobic and anoxic conditions, or in the presence of insulin.

The displacement from equilibrium of the individual glycolytic reactions for the aerobic and anoxic states is shown in Figure 2. The glycolytic reactions are depicted along the abcissa, while along the ordinate the log of the mass action ratio of non-equilibrium (K_{app}) divided by the thermodynamic equilibrium constant (K_{equil}), is plotted for each of the individual reactions (cf. Ref. 11). When this value is zero, the reaction is in equilibrium, while a negative number indicates that the products of the reaction in the K_{app} term are too low, relative to the reactants, for equilibrium conditions to hold. It is readily seen that hexokinase, phosphofructokinase, the product of glyceraldehyde-3-P dehydrogenase and P-glyceric kinase, and pyruvic kinase are far displaced from equilibrium, while P-glucose isomerase, aldolase, triose-P isomerase, P-glycerate mutase, and enolase are relatively closer to equilibrium. P-glucomutase, adenylate kinase, creatine-P-kinase, and glutamic aspartic transaminase may also be added to the near-equilibrium group.

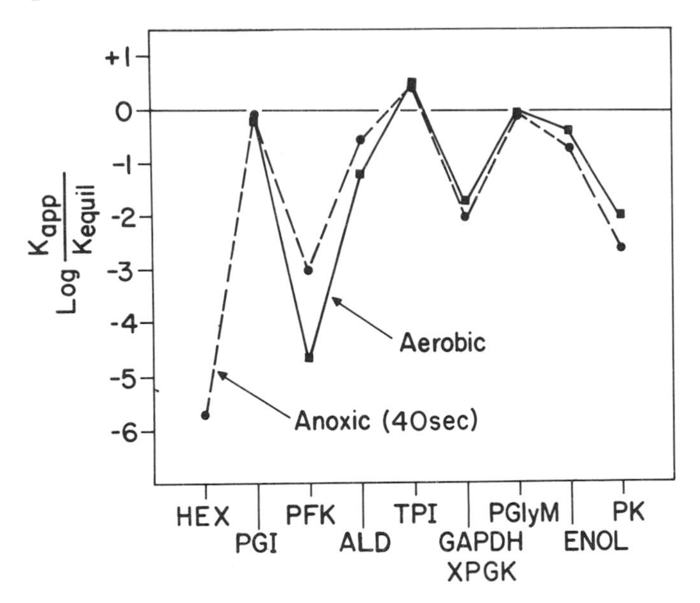

Figure 2. Deviations of the glycolytic reactions from equilibrium. Hearts were perfused without recirculation with fluid containing 20 mM glucose. Anoxic conditions were produced by changing the perfusate to a similar fluid saturated with carbon monoxide. The enzymic reactions of glycolysis are depicted along the abscissa, while the ordinate gives a measure of the deviation of each reaction from equilibrium (see text for details).

As discussed elsewhere by Hess (12, 13) and by Bücher (11), those reactions which are far displaced from equilibrium are generally not reversible, and may be considered as potential control sites, since they provide bottle-necks to the substrate flow. Reactions which are maintained close to equilibrium, being readily reversible, are not normally subject to control. During the aerobic-anoxic transition, phosphofructokinase is activated, as shown by the smaller deviation from equilibrium. Since this enzyme appears to be the rate-controlling enzyme of glycolysis in the aerobic heart, it is clear that it may be activated to a sufficient degree that control is transferred to another site further down the glycolytic chain. I shall present evidence for this shortly.

A consequence of the great deviation of the phosphofructokinase reaction from equilibrium is that when glyceraldehyde-P dehydrogenase is inhibited by iodoacetamide, fructose-1, 6-diP and the triose phosphates accumulate in the heart. This allows the observed deviations from equilibrium of aldolase and triose-P isomerase to be tested under conditions which allow the ratio of glyceraldehyde-3-P and dihydroxyacetone-P

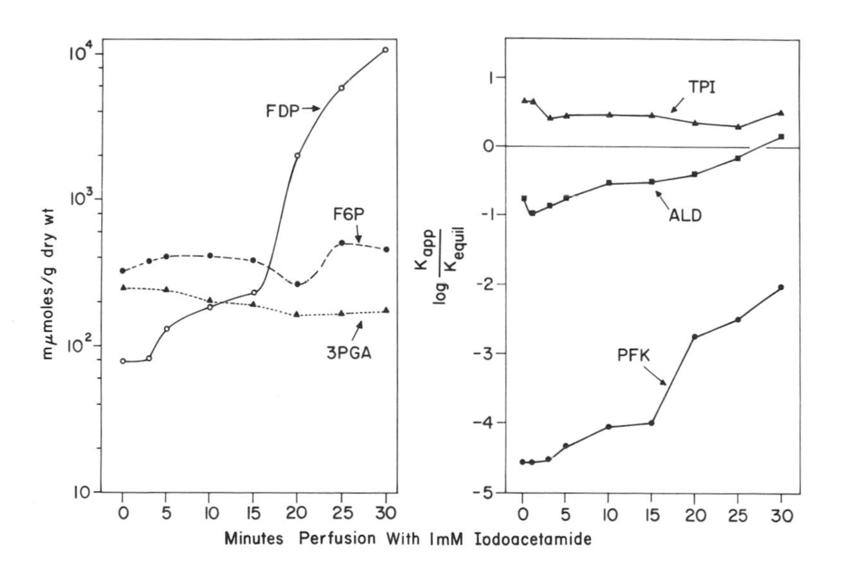

Figure 3. Effect of iodoacetamide in perfused rat heart. Hearts were perfused aerobically for 15 minutes with fluid containing 5 mM glucose and 2 x 10^{-3} units/ml insulin and then transferred for further perfusion to recirculation circuits containing a similar fluid plus 1 mM iodoacetamide.

to be measured accurately. The results of such an experiment are shown in Figure 3. Time in minutes after the addition of 1 mM iodoacetamide is shown along the abcissa and the units of the ordinate are shown on a log scale. In the left hand side of the Figure we see that F-6-P shows only a modest increase with time, while 3-P-glyceric acid decreases slightly. Fructose-1,6-diP levels, on the other hand, increase over 130 times, with the most rapid increase occurring after 15 minutes exposure to iodoacetamide. The deviations of PFK, aldolase and triose-P isomerase from equilibrium are shown in the right side of the Figure. The PFK mass action ratio increases 350-fold towards equilibrium during perfusion (30 min), but remains out of it by 2 orders of magnitude. Aldolase generally approaches equilibrium, while the triose-P isomerase equilibrium remains displaced in favor of G-3-P, relative to the thermodynamic equilibrium constant, with a mean ratio of DAP/GAP of about 10. These results support the suggestion of Lowry (16) that the fructose-1,6-diP may be distributed in different compartments within the cell, and also indicate the presence of two forms of G-3-P, possibly bound and free as suggested by Garfinkel (15). Unlike the large displacement of equilibrium at the PFK site, the small displacements of aldolase and triose-P isomerase do not reflect the property of control sites.

I shall now consider some specific examples of control at the PFK site in the rat heart. The crossover theorem has been used t identify rate-controlling sites, and for the present discussion it will be assumed that such sites are identified by the point at which there is a crossover point in the metabolite pattern between a relative accumulation and a relative depletion of intermediates with a decrease of flux, and _vice versa_. Figure 4 shows the effect of acetate addition to hearts perfused with glucose. The components of the glycolytic sequence are shown along the abcissa in 4A, while the ordinate shows the level of each component in the acetate-treated hearts expressed as a percentage of the values obtained in control hearts. Flux decreases by 50 and it is readily seen that a crossover occurs at PFK, indicatin inhibition and pinpointing it as the rate-controlling step. The lower part of the Figure indicates the relative changes of the citric acid cycle intermediates and the adenine nucleotides are shown in a similar plot. The adenine nucleotides show only mino changes but the citrate levels increase 10-fold, probably as a consequence of increased acetyl-CoA availability, since the aspartate and oxaloacetate levels decrease. PFK must normally be in a highly inhibited state in rat heart since the concentration of ATP, ADP and AMP are about 10 mM, 1.1 mM and 0.1 mM respectively, while F-6-P is only 70-80 μM. Hence these results imply that the inhibitory effects of ATP and citrate on PFK are synergistic in the intact organ, as in the isolated enzyme.

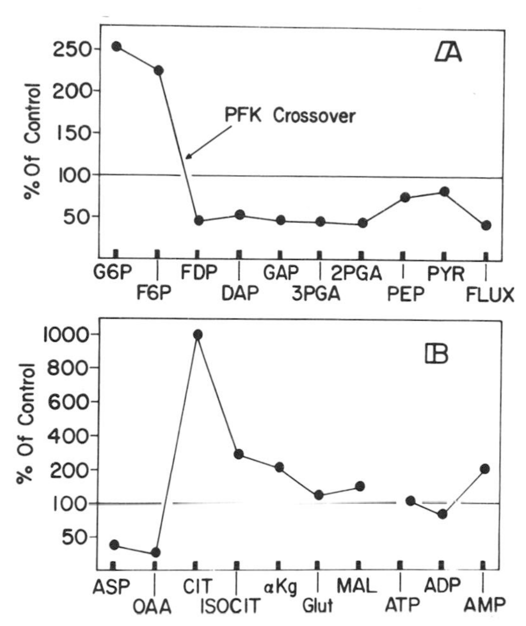

Figure 4. Metabolic effects of acetate on the perfused rat heart. Control hearts were perfused for 15 minutes with fluid containing 10 mM glucose, while other hearts were perfused similarly with fluid containing in addition 10 mM acetate. Metabolic components are shown along the abscissa, while the ordinate gives the percentage change of the components in the acetate-treated hearts with respect to the control hearts.

Considerably more information is yielded from the measurement of metabolite levels during the transition from one steady state to another, than from measurements at different steady states, and a kinetic approach has been used to study the aerobic-anoxic transition in rat hearts perfused with 20 mM glucose. In these experiments, anoxia was induced by changing from perfusate equilibrated with 95 % oxygen and 5 % CO_2 to a similar fluid equilibrated with 95 % carbon monoxide and 5% CO_2 (Figure 5). Time 0 represents the time at which a tap was turned to change the perfusate, and it is seen that about 10 seconds elapses before there is any increase of reduced pyridine nucleotide (as monitored by tissue fluorescence). The half time for the fluorescence increase from the aerobic steady state is about 30 seconds, and reduction of the pyridine nucleotides is complete after 80 seconds. Fructose-6-P levels decrease by about 50 % after 15 seconds and subsequently tend to increase. The levels of fructose-1,6-diP and 3-P-glyceric acid start to change somewhat later, and increase dramatically, reaching peak values between 40 and 60 seconds, before declining to new steady state values after 80-100 seconds.

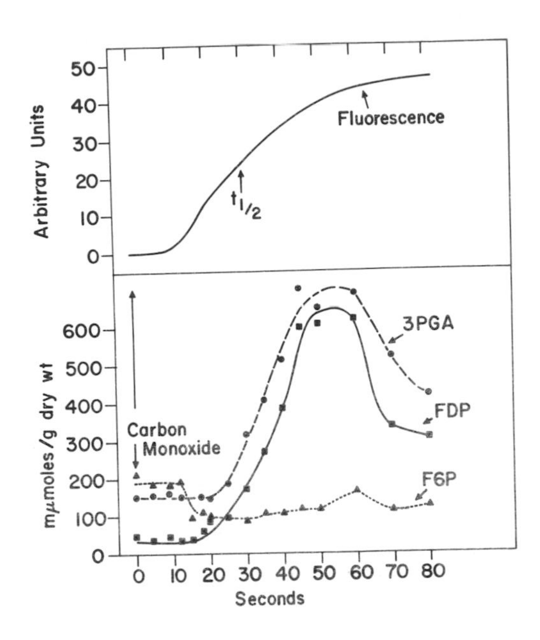

Figure 5. Kinetics of the glycolytic intermediate changes with anoxia. Hearts were perfused without recirculation with fluid containing 20 mM glucose, and anoxia was induced by carbon monoxide.

Figure 6 shows the relative changes of the glycolytic intermediates and adenine nucleotides after 20, 40, 60 and 80 seconds of anoxia. We see that 20 seconds after the onset of anoxia, phosphofructokinase is activated, but there is as yet no change of 3-P-glycerate, while pyruvate shows a depletion. There thus seems to be a push at phosphofructokinase and a pull at lactic dehydrogenase, with a bottle-neck at glyceraldehyde-P dehydrogenase. As seen on the right hand side of the figure, ADP, AMP and P_i show marked increases after 20 seconds. After 40 seconds of anoxia, there is one crossover at phosphofructokinase and another at pyruvic kinase in the opposite sense. From these results it appears that phosphofructokinase has been activated to such a degree that the rate-controlling step is transferred to pyruvic kinase. Possibly inhibition of pyruvic kinase by the increased levels of inorganic phosphate account for the transference of control. A limitation of the simple crossover theorem, however, as applied to glycolysis, is illustrated by the relative changes after 60 seconds of anoxia. At this time all the glycolytic intermediates are above the control values, and the rate-controlling step cannot be identified with certainty. However,

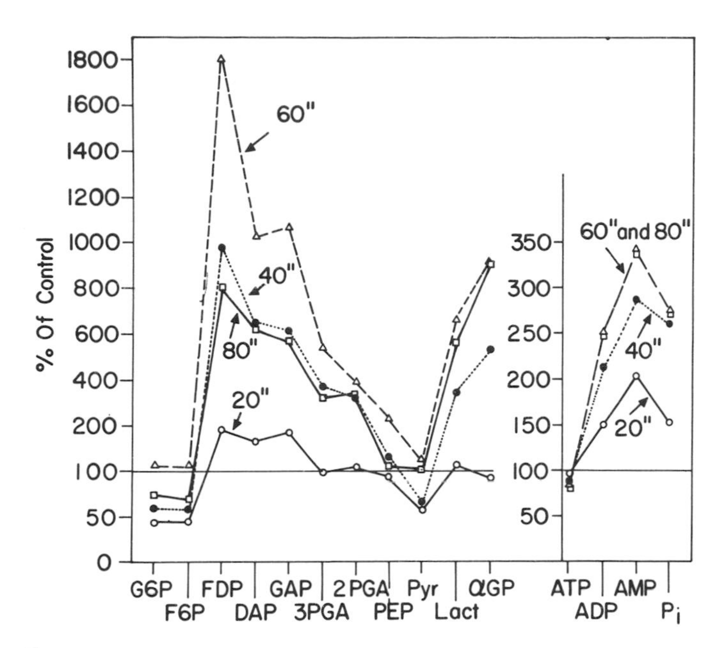

Figure 6. Relative changes of the glycolytic intermediates and the adenine nucleotides after 20, 40, 60 and 80 seconds of anoxia.

the very large accumulation of fructose-1,6-diphosphate indicates a further activation of phosphofructokinase, as borne out by the additional increases of ADP, AMP and P_i. Between 60 and 80 seconds the adenine nucleotides attain the steady state values, but phosphofructokinase apparently is partially deactivated as shown by the marked fall of FDP. Preliminary determinations of citrate show no marked increase between 60 and 80 seconds, indicating that some other factor, as yet undescribed, may contribute to the overall activity pattern of phosphofructokinase under these conditions. Changes of intracellular pH may possibly be involved here, as suggested from the work of Mansour (16).

Finally, I would like to show the results of some experiments in which glycolysis has been activated by the addition of epinephrine in the perfused rat heart. Figure 7 shows the accumulation-depletion curves of some of the glycolytic intermediates upon the addition of 1 µg epinephrine to hearts perfused without recirculation with medium containing glucose. Glycogen is metabolized to lactate very rapidly within the first minute or two of epinephrine action (1), and the intermediates accumulate transiently as their rate of production temporarily exceeds their rate of removal by the individual

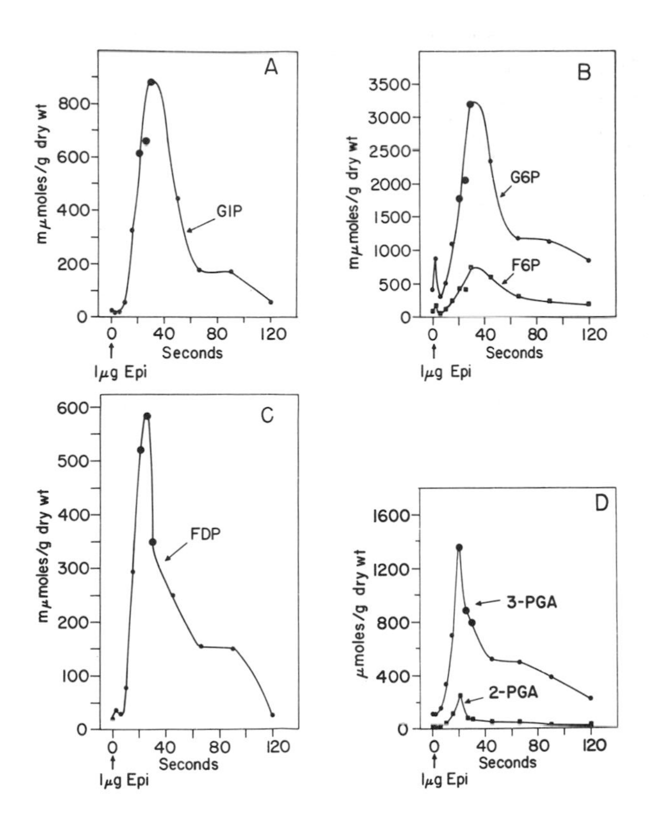

Figure 7. Kinetics of intermediate changes upon the addition of 1 μg epinephrine (Epi) to rat hearts perfused without recirculation with 10 mM glucose. The larger points in the time sequence of metabolite changes represents points at 21, 26 and 30 seconds, respectively, after the onset of the inotropic stimulus.

glycolytic reactions. I would like to draw your attention to the relative levels of the intermediates at the times indicated by the larger dots, which correspond to times 21, 26 and 30 seconds after the onset of the inotropic stimulus. It is seen that the peak accumulation of the hexose monophosphates occurs at about 30 seconds. Peak values of fructose-1,6-diP, dihydroxyacetone-P and glyceraldehyde-3-P are obtained at 26 seconds, while peak values of 3-P-glyceric acid and 2-P-glyceric acid are found at 21 seconds. This means that over the time interval 21-30 seconds, some intermediates are on the depletion phase while the hexose monophosphates are still accumulating.

Phosphofructokinase is initially activated during the epinephrine stimulus, as will become apparent presently, and what we are seeing here is a displacement of control from phosphofructokinase to glyceraldehyde-P dehydrogenase, and back to phosphofructokinase. This is more readily appreciated when the results are presented in the form of a crossover plot, as shown in Figure 8. In this figure C_{21}, C_{26} and C_{30} refer to the concentrations of the particular glycolytic intermediates at times 21, 26 and 30 seconds after epinephrine (cf. Figure 7). The changes in the levels of the individual intermediates over the two time intervals from 21 to 26 seconds and from 26 to 30 seconds are shown as a percentage of the levels at times 21 and 26 seconds, respectively.

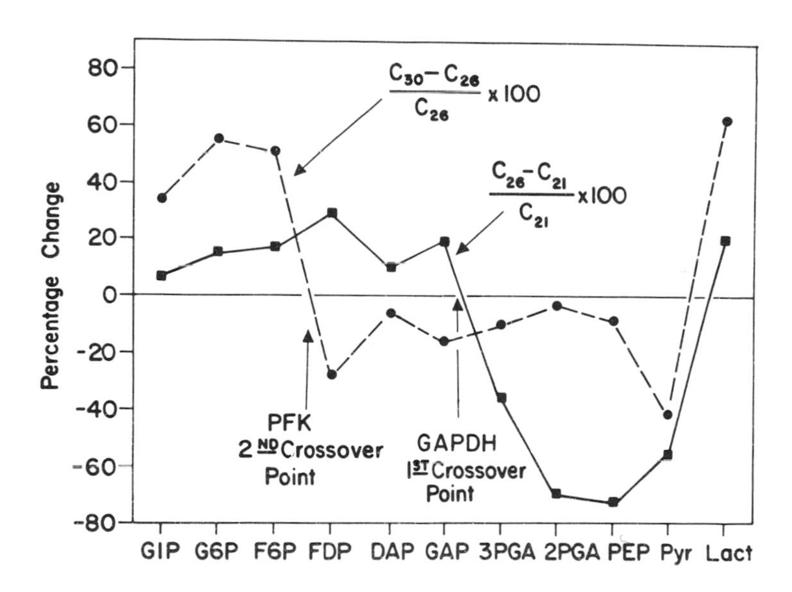

Figure 8. Identification of control sites during epinephrine-induced glycogenolysis in the perfused rat heart. The data in Figure 7, together with data on the levels of the glycolytic intermediates were used to derive this plot. (See text for further details.)

Flux is increasing over both time intervals as shown by the relative accumulation of lactate. We see here that over the time interval from 21 to 26 seconds, control of flux can be identified at the glyceraldehyde-P dehydrogenase step, while over the time interval from 26 to 30 seconds, control at PFK is re-established. This pattern of the glycolytic intermediate changes is reproducible, and a similar displacement of control from PFK to glyceraldehyde-P dehydrogenase has been observed in separate experiments in which glucose was omitted from the perfusate.

Relative changes in the levels of the cofactors affecting phosphofructokinase activity in the epinephrine experiment of Figure 7 are shown in Figure 9. Values shown here are plotted as a percentage of the values found at time 0. The relative activity of phosphofructokinase is depicted by the calculated mass action ratio ($K_{app} = \frac{[FDP][ADP]}{[F6P][ATP]}$) at each time.

During the first 26 seconds there is a 30-fold increase of the K_{app} towards equilibrium (i.e., activation), followed by an abrupt decrease between 26 and 30 seconds before a new steady state is established. AMP, ADP and inorganic phosphate start to increase immediately after the addition of epinephrine, and attain peak values at approximately the same time as the maximum increase of the phosphofructokinase mass action ratio. ATP shows only a small change since it is present in the heart at a much higher concentration than the other nucleotides. Deactivation of the phosphofructokinase apparently occurs primarily as a result of a fall in the concentrations of AMP and ADP. In addition, an increase of citrate may also be a factor contributing to the rapid deactivation of phosphofructokinase (17). The relative changes of cyclic AMP are also plotted in Figure 9, and it is seen that the response is large, very fast, but short-lived, with peak cyclic AMP values occurring after about 10 seconds (18). In view of these kinetic studies, I suggest that cyclic AMP is unlikely to be an important regulator of phosphofructokinase activity in heart muscle.

We can conclude from these results that glycolytic flux in heart muscle is mainly limited by the activity of phosphofructokinase. When the energy demand on heart is increased, as with epinephrine, or when mitochondrial respiration is decreased, as with anoxia, the production of glycolytic ATP is increased by increased phosphofructokinase activity as a result of a fall in the phosphate potential. On the other hand, when

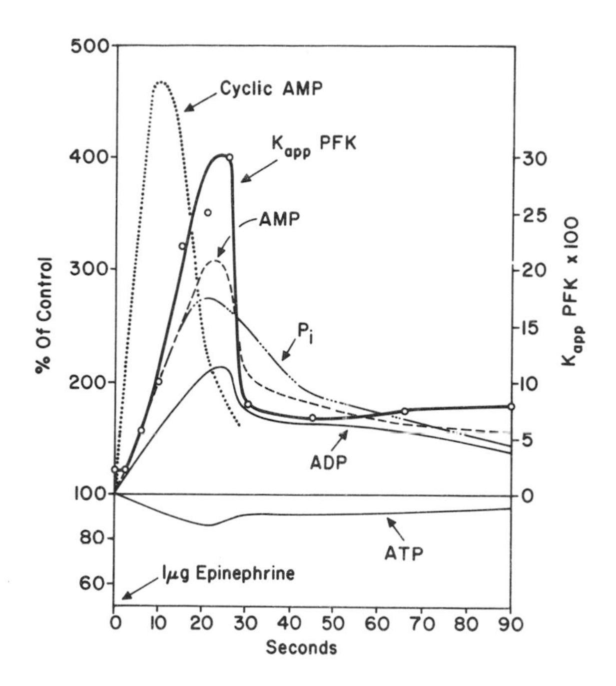

Figure 9. Relative changes of ATP, ADP, AMP, P_i and cyclic AMP in the perfused rat heart after epinephrine stimulation compared with the change in the mass action ratio of the phosphofructokinase reaction.

non-carbohydrate fuels are present in abundant supply, phosphofructokinase is inhibited by an increase in the level of citrate. There is thus multiple feed-back control between energy-producing steps in the mitochondria, and energy-producing steps in the cytoplasm.

REFERENCES

1. Williamson, J. R., J. Biol. Chem., 239, 2721 (1964).
2. Williamson, J. R., J. Biol. Chem., 240, 2308 (1965).
3. Chance, B., Williamson, J. R., Jamieson, D., and Schoener, B., Biochem. Z., 341, 357 (1965).
4. Estabrook, R. W., and Maitra, P. K., Anal. Biochem., 3, 369 (1962).
5. Bleehen, N. M., and Fisher, R. B., J. Physiol. (London), 123, 260 (1954).
6. Kreisberg, R. A., and Williamson, J. R., Am. J. Physiol., 207, 721 (1964).
7. Kreisberg, R. A., and Williamson, J. R., Am. J. Physiol., 207, 347 (1964).
8. Morgan, H. E., Henderson, M. J., Regen, D. M. and Park, C. R., J. Biol. Chem., 236, 253 (1961).
9. Morgan, H. E., this volume, p. 347.
10. Karpatkin, S., Helmreich, E., and Cori, C. F., J. Biol. Chem., 239, 3139 (1964).
11. Bücher, Th., and Rüssmann, W., Angew. Chem., Internat. Ed., 3, 426 (1964).
12. Hess, B., in Control Mechanisms in Respiration and Fermentation, ed. B. Wright, Ronald Press, Co., New York, 1963, p. 333.
13. Hess, B., and Brand, K., Chemical Chemistry, 11, 223 (1965).
14. Lowry, O. H., and Passonneau, J. V., J. Biol. Chem., 239, 31 (1964).
15. Garfinkel, D., Ann. N. Y. Acad. Sci., 108, 293 (1963).
16. Mansour, T., this volume, p. 81.
17. Williamson, J. R., Nature, 206, 473 (1965).
18. Cheung, W. Y., and Williamson, J. R., Nature, in press.

REGULATION OF GLUCOSE TRANSPORT*

H. E. Morgan+, J. R. Neely, J. P. Brineaux and C. R. Park

Department of Physiology, Vanderbilt University
Nashville, Tennessee

In muscle, glucose transport controls utilization of extracellular glucose. Transport is accelerated by insulin (1-3), muscular exercise (4,5) and anoxia (6,7) as shown by studies with glucose and non-metabolized sugars. Transport has properties suggesting that the sugar combines transiently with a mobile constituent, or carrier, in the membrane. These properties include a) saturation kinetics, b) stereospecificity, c) competition between pairs of sugars for transport, and d) counterflow (8-10). Transport in muscle leads only to equilibration of sugar concentrations across the cell membrane.

In the present paper, the role of transport in regulating carbohydrate metabolism in aerobic, anaerobic and working muscle will be examined. These studies indicate that acceleration of transport is of primary importance for a sustained increase in glucose uptake in anoxic or working muscle.

Experimental Procedure

The isolated perfused rat heart has been used for all of the studies that will be reported. Hearts were removed from heparinized rats, anaesthetized with Nembutal, and perfused with a Krebs-Henseleit bicarbonate buffer containing 0.5 mM CaEDTA, gassed with either $O_2:CO_2$ (95:5) or $N_2:CO_2$ (95:5). Perfusions of the Langendorff type were carried out by retrograde flow of perfusate into the aorta (11). Pressure for perfusion of the coronary bed was generated by a peristaltic pump. Although this preparation will be designated as "non-working," the ventricle develops pressure up to the level of the perfusion pressure (60 mm Hg) with each systole. Varying degrees of left ventricular work were studied in a "working"

* Supported by grants from the National Institutes of Health and the Life Insurance Medical Research Fund.
+ Investigator, Howard Hughes Medical Institute.

heart apparatus (12). In this case, the perfusate was introduced into the left atrium from an overflow type bubble trap whose position above the heart could be varied. The left ventricle pumped the buffer through an aortic cannula into a chamber which was 1/3 filled with air to provide some elasticity; from this chamber the fluid was pumped into a bubble trap 60 cm above the heart. In this preparation, pressure for perfusion of the coronary bed was generated by the heart itself.

Hearts were perfused for 10 minutes without recirculation under aerobic conditions with buffer containing heparin (10 mg/l). Glucose was added at a concentration of 16 mM. Glucose uptake was estimated by measuring changes in the perfusate concentration during either a 30 minute or 1 hour period of perfusion. Sorbitol-H^3 was used to estimate the volume of fluid recirculated during the uptake period and the extracellular space. Heparin was not added to the recirculation buffer. At the end of perfusion, hearts were frozen while still being perfused by clamping the tissue between blocks of aluminum cooled to the temperature of liquid nitrogen (13). The tissue was powdered in a percussion mortar at liquid nitrogen temperatures. Weighed aliquots of the powder were used for the estimation of dry weight and for preparation of perchloric acid extracts. These extracts were analyzed for glucose by the glucose oxidase method and for sorbitol-H^3 by liquid scintillation counting (12). Sugar and sorbitol spaces were calculated as described elsewhere (11). Insulin, free of glucagon, was obtained from Novo Therapeutisk Laboratorium, Copenhagen. All results are expressed per gram of dry heart weight.

Results

Glucose uptake of the aerobic heart was low (Table I). If all the glucose disappearing had been oxidized, it could have accounted for only 25 per cent of the oxygen consumed (12). Intracellular free glucose remained below the level of detection, indicating that glucose phosphorylation was able to keep pace with entry. Therefore, membrane transport was the major rate-limiting step for uptake. The rate was the same with glucose concentrations of 5 and 16 mM; at 2.5 mM glucose, the rate was 43 ± 6 µmoles·g^{-1}·hr^{-1}. These data indicate that the apparent K_m of transport was about 1 mM and V_{max} 65 µmoles·g^{-1}·hr^{-1}.

TABLE I

Effects of Insulin, Anoxia and Cardiac Work on Glucose Uptake and Intracellular Glucose in the Perfused Rat Heart

Perfusion Conditions	Left Atrial Pressure mm Hg	Insulin Added 20 m.units ml^{-1}	Glucose Uptake µmoles· $g^{-1} \cdot hr^{-1}$	Glucose Space $ml \cdot g^{-1}$	Sorbitol Space $ml \cdot g^{-1}$	Intracellular Glucose mM
Aerobic	-	0	60 ± 26 [a]	2.6 ± 0.1 [a]	2.7 ± 0.1 [a]	N. D.
	-	+	373 ± 17	3.4 ± 0.1	2.8 ± 0.1	5.9 ± 0.8
Anaerobic	-	0	638 ± 39	3.7 ± 0.1	3.4 ± 0.1	2.7 ± 0.7
	-	+	814 ± 52	3.9 ± 0.1	3.5 ± 0.1	2.9 ± 0.5
Working	0	0	76 ± 29	3.0 ± 0.2	2.9 ± 0.2	0.2 ± 0.7
	5	0	142 ± 34	3.2 ± 0.1	3.0 ± 0.1	1.8 ± 1.2
	10	0	219 ± 40	3.2 ± 0.1	3.1 ± 0.1	0.3 ± 0.9
	20	0	378 ± 83	3.5 ± 0.1	3.5 ± 0.2	N. D.

The experiments were carried out as described in the methods section. Six to eight hearts were perfused in each group.
a = standard error of mean
N.D. = none detected

Insulin accelerated uptake 6-fold and resulted in the accumulation of intracellular free sugar. Anoxia increased uptake 10-fold and also caused a measurable accumulation of intracellular sugar. These effects were due to an acceleration of transport. A rise in the V_{max} appears to be a major kinetic effect of these agents since the rates of uptake were well above the maximal rate of aerobic transport. Accumulation of intracellular glucose indicated that phosphorylation was no longer able to keep pace with the rate of transport and, as a consequence, became rate-limiting for glucose uptake.

Anoxia also accelerated glucose uptake in the heart treated with insulin (line 4 compared with line 2). Since saturating levels of intracellular free glucose were already present in the aerobic heart, this anaerobic stimulation of uptake could be explained most easily by a rise in the apparent V_{max} of glucose phosphorylation. In earlier studies, the anoxic acceleration of glucose phosphorylation was localized to the hexokinase and phosphofructokinase steps (14-16). With anoxia, intracellular concentrations of P_i and AMP increased about 3-fold while ATP decreased about 20 per cent (16). AMP and inorganic phosphate are known to overcome an ATP inhibition of phosphofructokinase (17, 18), while P_i may counteract the glucose-6-P inhibition of hexokinase (19, 20).

Transport limited the rate of glucose uptake in the "non-working" rat heart. When progressively greater work loads were imposed by increasing left atrial filling pressure, glucose uptake increased as much as 5-fold (lower panel, Table I). Levels of free glucose statistically greater than zero were not detected at any left atrial pressure. These findings indicated that glucose transport was accelerated by muscular work and that transport was still a major rate controlling step. The degrees of work that were studied did not result in hypoxia since the oxygen tension of the coronary effluent was maintained above the normal *in vivo* arterial oxygen tension. The mechanism of transport stimulation in either anaerobic or working muscle is unknown.

The data obtained with 20 mm left atrial filling pressure, as compared to those obtained with insulin addition to the non-working heart, indicate that intracellular phosphorylation was stimulated by cardiac work. In the insulin-treated tissue, glucose uptake was 373 $\mu moles \cdot g^{-1} \cdot hr^{-1}$ when the intracellular glucose concentration was 5.9 mM. In the working tissue, approximately the same rate of uptake was found with an intracellular glucose level below detection by the methods employed.

Factors regulating monosaccharide transport can be studied more directly be meausring intracellular accumulation of a non-metabolized sugar. L-arabinose and glucose have been shown to be transported by the same mobile carrier system by demonstration of competitive inhibition and counter flow (3, 21). After 10 minutes of perfusion with L-arabinose, the aerobic non-working hearts contained very small amounts of intracellular pentose (Table II). Accelerated accumulation of L-arabinose was observed in anaerobic or working muscle or following the addition of insulin.

TABLE II

Effects of Insulin, Anoxia and Cardiac Work on L-Arabinose Transport in the Perfused Rat Heart

Perfusion Conditions	Insulin Added 900 μ units $\cdot ml^{-1}$	L-Arabinose Space $ml \cdot g^{-1}$	Per cent Equilibrium
Aerobic	0	1.92 ± .06[a] (22)	4 ± 4[a]
	+	2.42 ± .09 (12)	29 ± 4
Anaerobic	0	3.02 ± .05 (28)	28 ± 3
	+	3.37 ± .06 (12)	46 ± 3
Working-Aerobic 10 mm Left Atrial Pressure	0	2.34 ± .07 (19)	23 ± 3
	+	2.92 ± .11 (6)	61 ± 7

The number of hearts in each group is indicated by the figure in parenthesis.
a = standard error of mean.

After a preliminary 10 minute perfusion with arabinose-free buffer, perfusion was switched to buffer containing pentose (13 mM) and sorbitol-H^3. This buffer was recirculated for an additional 10 minutes. Insulin was added only to the recirculating buffer. At the end of perfusion, tubes leading to the heart were clamped and the heart cut off into a beaker of saline in ice. The chambers were cut open and the heart rinsed. The tissue was blotted on filter paper and frozen with a Wollenberger clamp. A portion of the tissue was taken for the estimation of dry weight and the remainder used for the preparation of a boiling water extract (11). L-arabinose was estimated by the method of Roe and Rice (22). In the non-working heart, sorbitol space was 1.83 ml • g^{-1} and total water 4.38 ml • g^{-1}. With work, sorbitol increased to 1.97; total water was unchanged. In the anaerobic heart, sorbitol space was 2.47 and total water 4.90. Eighty-one per cent of intracellular water has been found to equilibrate with monosaccharides (9).

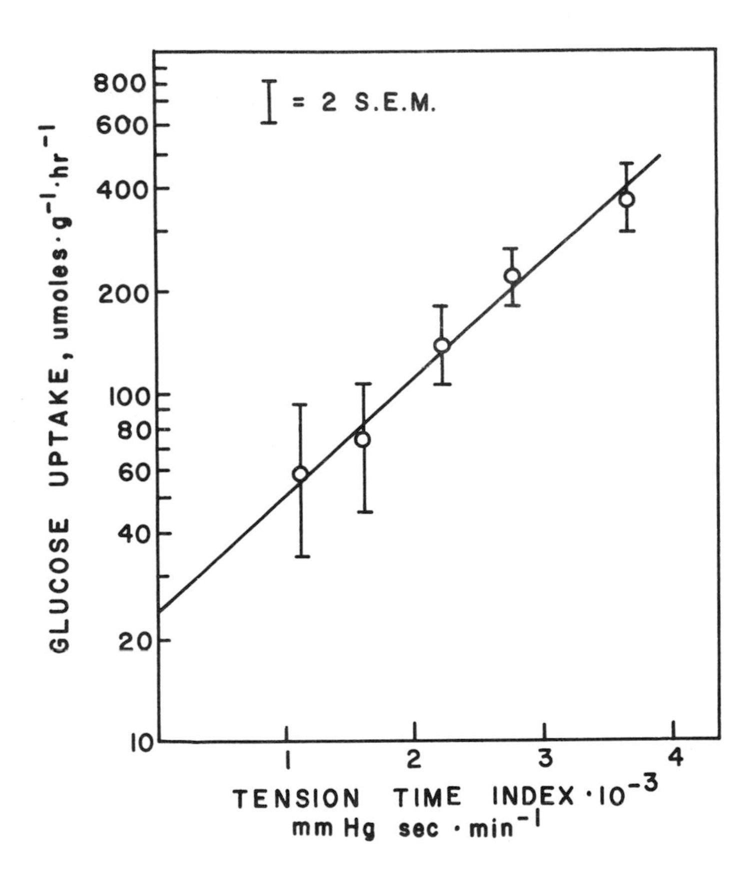

Figure 1. Effect of tension development on glucose uptake of the isolated rat heart. Uptake measurements are taken from Table I. Tension development was measured either by integrating the area under aortic or ventricular pressure curves. Ventricular pressures were measured by inserting a needle into the left ventricle through the apex of the heart.

Discussion

Glucose transport controls the utilization of exogenous glucose in muscle (11, 23), adipose tissue (24), and erhthrocytes of several species (12, 23). In muscle, virtually the whole range of transport rates is controlled by metabolic and hormonal regulatory mechanisms. If glucose uptake is plotted as a function of tension development (Figure 1), the line extrapolates to 23 μmoles • g^{-1} • hr^{-1} when zero tension is produced. This value is 4 per cent of the rate observed at the same glucose concentration under anaerobic conditions (Table I). If the tissue were free of insulin, the rate could be expected to be still lower. It may be, in fact, that any measurable rate in heart muscle indicates a degree of stimulation by metabolic or mechanical work, incomplete oxygenation or insulin.

The mechanisms of the effects of insulin, anoxia and work on transport remain obscure. Accelerated transport in exercising skeletal muscle has been observed earlier (4, 5). In contrast to these studies, the isolated working rat heart allows a separation of the effects of work and anoxia. Accelerated arabinose transport has been observed in hearts that were producing only small amounts of lactate and had high oxygen tensions in the coronary effluent. Demonstrations of counterflow and maintenance of stereospecificity of transport in insulin-treated and anaerobic tissue have indicated that these agents stimulate the specific carrier mediated transport system rather than opening accessory pathways for free diffusion of sugar into the cell (21).

The importance of transport acceleration in the Pasteur effect is frequently overlooked. In recent years, considerable attention has been given to mechanisms controlling the intracellular utilization of glucose and glycogen by allosteric factors regulating hexokinase, phosphofructokinase and phosphorylase. These regulatory mechanisms provide sensitive controls on these rates. In muscle tissue, however, the regulation of intracellular glucose utilization is of secondary importance. Only after transport is stimulated, can these control mechanisms result in large sustained changes in utilization of glucose. Analogous control of carrier activity by allosteric substances in environment of the membrane has been discussed earlier (12).

Summary

Glucose transport in heart muscle is regulated by hormonal and metabolic mechanisms. Insulin accelerated transport at least 6-fold; anoxia at least 10-fold; and muscular work at least 5-fold. These stimulations appear to involve an accelerated rate of carrier transport rather than the opening of accessory pathways for diffusion of sugar. These accelerations are of primary importance in the stimulation of glucose uptake in anaerobic of working muscle. Intracellular phosphorylation of glucose is also accelerated in working or anoxic muscle.

REFERENCES

1. Park, C. R., Bornstein, J. and Post, R. L., Am. J. Physiol., 182, 12 (1955).

2. Fisher, R. B. and Lindsay, D. B., J. Physiol., 131, 526 (1956).

3. Park, C. R., Reinwein, D., Henderson, M. J., Cadenas, E. and Morgan, H. E., Am. J. Med., 26, 674 (1959).

4. Goldstein, M. S., Mullick, J., Huddlestun, B., and Levine, R., Am. J. Physiol., 173, 212 (1953).

5. Helmreich, E. and Cori, C. F., J. Biol. Chem., 224, 663 (1957).

6. Randle, P. J. and Smith, G. H., Biochem. J., 70, 490 (1958).

7. Morgan, H. E., Randle, P. J. and Regen, D. M., Biochem. J., 73, 573 (1959).

8. Wilbrandt, W. and Rosenberg, Th., Pharmacol. Revs., 13, 109 (1961).

9. Morgan, H. E., Regen, D. M. and Park, C. R., J. Biol. Chem., 239, 369 (1964).

10. Regen, D. M. and Morgan, H. E., Biochim. Biophys. Acta, 79, 151 (1964).

11. Morgan, H. E., Henderson, M. J., Regen, D. M. and Park, C. R., J. Biol. Chem., 236, 253 (1961).

12. Morgan, H. E., Neely, J. R., Wood, R. E., Liebecq, C., Liebermeister, H. and Park, C. R., Fed. Proc., in press.

13. Wollenberger, A., Ristau, O. and Schoffa, G., Arch. ges. Physiol. Pfluger's, 270, 399 (1960).

14. Park, C. R., Morgan, H. E., Henderson, M. J., Regen, D. M., Cadenas, E. and Post, R. L., in G. Pincus (Editor), Recent Progress in Hormone Research, Vol. 17, Academic Press, Inc., New York, 1961, p. 493.

15. Newsholme, E. A. and Randle, P. J., Biochem. J., 80, 655 (1961).

16. Regen, D. M., Davis, W. W., Morgan, H. E. and Park, C. R., J. Biol. Chem., 239, 43 (1964).

17. Passonneau, J. V. and Lowry, O. H., Biochem. Biophys. Res. Comm., 7, 10 (1962).

18. Mansour, T. E., J. Biol. Chem., 238, 2285 (1963).

19. von Tiedemann, H. and Born, J., Z. Naturforsch., Pt. b, 14, 477 (1959).

20. Rose, I. A., Warms, J. V. and O'Connell, E. L., Biochem. Biophys. Res. Comm., 15, 33 (1964).

21. Morgan, H. E., Regen, D. M. and Park, C. R., J. Biol. Chem., 239, 369 (1964).

22. Roe, J. H. and Rice, E. W., J. Biol. Chem., 173, 507 (1948).

23. Park, C. R., Post, R. L., Kalman, C. F., Wright, J. H., Jr., Johnson, L. H. and Morgan, H. E., Ciba Foundation Symposium on Endocrinology, Vol. 9, Little Brown and Co., Boston, 1956, p. 240.

24. Crofford, O. B. and Renold, A. E., J. Biol. Chem., 240, 14 (1965).

FATTY ACID INDUCED ALTERATIONS IN CITRIC ACID CYCLE INTERMEDIATES*

R.H. Bowman

Department of Physiology, Vanderbilt University
Nashville, Tennessee

The finding that citrate is an inhibitor of phosphofructokinase (1,2,3) led naturally to the question of how the level of intracellular citrate is regulated. In hearts of diabetic rats we have found (1,4,5) that citrate, isocitrate and malate are elevated. Preliminary measurements show that succinate is also higher in hearts of diabetic rats, but α-ketoglutarate is not significantly altered. Perfusion of normal hearts with fatty acids elevates these same intermediates, and has no effect on α-ketoglutarate. Figure 1 shows the development of the altered levels during a 1, 3 and 10 minute perfusion with octanoate.

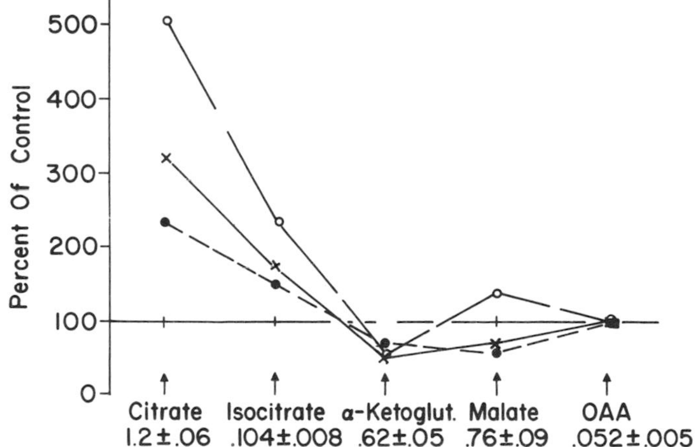

●-----● = 1 minute perfusion

X——X = 3 minute perfusion

O—— —O = 10 minute perfusion

Figure 1. Change in concentrations of citric acid cycle intermediates during perfusion of rat hearts with octanoate. (Control values expressed as μmoles/g dry wt.)

* Supported by the American Heart Association.

Citrate rises very rapidly and isocitrate more slowly. α-ketoglutarate falls during this time as does malate for the first 3 minutes. After 10 minutes malate is significantly elevated. These data suggest that a primary block of isocitric dehydrogenase following exposure of the heart to octanoate may occur. There also appears to be some change in the aconitase equilibrium. A longer (20 minute) perfusion results in levels of citrate, isocitrate and malate that are more nearly equivalent in terms of the present increase over their respective concentrations in hearts perfused for 20 minutes without octanoate.

In addition to an isocitric dehydrogenase block as a cause for elevated citrate, fixation of carbon dioxide has been considered. Figure 2 is a profile of heart extracts chromatographed for citric acid cycle intermediates. These hearts had been perfused with $NaHC^{14}O_3$ plus or minus octanoate. The predominant amount of radioactivity was detected in citrate with the only other significant identified amount appearing in malate. Octanoate increased the total radioactivity in citrate, but there was a decrease in the specific activity.

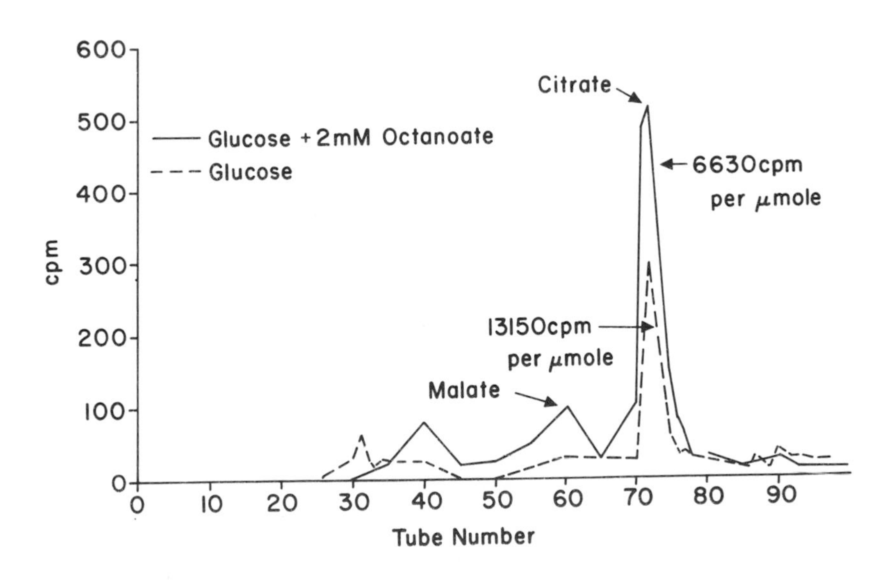

Figure 2. Radioactivity of citric acid cycle intermediates from hearts perfused with $NaHC^{14}O_3$ with or without octanoate.

The results are interpreted to indicate that a certain amount of the increased citrate in hearts perfused with fatty acids is due to an increase in CO_2 fixation. The specific activity of citrate greatly exceeded that of malate in hearts perfused with or without octanoate, suggesting that a part of the CO_2 fixation may be due to carboxylation of α-ketoglutarate via reversal of the isocitric dehydrogenase reaction.

REFERENCES

1. Parmeggiani, A., and Bowman, R. H., Biochem. Biophys. Res. Comm., 12, 268 (1963).
2. Passonneau, J. V., and Lowry, O. H., Biochem. Biophys. Res. Comm., 13, 372 (1963).
3. Garland, P. B., Randle, P. J., and Newsholme, E. A., Nature, 200, 169 (1963).
4. Bowman, R. H., Fed. Proc., 23, 118 (1964).
5. Bowman, R. H., and Parmeggiani, A., Nature, in press (1965).

DISCUSSION

Hempfling: I wish to present the results of experiments on glycolysis in E. coli B which have comparative significance in this discussion. Figure 1 shows a cross-over plot obtained

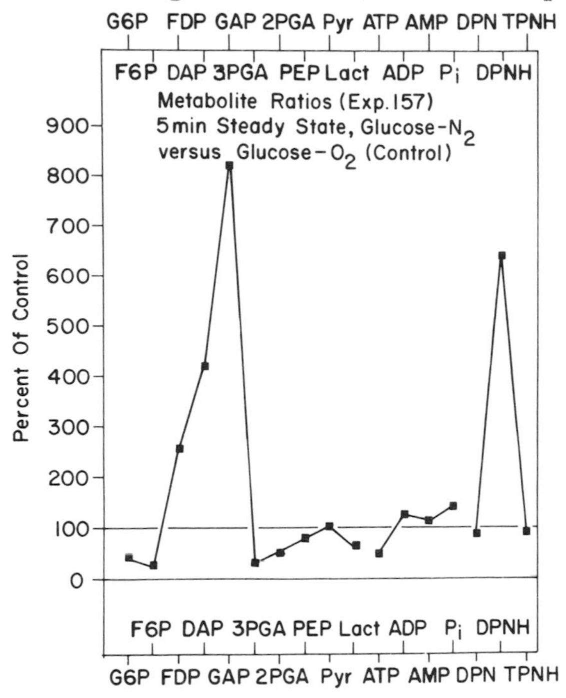

Figure 1. Cross-over plot of steady state anaerobic glycolysis in E. coli B. 15 mg/ml dry weight cells in 20 mM triethanolamine-Cl containing 3 mM $MgSO_4$, pH 7.4 (20°). Bacteria withdrawn 5 min. after addition of glucose and the reaction terminated in 0.5 N $HClO_4$. Assays of metabolites were performed in the neutralized extracts by the methods of Estabrook and Maitra (3) and Maitra and Estabrook (4). Values expressed are derived from intracellular concentrations.

* Supported from PHS GM 12202 and 5T1 GM 2G 277.

from E. coli B which had been grown aerobically in tryptic soy broth and then starved. Samples were withdrawn 5 minutes following the addition of glucose at which time the suspensions of cells were in the steady state of glucose utilization. A comparison is made between the steady state concentrations of glycolytic metabolites in the absence of oxygen and concentrations in the aerobic steady state (which serves as the 100 per vent control.) Under anaerobic conditions cross-overs are obtained at PFK in the direction of activation and the kinetic region of glyceraldehyde-3-phosphate dehydrogenase and 3-phospoglycerate kinase in the direction of inhibition, that is the steady state levels of FDP, DAP and GAP are higher anaerobically than aerobically, while the steady state levels under anaerobic conditions of G-6-P, F-6-P, 3-PGA, 2-PGA and PEP are below those levels obtained under aerobic conditions, The glycolytic flux measured by the disappearance of glucose at the 5 minute aerobic steady state is 57 per cent of that rate which occurs under anaerobic conditions.

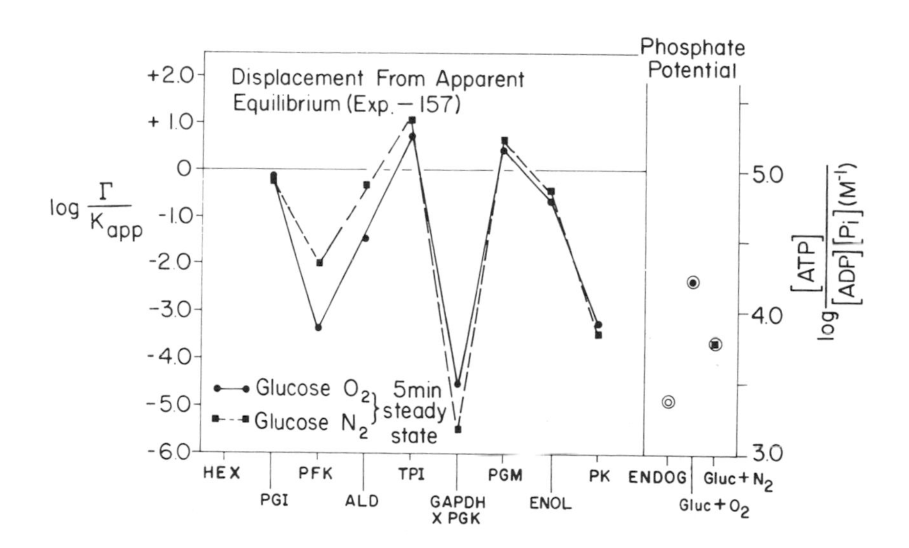

Figure 2. Data from Figure 1 calculated as $\frac{[\text{Products}]}{[\text{Reactants}]}$, giving the non-equilibrium mass action ratio (1). These functions were then compared with K_{app} (equilibrium) as given by Williamson (J. Biol. Chem., 240, 2308 (1965)), using mean values where necessary.

Figure 2 shows these data expressed as the log of deviation from apparent equilibrium at each reactant-product couple as suggested by Bücher (1). Gamma in this case is defined as in Bücher's original paper and is the mass action ratio in the non-equilibrium steady state. PGK, GAPDH x PGK and PK are relatively far displaced from equilibrium; that is, favoring the reactant concentration. These phenomena have been previously described by Dr. Williamson in this colloquium (p. 333), and we were disappointed to find that glycolysis in E. coli B is much the same as glycolysis in rat heart. As in the rat heart, the effect of anaerobiosis (the dashed line) is to reduce the displacement of PFK and aldolase from equilibrium by almost one and one half log units and by about one log unit, respectively. However, in this case, the GAPDH x PGK region is displaced significantly farther from equilibrium under anaerobic conditions than in the presence of oxygen. The steady state mass action ratio of pyruvate kinase is not much affected. The phosphate potential for three different steady states -- the endogenous steady state, the aerobic steady state with glucose, and the anaerobic steady state with glucose -- is on the right hand side of the figure. The values change in the expected direction. Hexokinase is not plotted here because we are not certain of the internal glucose concentration of the cells. When experiments are carried out in which cells are separated rapidly from the suspending medium by millipore filtration and total glucose and glucose in the filtrate are estimated we find that more than 95 per cent of the total glucose is outside the cell. However, if we choose some reasonably small concentration for glucose in this case, such as .1 μmole/gm dry weight, we arrive at a figure of about 2 to 3 log units displacement from equilibrium in the negative direction for hexokinase. This does not change much during the aerobic to anaerobic transition. Available internal phosphate is not much changed in the presence or absence of oxygen and in this regard we disagree with Holzer (2) as to the significance of phosphate availability and the Pasteur effect on E. coli B. We suggest that the mechanism of the displacement of GAPDH x PGK in the anaerobic situation lies in the inhibition of GAPDH by accumulated DPNH which on the cross-over plot increased about 6-fold under anaerobic conditions. However, inhibition of GAPDH by accumulated 1,3-diPGA is certainly not eliminated. It is of interest to compare the transient nature of GAPDH control in the rat heart as shown by Williamson with the relatively longer-lived and greater displacement from equilibrium of GAPDH x PGK in the case of this organism. Certainly, control of some glycolytic sites other than PFK (which is de-inhibited in the absence of oxygen) would be of value to an organism which is facultatively anaerobic in contradistinction to the perfused rat heart.

1. Bücher, Th., and Rüssmann, W., Angew. Chem. Internat. Ed., 3, 426 (1964).
2. Holzer, H., and Grunicke, H., Biochim. Biophys. Acta, 53, 591 (1961).
3. Estabrook, R. W., and Maitra, P. K., Anal. Biochem., 3, 369 (1962).
4. Maitra, P. K., and Estabrook, R. W., Anal. Biochem., 7, 472 (1964).

Olson: I would like to ask Dr. Morgan whether or not the nice linear relationship between glucose uptake by the working heart and the amount of cardiac work persists as the heart fails at high filling pressures. I notice that some aerobic glycolysis is observed at the highest filling pressures which you used. We have observed in intact dogs in which heart failure is induced by surgical valvulotomy that the glucose extraction by the heart tends to be higher and the fatty acid extraction lower than by comparably treated non-failing controls. This is so, despite no detectible change in myocardial CP or ATP levels.

Morgan: Thus far, we haven't really pushed this preparation to the point of cardiac failure. With the highest degree of work that we have tested, about 80 percent of the oxygen consumption can be accounted for by the consumption of exogenous glucose and glycogen, so that glucose is the primary fuel for this preparation.

In association with Drs. Robinson, Bücher, and Sutherland, we have been looking at the effects of epinephrine on the levels of cyclic AMP, the inotropic effect, and the activation of phosphorylase. In the working rat heart preparation, Dr. Robinson has found that after 3 seconds of exposure to epinephrine, the cyclic AMP level reached its peak, while the peak of the inotropic response occurred at 10 to 20 seconds, and the peak of the phosphorylase activation was delayed as much as 40 seconds. I think this would support the idea that Dr. Krebs suggested, that there could be an inactivation of some enzyme that follows in time the changes in the level of cyclic AMP.

The shift from aerobic to anaerobic conditions results in a rapid increase in glycogenolysis in the perfused heart (Cornblath, M., Randle, P.J., Parmeggiani, A. and Morgan, H.E., J. Biol. Chem., 238, 1592 (1963). In the aerobic tissue, nearly all of the phosphorylase is the the b form. Enzyme activity is maintained at a low level by ATP and G-6-P inhibition of the AMP activation of the b form (Morgan, H.E. and Parmeggiani, A., J. Biol. Chem., 239, 2440 (1964). These inhibitions appear to be particularly important since the intracellular level of AMP is high enough to induce nearly maximal activity of the enzyme (Morgan, H.E. and Parmeggiani, A., J. Biol. Chem., 239, 2435 (1964)). Low levels of inorganic phosphate (< 3 mM) in aerobic muscle also contribute to a slow rate of glycogenolysis. In the presence of aerobic AMP and ATP levels, the phosphate K_m was approximately 18 mM, indicating that the rate of glycogenolysis in aerobic muscle would be a linear function of intracellular phosphate within the range of tissue concentrations. When the tissue is made anoxic, AMP levels increase and counteract to a large extent the inhibition of phosphorylase b by ATP and G-6-P. Since intracellular P_i levels are also increased, phosphorylase b activity can be estimated to increase 30-90 fold. Anoxia also accelerates disposal of hexosemonophosphate via phosphofructokinase and prevents the accumulation of high levels of G-6-P. In addition 15-25 percent of the phosphorylase is converted to the a form. In an anaerobic environment, the rate of glycogenolysis induced by the a form was accelerated due to increased intracellular P_i. These observations have led us to suggest that control of phosphorylase b activity by changes in concentrations of nucleotides, G-6-P and P_i is as important for the control of glycogenolysis as shifts between the b and a forms of the enzyme.

Hess: I have a question to Dr. Williamson with respect to the figures on the aerobic-anaerobic transition in which you combined the reaction of GAPDH and PGK, as we have done in our earlier experiments (Hess, B., Proc. Vth Int. Cong. Biochem., 5, 818 (1961); Hess, B., J. Gen. Physiol., 45, 603A (1962)). Because of the general problem of the control of DPN and DPNH in the cytoplasmic compartment it is necessary to analyze both reactions separately. In our earlier experiments we calculated the level of DPG in Ehrlich ascites tumor cells to be 80 μM based on the known redox potentials of the lactate-pyruvate ratio and the α-glycerol phosphate-dihydroxyacetone phosphate ratio. More recent assays (based on the enzymic assay system using the fluorometric technique) revealed far lower figures (Hess, B., and Brand, K., unpublished experiments): in Baker's yeast (anaerobiosis, glucose saturated steady state) 4.8 μM (maximum values), in Ehrlich ascites tumor cells (anaerobiosis, glucose saturated steady state) between 3-17 μM. In the latter case, the ratio of the GAP/DPG was between 2 and 3. Thus, in Ehrlich ascites tumor cells the GAPDH reaction is near equilibrium, pointing to the PGK reaction as being displaced from equilibrium. We have not finished this study for yeast and I would like to know your opinion on this problem.

Williamson: The content of 1,3-DPG has not yet been measured in heart; therefore it is not possible to determine the mass action ratios of the GAPDH and PGK steps separately. All we can say for certain is that the product of the mass action ratios for these two reactions is displaced from equilibrium. However, one indirect method may be used to provide information on the state of equilibrium or lack of it in these reactions, namely from a calculation of the steady state levels of 1,3-DPG, by assuming equilibrium, in turn, at either the GAPDH or the PGK steps. For instance, if equilibrium at PGK is assumed, 1,3-DPG values of the order of 0.2 µM may be calculated from the observed contents of 3-PGA, ADP and ATP. If on the other hand, equilibrium at GAPDH is assumed, the corresponding calculated level of 1,3-DPG is about 30 µM (Williamson, J. R., J. Biol. Chem., 240, 2308 (1965)). It is unlikely that the steady state level of 1,3-DPG would be as high as 30 µM, firstly because it is incompatible with the measured Ki for inhibition of GAPDH by 1,3-DPG of 0.8 µM, and secondly, the fluorescence assay technique has a sensitivity capable of measuring amounts equivalent to a tissue concentration of 1 µM with an accuracy of less than 20 per cent. Our present failure to detect 1,3-DPG in heart suggests that the actual concentration is below 1 µM. Therefore, for the time being, I prefer to consider a lack of equilibrium at GAPDH rather than at PGK. The situation may be difficult in other tissues, as you suggest.

Hempfling: Professor Bücher, what is the significance of the energy which might go into displacing a glycolytic chain from the true equilibrium state? Would it be large or small? Would it fluctuate under anaerobic/aerobic conditions?

Bücher: You may calculate the energy required according to a formula developed by W. Kuhn (Ergebnisse d. Enzymologie, 5, 1 (1936); Angew. Chem., 48, 215 (1936); see also Bücher, Th., and Rüssmann, W., Angew. Chem., International Edition, 3, 426 (1964)). Due to the higher potential of the adenylate system, it enlarges under aerobic conditions, but not by orders of magnitude.

E. Krebs: Dr. Williamson, why were you willing to dismiss cyclic adenylic acid as a regulatory factor so quickly? It seems to me thatthe cell might "remember" the high level of this substance which occurred immediately after epinephrine administration.

Williamson: This is unlikely. I would suggest that the main effects of cyclic AMP are on the phosphorylase cascade. The kinetic data on the accumulation/depletion of cyclic AMP relative to changes in the activity of PFK seem to me to indicate that it is not involved, or at least is unlikely to be an important factor, in PFK activation. In any case, the concentrations of cyclic AMP necessary to activate PFK *in vitro* appear to be much higher than those found in this tissue. In these studies, which were done in collaboration with Dr. Cheung, cyclic AMP increased from control levels of 1-2 μmoles/gm dry weight to values of 10-14 μmoles/gm dry weight after epinephrine addition (an increase from 1-7 μM).

Mansour: We have found that cyclic 3'5'-AMP by itself is not a very good activator of the pH 5.8 inactivated enzyme. However, when it was combined with the hexose phosphate F-6-P or FDP, it was a very potent activator. In general, there is a synergism between activation by a hexose phosphate and adenylic nucleotide. I might add that I have noticed in Dr. Williamson's figures that there is an overlap between the levels of cyclic 3'5'-AMP and PFK activation; the two graphs are really not completely independent.

Lowry: I would raise an objection to cyclic adenylate as an activator of PFK purely on concentration grounds. Towards cardiac PFK as towards the various mammalian PFK's, cyclic adenylate is only about twice as active as AMP itself and they both act, as far as we can see, in exactly the same manner. There must be between 20 and 50 times more adenylic acid than cyclic adenylate in the heart, so it seems unreasonable that cyclic adenylate would play much of a role in regard to PFK unless there is some very strict compartmentation. I think we shouldn't rely completely on cyclic adenylate anyway; we need a few other controls as well.

Chance: Dr. Krebs, what physical-chemical process do you envisage in which the concentration of the activator decreases while that of the "activatee" is increasing? I think that you must mean that cyclic AMP is converted into the activator of PFK; the concentration of cyclic AMP is falling while that of PFK is rising.

E. Krebs: It seems to me that the chemistry of PFK is quite complicated, and it is conceivable that a structural change in this enzyme caused by cyclic AMP could last for 15 to 20 seconds. While we have not seen active and inactive forms in our laboratory, Dr. Mansour observed conversion from an inactive to an active form; the only type of more or less permanent change in an enzyme need not be phosphorylation, as occurs with phosphorylase. There may be other mechanisms whereby PFK can be converted from a less active to a more active form.

Chance: It still seems unlikely that there is a 10-20 second delay in the structural change and that it should last for 10-20 seconds. One of the few protein conformation changes that has been followed effectively from the kinetic standpoint is that in hemoglobin by Gibson. The relaxation time of the conformation change can be measured in milliseconds, very short times compared with the 15-20 second interval you mention.

Helmreich: Dr. Williamson, the G-1-P and G-6-P concentrations which you have reported in the epinephrine treated heart seem to indicate that the ratio of G-6-P to G-1-P was about 4:1. This would indicate that the equilibrium of the PGM reaction is quite displaced in these conditions.

Williamson: In this particular experiment, the G-1-P values do appear to be a little high. In other, similar experiments, the G-6-P:G-1-P ratio approaches 20:1. On Dr. Lowry's suggestion, I checked out the PGM enzyme used for the G-1-P assay, and I could not detect any FDPase contaminating activity which would give values too high. Probably the enzyme is maintained fairly close to equilibrium when glycogen utilization is high. It does appear, however, to be off equilibrium when glycogen is not being used and values for the G-6-P:G-1-P ratio as high as 60:1 have been observed.

Helmreich: My second point, Dr. Williamson, is that you showed data indicating that in the epinephrine treated heart there is actually an increase in P_i. I find this surprising because in the epinephrine treated muscle there is a large increase in hexose phosphate, which might be expected to take away P_i. Dr. Cori, Dr. Karpatkin, and I have recently published data on the effects of epinephrine on the glycolytic system in frog sartorius (J. Biol. Chem., 239, 3139 (1964). In keeping with the previous data from Dr. Cori's laboratory (Hegnauer, A. H., and Cori, G. T., J. Biol. Chem., 105, 691 (1934), these results show that there is actually a decrease in the P_i level in the epinephrine-treated anaerobic frog muscle.

Williamson: In the rat heart treated with epinephrine, the increase of P_i is a consequence of CP breakdown. Since the levels of creatine-P in heart are of the order of 37 μmoles/gm dry weight, and there is a transient decrease of CP of about 60 per cent, the relative P_i production is very much greater than the increase of bound phosphate in the glycolytic intermediates.

Danforth: The heart is changing its work load when exposed to epinephrine, while frog skeletal muscle is resting. That might make a lot of difference.

Chance: May we now consider whether the "*in vivo* concentrations" are relevant to the *in vitro* tests of enzyme activities?

Lowry: I agree with Dr. Chance that in spite of uncertainties about absolute local concentrations of metabolites in tissues, it would be of value to compare average tissue concentrations of known PFK affectors with concentrations necessary to activate or inhibit. I will confine myself to brain PFK and brain metabolite levels since we have the most complete information in this case. In getting at this problem we must think of ranges rather than fixed levels. Metabolite levels vary; activator and inhibitor constants are profoundly affected by other substances present.

It is obvious that almost any of the substances listed in the Table below with the probable exception of cyclic AMP, could have influence of PFK *in vivo*. Because of the interactions of the various components listed it would be helpful to evaluate the influence of each of the components when the other components are present at levels approximating the average concentration in tissue. Present data are too fragmentary to make this evaluation possible.

TABLE I

	Range of tissue concentration mmoles/kg	Range of concentration for 50 per cent inhibition or 50 per cent of maximal activation mmoles/kg
Inhibitors		
ATP	2.3 - 3	0.005 - 5
Citrate	0.2 - 0.4	0.01 - 1.0
Activators		
Fructose-6-P	0.01 - 0.05	0.05 - 1
Fructose-1,6-diP	0.05 - 0.2	0.001 - 0.1
ADP	0.4 - 0.8	0.5 - 2
AMP	0.05 - 0.2	0.02 - 1
Cyclic-AMP	0.0008 - 0.0015	0.01 - 0.5
P_i	2 - 4	0.05 - 15
NH_4	0.2 - 1	0.2 - 10

Williamson: It seems to be important to develop methods for isolating the individual factors which are responsible for PFK activation and inhibition. So far we have only been able to say that during a particular change of PFK activity, 20 per cent of the total activation is due to ADP, 50 per cent to AMP, and so on.

Lowry: I can think of a number of examples of studies, including your own, in which there were large increases of citrate but nothing else was very much changed. I think in these cases it is reasonable to attribute the PFK inhibition to citrate. In other situations, however, I think it is going to be very difficult to say whether a change in P_i or AMP, etc., was responsible. The point has been made that it is the synergistic effect of changes in several factors that is probably responsible.

Bücher: There is one problem. You will never get the actual concentration in the tissue; the best thing you can get is the content of the tissue. Professor Cori has just reminded us that there might be at least 6 forms of ATP -- bound ATP in the mitochondria, free ATP, extra-mitochondrial ATP, and so on.

Davies: I thoroughly agree with Dr. Bücher. It is also incorrect to use the ATP/ADP ratio without regard to the fact that these are just contents and not concentrations. This is certainly true for the Ca^{++} content of muscle. There is no question of Ca^{++} changing into anything else; the amount that diffuses out is negligible compared to the total amount that is there. The amount in muscle is a few mmoles/kg wet weight, and the actomyosin ATPase is activated unless the concentration is below 10^{-7} M. When it is as high as 10^{-5} M, the ATPase is fully activated; so clearly, in the resting muscle the concentration of free Ca^{++} in the sarcoplasm must be less than 10^{-7} M, although the muscle has an apparent "concentration" 10,000 times greater than this. Thus it is perfectly clear that the Ca^{++} must be compartmentalized, and no amount of measurement on the intact muscle will tell you where it is. You must use other techniques for this and for other compounds; until you have them, you cannot, in my opinion, be certain about which compound is the one that is causing the change at the particular site you are interested in.

Chance: One must employ intracellular indicators to measure intracellular concentrations. There are two possibilities. First, we may study the "affinities" of intracellular enzymes or enzyme systems (such as mitochondria) for various control chemicals *in vitro*, and then observe whether they respond half-maximally *in vivo* (Chance, B., and Connelly, C. M., Nature, 179, 1235 (1957)). Alternatively, one may microinject the control chemicals into the appropriate region of single cells and observe responses of reduced pyridine nucleotide fluorometrically as is being attempted here by Dr. Kohen.

Bücher: I would like to emphasize what Dr. Davies just stated. I generally dislike the use of the term "*in vivo* concentration" in discussing the amounts of metabolites extracted from a specimen of tissue referred to its fresh weight. Professor Cori has already stressed that the inhomogeneity of the intracellular distribution might limit the interpretation of the analyses. The analytical figures give us the average of the amounts of metabolites probably bound at many sites, e.g., those complexed with various cations, as well as with the true concentrations which are spread through various physically separated compartments. In many cases, the actual concentration might be quite different from the amounts analyzed; in other cases, not.

Referring to the ratio of the amount of reactant-product couples, I would like to caution against the possible errors inherent in this approach; their applicability must be carefully investigated in each and every case.

Two examples may serve to illustrate the situation: the ratio of "contents" (amount extracted) of DPN/DPNH in normoxic liver is about 10. The ratio of lactate to pyruvate is also about 10. Now, we may assume that the LDH reaction approaches mass action equilibrium in the extramitochondrial spaces of the normoxic liver cell, so that the true DPN/DPNH ratio is more like 1,000 instead of 10. This is ample evidence for the incorrectness of an approach based solely on the tissue content.

A second instance is provided by the ATP/ADP ratio. The ratio of these concentrations extracted from the normoxic liver is about 5; in anoxia, it decreases to about 2. However, the corresponding figures for the CTP/CDP couple are 30 and 3. A better approach to the true concentrations expressed in the ATP/ADP ratio appears to be closer to 30 than 5, since ADP is the primary phosphate acceptor during oxidative phosphorylation.

Hess: From the approach I expressed previously (see page 111) I would like to mention that the figure for concentration and "active concentration" (as defined by Meyerhoff) cannot differ by a large factor for such simple enzyme reactions as enolase and PGM and because the calculation on a molar basis for the maximum activities of both enzymes agrees well with the calculation on the kilogram basis.

BICENTENNIAL LECTURES ON CONTROL OF ENERGY METABOLISM

LECTURES CELEBRATING THE BICENTENNIAL OF
THE UNIVERSITY OF PENNSYLVANIA SCHOOL OF MEDICINE
ON
CONTROL OF ENERGY METABOLISM
May 21, 1965

Chairman: Sir Hans Krebs, University of Oxford

"Energy Transformations in the Generation of Bioelectricity"
Dr. Richard D. Keynes, Cambridge, England

"Bioenergetics of Muscular Contraction"
Dr. Robert E. Davies, University of Pennsylvania

"Enzyme Control of Anaerobic Muscle Metabolism"
Dr. Carl F. Cori, Washington University
(The main substance of this paper may be found on p. 299 of this text)

"Control of Liver Metabolism"
Prof. Theodor Bücher, University of Munich, München

"Enzyme Control of Aerobic Metabolism"
Dr. Britton Chance, University of Pennsylvania

ENERGY TRANSFORMATIONS IN THE GENERATION OF BIOELECTRICITY

R. D. Keynes

Agricultural Research Council, Institute of Animal Physiology
Babraham, Cambridge, England

All the available evidence supports the view that the immediate source of energy for the electric current that flows when an impulse is propagated along a nerve or muscle fiber, or when an electric organ discharges, is the pre-existing ionic concentration gradient. In general, current flowing into a cell is carried by Na^+ ions moving from a high extracellular concentration to a low intracellular concentration, while outward current is carried by K^+ ions moving similarly down their gradient from a high internal level. Under some circumstances some outward current may also be carried by an inward transfer of Cl^- ions, but usually the anion movements are relatively small. The first transformation that we have to consider is therefore the conversion of energy stored in the form of concentration gradients into energy released as electric current. The process that allows this conversion to take place is a highly organized sequence of changes in the ionic permeability of the cell membrane, which I shall refer to as the "excitability mechanism". In the membrane of the squid giant axon, whose properties have recently been reviewed by Hodgkin (1), the ease of passage of Na^+ and K^+ ions through the passive permeability channels is both voltage- and time-dependent; depolarization causes an immediate rise in the sodium permeability of the membrane, which declines a millisecond or so later through an inactivation process, followed by a delayed rise in the potassium permeability, which is reversed when the membrane potential returns to its original resting level, but is not subject to inactivation with time. Other types of nerve and muscle fiber behave in a similar way, though with some variation in the details of the mechanism. It is of interest in this connection that Nakamura, Nakajima and Grundfest (2) have recently reported that the potassium permeability of the innervated face of the electroplate of Electrophorus (the electric eel) is very high at all times, and does not increase during the repolarization phase of the spike. But although the behavior of the excitability mechanism has been very closely investigated in a variety of tissues, and has been described quantitatively and accurately by sets of mathematical equations, it would be fair to say that we are still very much in the dark as to exactly how the cell membrane discriminates so well and in such a complicated fashion between ions as like one another chemically as Na^+ and K^+. The important advances that have been made in the past fifteen years in our knowledge of the mechanism of propagation of impulses in nerve and muscle, and of the additive discharge in electric organs, have not yet led to a proper understanding in which, at the molecular level, cell membranes operate.

This statement is equally true of the second transformation of which I have to speak - that is to say the utilization of energy stored in chemical bonds to restore the ionic concentration gradients that are drawn upon in the first stage of energy conversion. There is no doubt whatever of the existence of mechanisms for the active transport of ions against electrochemical potential gradients, and in the case with which I am concerned the "pump mechanism" certainly is able to bring about a coupled uphill transport of both Na^+ and K^+ ions. But although there is now good evidence, which I shall summarize in a moment, that the sodium pump derives its energy supply, like the mechanism of muscular contraction which Dr. Davies will describe, from the terminal energy-rich phosphate bonds of ATP, there is still virtually no indication at all as to how the pump selects the appropriate ions and transfers them through the membrane. Probably the most popular theory is the circulating carrier hypothesis, according to which a carrier X^- with a specific affinity for K^+ is converted by phosphorylation at the inside of the membrane into a sodium carrier Y^-; as long as an adequate supply of ATP is available, a steady stream of NaY then moves through the membrane to release its sodium outside, where Y^- is reconverted to X^-, which ferries K^+ inwards on its return journey. However, we have little information about the chemical identity of X^- and Y^-. The idea that phosphatidic acid is somehow involved in the cycle (3) no longer has many supporters, and experiments with $AT^{32}P$ on electric organ ATPase seem to argue against the direct participation of any membrane phospholipid (4). Several attempts have been made with labelled ATP to isolate phosphorylated intermediates which might form part of the pump mechanism (see, for example, references 5, 6, and 7), but although they seem to implicate some kind of phosphoprotein, perhaps containing phosphoserine, no really clear-cut characterization has yet been achieved. It is, of course, quite possible that the specificity of the pump depends on maintenance of the membrane structure in which it is located, and that attempts to extract the mechanism by applying standard biochemical fractionation procedures are therefore doomed to failure. The striking successes that have been reported in studies of the Na- and K-activated ATPase systems first described by Skou (8) for microsomal preparations from minced crab nerve are not inconsistent with this rather pessimistic view, since they appear to consist largely of relatively intact pieces of cell membrane.

Apart from the work on ATPase systems that I have just mentioned, the most direct evidence that the pump mechanism is driven by phosphate-bond energy is probably that obtained by Caldwell, Hodgkin, Keynes and Shaw (9) for the squid giant axon, in which they showed that in axons whose endogenous supply of ATP had been blocked by treatment with cyanide, the sodium efflux could be restored temporarily by injection of ATP, arginine phosphate or phosphoenolpyruvate. This work revealed interesting variations in the closeness of coupling between the sodium efflux and the potassium influx when the ratio of [ATP] to [ADP] was changed, simulation of normal operation of the sodium pump in an unpoisoned axon only being achieved when the ratio was high. In muscle it is less easy to provide a direct demonstration that the sodium pump is driven by ~P bonds, and since I do not pretend that this is anything but a partisan account of the situation, I will only say that the evidence seems to me far more consistent with this view than with Conway's redox pump theory, according to which sodium movements are coupled to electron transport in the cytochrome system (10). In the one tissue which is specially adapted for the production of electricity, the electric organ, there is also good evidence for the intervention of ~P bonds, since a breakdown of phosphocreatine which is large enough to account quantitatively for the electric power generated has been shown to precede the activation of glycolysis which then replenishes the stores of energy-rich phosphate (11, 12). The third and later energy transformations in the generation of bioelectricity are hence the chains of reactions involved in aerobic and anaerobic metabolism which result in the resynthesis of ATP from ADP and inorganic phosphate at the expense of a breakdown of glycogen and other metabolic intermediates. I need say nothing further about them, since they will be discussed fully by later speakers.

In discussions of the subject of this talk I have often encountered considerable confusion between the concepts of the excitability mechanism and of the pump mechanism, and I will therefore try to summarize the reasons for thinking that they involve entirely separate, albeit parallel channels for the passage of ions across the cell membrane. Almost the only characteristic which the two mechanisms have in common is their ability to discriminate between sodium and potassium, although even here the similarity is lost when their behavior towards the other alkali metal ions is considered. It is possible that both mechanisms exploit the same fundamental physicochemical differences between hydrated Na^+ and K^+ ions that provide a basis for the selectivity of the glasses studied by Eisenman (13), but in every other respect their behavior can readily be contrasted, as will be seen in the following list of their properties:

(a) The direction of ion movements

Operation of the excitability mechanism involves movement of the ions down their concentration gradients, i.e. sodium is transferred inwards and potassium outwards; the pump moves the ions uphill, against the gradients. These statements refer strictly to net movements, not to movements of labelled ions, since both mechanisms permit a transfer of labelled sodium or potassium in the opposite direction to the main stream.

(b) Coupling with metabolism

The excitability mechanism can operate quite independently of cellular metabolism, whereas the pump has to have a steady supply of ATP. This vitally important contrast between the two systems was first made clear in experiments on cephalopod giant axons (14), in which it was shown that treatment with cyanide or dinitrophenol abolished active transport but left the resting and action potentials wholly unimpaired. The most dramatic demonstration of the independence of the excitability mechanism of metabolism has been provided by recent experiments on squid giant axons whose cytoplasm has been squeezed out and replaced by solutions of inorganic ions. Baker, Hodgkin and Shaw (15) found that such axons could conduct hundreds of thousands of virtually normal impulses when they contained nothing but isotonic potassium sulphate solution. Attempts to activate the pump mechanism in these perfused axons have so far been unsuccessful, but the dependence of the pump on ~P bonds has been amply proved by the injection studies with poisoned axons that have already been mentioned (9). It is, of course, mainly the large size of these axons that makes it possible to dissociate the two mechanisms so clearly, because the internal ionic concentration changes after the passage of a single impulse are relatively small; in small nonmyelinated nerve fibers, such as the C fiber of mammals, the excitability and pump mechanisms are more difficult to disentangle, though in all probability the same distinctions apply.

(c) Effect of temperature

It can be said that, in general, temperature has a larger

effect on excitability than on active transport. Certainly in squid axons the uphill fluxes of labelled ions have larger temperature coefficients than the downhill ones (14). However, some features of the excitability mechanism, such as the rate of change of passive sodium and potassium conductance when the membrane is depolarized, do have a large temperature coefficient.

(d) Effect of membrane potential

The interaction between membrane potential and downhill membrane permeability constitutes an integral part of the excitability mechanism, and the permeability changes very steeply as a function of potential (1). Although there is some evidence that the sodium efflux from frog muscle may be increased by lowering the membrane potential (16), the sodium efflux from a *Sepia* axon was not changed at all by raising it (17), and there can be little doubt that the pump mechanism is relatively independent of the potential across the membrane.

(e) The rate of transfer of ions

During the rising phase of the action potential in a squid axon, Na^+ ions flow downhill through the excitability channel at a rate which may momentarily reach a value of 20,000 pmole/cm^2.sec; shortly afterwards K^+ ions move outwards at a similar rate. The maximum rate at which the sodium pump can operate is of a very different order, since the sodium efflux in a squid axon is unlikely to exceed 100 pmole/cm^2.sec.

(f) Effect of calcium

A lowering of the external calcium concentration has a well known effect on the excitability of nerve fibers, reducing the threshold for excitation and even giving rise to spontaneous firing. This arises from an interaction with the passive ionic permeability which has been examined in detail by Frankenhaeuser and Hodgkin (18). The sodium pump, on the other hand, is unaffected by changes in external [Ca].

(g) Discrimination between sodium and lithium

As was originally discovered by Overton (19), lithium is the only cation other than sodium that will maintain the excitability of a frog muscle. The action potentials generated by nerve and muscle fibers are, indeed, almost unaltered if Li^+ is substituted for Na^+ (20), so that the two ions are treated in a nearly identical fashion by the excitability mechanism. However, lithium which has entered a muscle fiber is extruded relatively slowly (20), and the pump mechanism certainly discriminates against lithium.

(h) Effect of drugs

Cardiac glycosides are potent inhibitors of the pump mechanism, in squid axons (21) and frog muscle (22), as well as in many other types of tissue. At the same time, they do not affect the ability of the fibers to conduct impulses, and thus do not attack the excitability mechanism. There are other drugs, such as local anaesthetics like procaine, which block excitability without, as far as I know, affecting the pump mechanism.

In many different ways, therefore, the excitability mechanism and the pump mechanism have contrasting properties, and the behavior of the one can be drastically changed without any effect on the other. It can hardly be doubted that when ions move through the membrane down their concentration gradients, they follow pathways which are quite separate from those traversed when the sodium pump transfers them back again. How far the channels for sodium and potassium in either mode should also be regarded as separate is a harder question, and a fair amount of research is currently being done on the way in which the ion fluxes are coupled together.

There is a special relevance in mentioning research on the electric organ on the occasion of these celebrations. Not only did the first paper to be published in the English language on an electric fish, that of Walsh on *Torpedo* (23), take the form of a letter addressed to Benjamin Franklin, but also the first paper in English on the electric eel originated from Philadelphia, and was written by Hugh Williamson, who graduated in the first class from the College of Philadelphia (24). Philadelphia was, therefore, one of the earliest homes of research on the electric eel, and the work that Dr. Chance and I have done at the Johnson Foundation (12) is in the best tradition.

REFERENCES

1. Hodgkin, A.L., *The Conduction of the Nervous Impulse*, Liverpool University Press (1964).

2. Nakamura, Y., Nakajima, S., and Grundfest, H., Science, 146, 266 (1964).

3. Hokin, L.E., and Hokin, M.R., Nature, London, 184, 1068 (1959).

4. Glynn, I.M., Slayman, Carolyn W., Eichberg, J., and Dawson, R.M.C., Biochem. J., 94, 692 (1965).

5. Skou, J.C., Progr. Biophys., 14, 131 (1964).

6. Whittam, R., Wheeler, K.P., and Blake, A., Nature, 203, 720 (1964).

7. Post, R.L., Sen, Amar K., and Rosenthal, A.S., J. Biol. Chem., 240, 1437 (1965).

8. Skou, J.C., Biochim. Biophys. Acta, 23, 394 (1957).

9. Caldwell, P.C., Hodgkin, A.L., Keynes, R.D., and Shaw, T.I., J. Physiol., 152, 561 (1960).

10. Conway, E.J., Internat. Rev. Cytol., 11, 419 (1953).

11. Caldwell, P.C., and Keynes, R.D., J. Physiol., 169, 37P (1963).

12. Aubert, X., Chance, B., and Keynes, R.D., Proc. Roy. Soc. B, 160, 211 (1964).

13. Eisenman, G., Biophys. J., 2, 259 (1962).

14. Hodgkin, A.L., and Keynes, R.D., J. Physiol., 128, 28 (1955).

15. Baker, P.F., Hodgkin, A.L., and Shaw, T.I., J. Physiol., 164, 330 (1962).

16. Horowicz, P., and Gerber, C.J., J. Gen. Physiol., 48, 489 (1965).

17. Hodgkin, A.L., and Keynes, R.D., Sump. Soc. Exp. Biol., 8, 423 (1954).

18. Frankenhauser, B., and Hodgkin, A.L., J. Physiol., 137, 217 (1957).

19. Overton, E., Pflüg. Arch. Ges. Physiol., 92, 346 (1902).

20. Keynes, R.D., and Swan, R.C., J. Physiol., 147, 626 (1959).

21. Caldwell, P.C., and Keynes, R.D., J. Physiol., 148, 8P (1959).

22. Edwards, C., and Harris, E.J., J. Physiol., 135, 567 (1957).

23. Walsh, J., Philos. Trans., 63, 461 (1773).

24. Williamson, H., Philos. Trans., 65, 94 (1775).

CONTROL OF ENERGY METABOLISM. BIOENERGETICS OF MUSCULAR CONTRACTION*

R. E. Davies

School of Veterinary Medicine, University of Pennsylvania
Philadelphia, Pennsylvania

Muscle is a complex living tissue containing a delicately balanced mechanism with many negative feedback controls which precisely demark the force it can develop, the velocity with which it can move, and the distance it can shorten. The controls are variously anatomical, physiological and biochemical. The anatomy determines whether the muscle is intrinsically fast or slow, whether it can develop large forces over short distances, small forces over long distances, or maintain forces for very long periods. The physiological situation determines what actually happens. Are few, many or all of the individual muscle fibers fully stimulated? Is the muscle lightly or heavily loaded? Is it stretched or pre-shortened? All these affect the energy output. The biochemical situation determines the mechanism for ensuring continued action, the mobilization of several metabolic pathways to produce more energy supplies, and the initiation of the recovery processes. The amount and type of activity then control the subsequent atrophy or hypertrophy of the muscle. How does all this come about?

Today we are celebrating the 200th anniversary of the founding of this School of Medicine, but it is over 2,200 years since the first recorded theory of muscle contraction. This was by Erasistratus of Chios (1), who believed that pneuma or vital spirits passed down the nerves and caused the muscle to expand. This theory is interesting because it was accepted for about 1900 years which is far longer than any other theory of muscle contraction has been believed. However, before we can consider theories, we must know some facts. Some vertebrate muscles have the appropriate anatomy to be fast and quick-acting.

* This investigation was supported in part by the U. S. Public Health Service Research Grant 2R01-HE-02520-09 from the National Heart Institute.

Others, such as those which hold the body together, are slow and able to maintain forces for quite long periods. For example, there is the fast frog sartorius muscle, a classical muscle about which more is known than any other in nature, and the relatively slow rectus abdominis. The edible mussel contains the very slow ABRM, the anterior byssus retractor muscle, and this mussel muscle has the really remarkable property of being able to maintain a continuous force for a whole month without either food or rest.

In some, the individual muscle fibers go from end to end of the muscle, so it can develop a relatively low force but can contract a long distance. In other muscles there are feather-like arrangements of the fibers which allow the development of large forces over quite short distances. An individual fiber is composed of many fibrils and in voluntary muscles these are striated which is why they are also called striated muscles. The fibrils are associated with mitochondria which is where the respiration occurs. They also have a complex network around them. This network is important because it is associated with the activation mechanism. The nerves which go to the individual fibers stimulate all the myofibrils and this causes the release of calcium which is normally sequestered in this particular structure -- the sarcoplasmic reticulum. If the calcium concentration in the sarcoplasm inside the myofibrils is less than one ten millionth molar the muscle relaxes; if it's higher than one hundred thousandth molar the muscle will fully contract (2), and to maintain this concentration one or two calcium atoms must be released per myosin molecule. The view that calcium is important in muscle contraction was held by Professor Heilbrun of this University for many years, and it was only after his tragic death that this has become generally accepted. This effect of calcium is able to explain such different things as milk fever in cows, where in the absence of sufficient calcium in the diet, lactating cows, who need lots of calcium for the milk, can die in flaccid paralysis, but can recover in a few seconds if calcium is injected. It can also explain the well known "Treppe" or staircase phenomenon in the heart when several stimuli may be needed before the cells are fully activated.

In very fast acting muscles, such as those that cause the croaking or drumming noise of the toadfish, or some in the larynx of the bat there is a very well developed sarcoplasmic reticulum. This is much reduced in slower muscles, such as the rabbit psoas muscle. The fibrils are made up of sarcomeres, which cause the visible striations, and the sarcomeres are composed of relatively thick filaments which contain myosin and relatively thin filaments which contain actin. Figure 1 shows

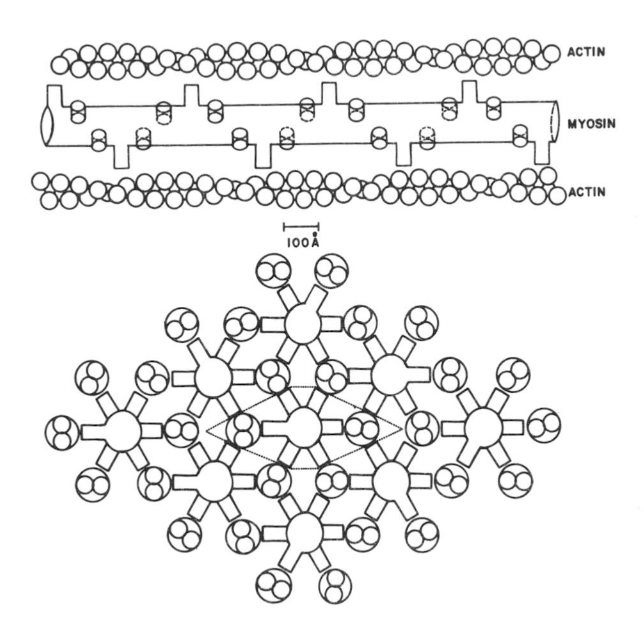

Figure 1. Spatial arrangement of myosin and actin filaments in striated muscle (rabbit psoas). Courtesy, Nature, 199, 1068 (1963).

the open helical nature of the actin filament and the more complex hexagonal helices of the myosin filament. The individual myosin molecules contain one of the side pieces and part of the longitudinal filaments. In cross section, these are arranged in a beautiful hexagonal array, each thick filament having six thin filaments around it, and each thin filaments having three thick filaments around it (3).

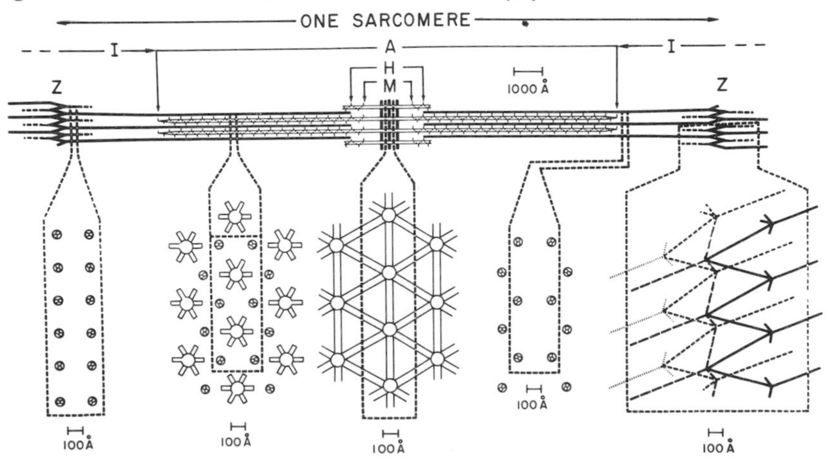

Figure 2. Molecular anatomy of part of one sarcomere of striated muscle.

Figure 2 shows part of a sarcomere and the lengths of the filaments. There are 216 cross bridges in each thick filament. The structure is quite complex and the hexagonal array of actins becomes a square array at the Z line. There are cross links in the middle of the M zone of the sarcomeres which have just been described (4). It is interesting that a blowfly flight muscle, for example, can be stained in such a way as to show up the activity of an enzyme, ATPase, that can break down the important energy transducer adenosine triphosphate or ATP. The activity of the enzyme is apparent in the side pieces of the myosin filaments in the region where they overlap with the actin filaments, besides being in the Z line and in the cristae of the mitochondria (5). The individual molecules of myosin are rather tadpole shaped (6), and enzymic studies on fragmented myosin show that the ATPase is in the head of these molecules (7).

One of the more surprising findings of recent years in this field has been the discovery that when muscles contract the individual filaments do not contract but remain the same overall length. The I band changes in length, the A band remains the same, and an overlap region can occur in the middle (8, 9).

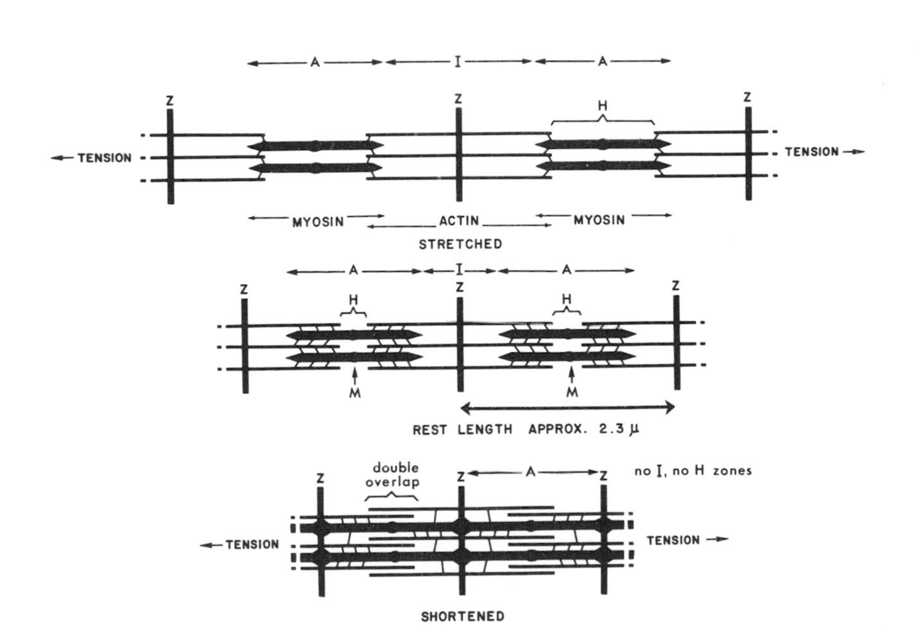

Figure 3. Schematic diagram of contraction of skeletal muscle showing some completed cross bridges at various lengths.

This is shown in Figure 3 where it can be seen that the overlap of the thick and thin filaments changes with the state of the muscle and that a double overlap can occur when the muscle shortens. This isn't the occasion to discuss theories of the precise molecular biology of muscle contraction or the precise chemical mechanism, but it seems likely that the method of creeping of the actins over the myosin depends on some cyclic process going on in the side bridges shown diagrammatically in Figure 4 as a conformational change of part of these cross bridges. This process requires the action of calcium and of adenosine triphosphate (10) and is believed to be a cyclic change from a coil to a helix to a coil of a specific polypeptide with ATP bound to it within the head of the myosin (Figure 5). Calcium is believed to form the transient link between actin and myosin. The ATPase breaks the link and allows the ratchet-like process to continue.

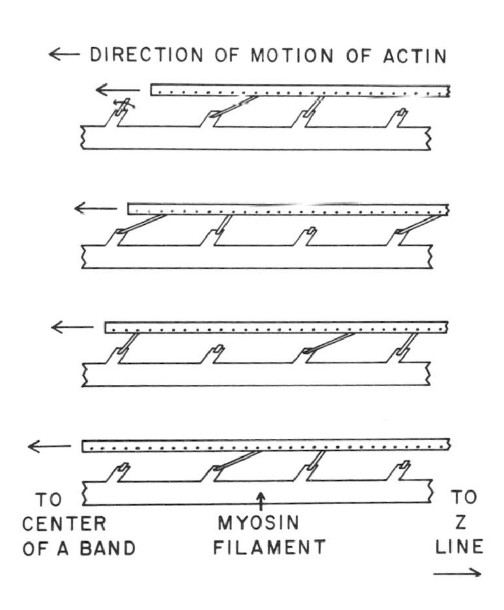

Figure 4. Diagram of assumed contractions and extensions of part of the cross bridges during muscle contraction.

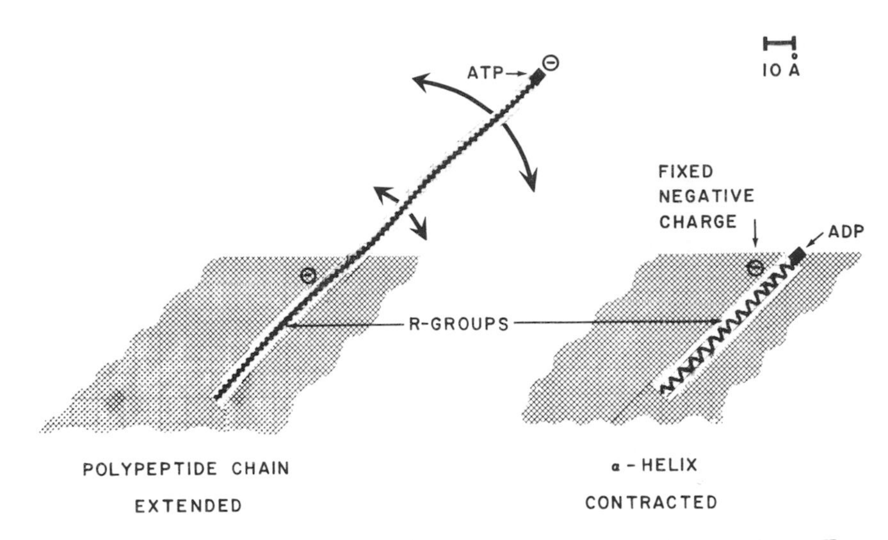

Figure 5. Diagram of a flexible polypeptide chain of an H-meromyosin in the extended and contracted state. Courtesy, Nature, 199, 1070 (1963).

Much work on isolated myosin and actin and on muscles treated with glycerol suggest that adenosine triphosphate is the actual energy source although this proved very difficult to demonstrate in living muscles (11). There are several mechanisms by which the adenosine triphosphate can be resynthesized partly by the action of a storage molecule phosphorylcreatine and also by the action of an enzyme, myokinase, which operates so that the product of the activity of the ATP, that is adenosine diphosphate (ADP)can go through a dismutation to form both ATP and adenosine monophosphate (AMP). It is interesting that the product of the action of the myosin ATPase, ADP and also AMP are able to stimulate glycolysis. Now Dr. Keynes has talked about the mechanism of stimulation by nerves, and Professor Cori will talk about the stimulation of glycolysis by ADP and AMP. It is interesting that ADP also stimulates oxidative phosphorylation and this will be Professor Chance's topic. Part of the biochemical processes cause the production of lactic acid which is liberated from the muscle to the blood and turned into glucose in the liver. This will be Professor Bücher's province.

Our experiments have been done in collaboration with Drs. Delluva, Cain, Infante, Kushmerick and Minihan and have been mainly on frog muscles at 0° C. Experiments have usually lasted about 1 second with a home-made apparatus. This apparatus has the peculiar property that virtually everything in it was borrowed. Professor Krebs may recognize the stimulator and stopwatch borrowed from Oxford. Professor Brobeck may recognize the kymograph we scavenged from his stockroom, and Professor Chance lent us the ergometer for the experiments. The total apparatus cost me only \$2.50. Its purpose was to make it possible to freeze the muscle rapidly in situ. This was done by this little device which is an old automobile pump operated by a derelict washing machine relay which lifts some liquid freon and rapidly freezes the muscle. With this apparatus the muscle can be frozen in situ at any point in the contraction-relaxation cycle.

We found that, in a single isotonic twitch, activation requires no significant amount of energy at the time it occurs, i.e., there is no usage of ATP. The work done in contraction does, however, and to our surprise there was an extra breakdown of ATP as the muscle relaxed during the decline of the active state (Figure 6), which we now believe is a measure of the removal of calcium from the myofibrils (12).

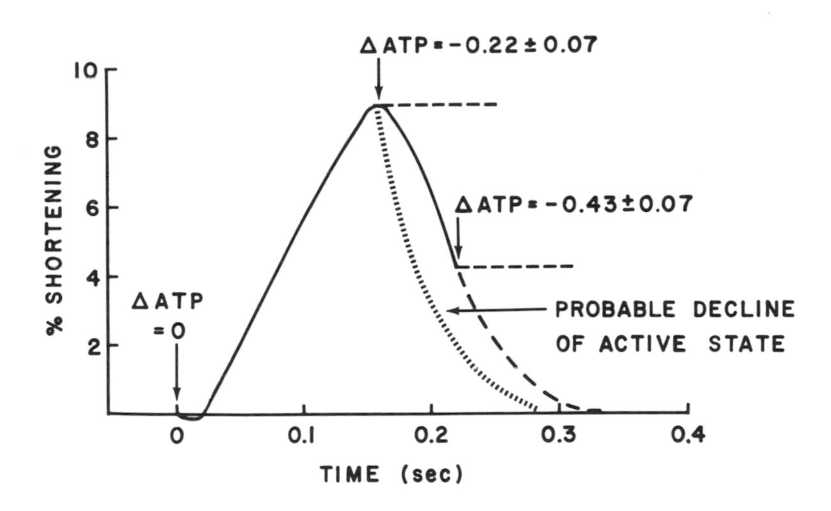

Figure 6. Changes in the ATP content of the frog sartorius muscles during a single isotonic twitch. (0° C, muscles pretreated with 2,4 dinitrofluorobenzene. Work done approximately 17 g-cm/g.

Now Professor A. V. Hill and his colleagues had made the major discovery that the heat output of a muscle during a contraction depends on the distance shortened and was independent of the load that the muscle was bearing at the time (13). We therefore measured the ATP needed both for work and for shortening and found that whereas there was a linear relationship between work and the usage of ATP, none at all was needed for shortening. In fact, calculations based on the theory of contraction I've just outlined show that shortening heat and all its various complexities apparently can be accounted for quantitatively from the formation of hydrogen bonds during the helix-coil transformation (10). From experiments such as this the efficiency of muscle, that is the external work done per molecule of ATP used can be calculated and surprisingly this seems to vary with the type of muscle. A slow muscle, the anterior byssus retractor operated at 51 per cent efficiency, the rather faster rectus abdominis at 44 per cent efficiency, and the fastest muscle that we've tried, the sartorius, operated at 35 per cent efficiency.

Professor Andrew Huxley and his colleagues have shown how the maximum isometric tension that can be developed is controlled by the length of the muscle (14). This depends on the overlap of the thick and thin filaments in the sarcomere. When the muscle is stretched so that no overlap occurs then no tension can be developed. When the muscle is so much contracted that the thick filaments hit the Z line and crumple, then again no tension can be developed and the shape of the length-developed tension curve follows from the different relationships of the thick and thin filaments. In particular, the maximum force depends on the amount of overlap.

We did experiments to find out how the usage of ATP would be affected by this. We measured the length-tension curve and the actual usage of ATP during isometric tetani at various lengths. We found that the two curves followed each other but that there was a residual basal turnover which seems to be just that expected from the calcium pumping mechanism associated with the sarcoplasmic reticulum (15).

One of the most important findings concerning the biophysics of muscle was made over the last several years by Professor Hill and his colleagues who found that when an activated muscle was stretched the energy output decreased, there was an apparent disappearance of energy which could be interpreted as a reversal of the final chemical reaction (16). It was, therefore, of interest to try and find out what happens under these circumstances. We repeated these experiments as near identically as we could except that we used American frogs instead of English toads, and showed that without doubt there was a reduction of the ATP usage and there was not a resynthesis (17). This, in fact, fits the theory I have outlined earlier. Stretching an activated muscle should physically break hydrogen bonds and cause a cooling of the muscle as was actually observed, and ATP breakdown should be reduced but no resynthesis should occur. It's interesting that negative work is at least ten times more "efficient" than positive work and this accounts for why it's possible to go downstairs backwards with very much less effort than to go upstairs at the same speed even though the muscles are developing the same forces, and moving through the same distances for the same times. However, they are doing negative rather than positive work.

The force-velocity and length-tension relationships have been further investigated and we've found that the faster the muscle moves, the less ATP is required for a given distance moved; the slower it moves, the more ATP is required, and this is related to the fact that whereas a fully stimulated, lightly-loaded muscle can move at high speeds, a heavily-loaded muscle can only move slowly. Clearly this means that a velocity-dependent chemical reaction is involved and the chance of link formation between the actin and myosin is reduced at high speeds. Here is yet another control of the bioenergetics of muscle contraction (18).

Some new control mechanisms have been found recently. Maximal isometric contractions of only a few seconds per day cause the muscle to grow more filaments, more of the muscle material that can develop force. Isotonic contractions apparently cause the growth of more of the reticulum, and this involves the calcium pump and the glycolytic enzymes. There is also an increase in the number and activity of the mitochondria that are associated with oxygen uptake. The two situations can be exemplified by considering the pole vaulter who develops maximal isometric contractions and develops very strong shoulder muscles, and the swimmer who remains lithe with great endurance but without great hypertrophy (19). The mechanism of this control mechanism is a problem for the future. It is possible that the explanation of this will be understood from recent discoveries in the molecular biology of the mode of action of the repression and induction phenomena in genes and the mode of action of hormones on chromosomes.

I think you will agree that muscle is a very complex system and that, though much yet remains to be done, the outlines of our eventual understanding are at last becoming clear.

REFERENCES

1. Erisistratus, (290 B. C.) quoted by Galen. Seen in Wilson, L. G., Notes Roy. Soc. Lond., 16, 158 (1961).

2. Caldwell, P. C., Proc. Roy. Soc., B, 160, 433 (1964).

3. Huxley, H. E., in J. Brachet and A. E. Mirsky (Eds.), The Cell, IV, Academic Press, London, 1960, p. 365.

4. Huxley, H. E., in W. M. Paul, E. E. Daniel, C. M. Kay and G. Monckton (Eds.), Muscle, Pergamon Press, Oxford, 1965, p. 3.

5. Zebe, E., and Falk, H., Zeit. Naturforsch, 18b, 501 (1963).

6. Rice, R., in J. Gergely (Ed.), Biochemistry of Muscle Contraction, Little, Brown and Co., Boston, 1964, p. 41.

7. Mueller, H., and Perry, S. V., Biochem. J., 85, 431 (1962).

8. Huxley, A. F., and Niedergerke, R., Nature, Lond., 173, 971 (1954).

9. Huxley, H. E., and Hanson, J., Nature, Lond., 173, 973 (1954).

10. Davies, R. E., Nature, Lond., 199, 1068 (1963).

11. Davies, R. E., in P. N. Campbell and G. D. Greville, (Eds.), Essays in Biochemistry, I, Academic Press, London, 1965, p. 2

12. Infante, A. A., and Davies, R. E., Biochem. Biophys. Res. Commun., 9, 410 (1962).

13. Hill, A. V., Proc. Roy. Soc., B, 141, 161 (1953).

14. Gordon, A. M., Huxley, A. F., and Julian, F. J., J. Physiol., 171, 28P (1964).

15. Infante, A. A., Klaupiks, D., and Davies, R. E., Biochim. Biophys. Acta, 88, 215 (1964).

16. Hill, A. V., Science, 131, 897 (1960).

17. Infante, A. A., Klaupiks, D., and Davies, R. E., Science, 144, 1577 (1964).

18. Kushmerick, M. J., Minihan, K., and Davies, R. E., Fed. Proc., 24, 598 (1965).

19. Gordon, E. E., personal communication (1965).

HEMOGLOBIN-FREE PERFUSION OF RAT LIVER*

Roland Scholz and Theodor Bücher

Physiologisch-chemisches Institut
der Universität München
München, Germany

There are no difficulties, theoretically, in securing a sufficient oxygen supply by perfusing an isolated liver in the absence of erythrocytes. For instance, a rat liver may easily be perfused with 5 ml of fluid per minute per gram tissue by way of the portal vein. 500 µatoms of oxygen per hour per gram tissue would be supplied by saturating the perfusion fluid (Table I) with oxygen at normal pressure. The stationary respiration of the organ amounts to about one half of that.

TABLE I

Composition of perfusion fluid (mM) and conditions of perfusion

Composition (mM)	Conditions
137.0 NaCl	T = 36° C
2.7 KCl	pH = 7.40
0.7 NaH_2PO_4	
0.5 $CaCl_2$	gas mixtures:
0.5 $MgCl_2$	normoxia 95 °/o O_2 + 5 °/o CO_2
23.0 $NaHCO_3$	anoxia 95 °/o A + 5 °/o CO_2
5.5 glucose	
1.5 lactate	perfusion:
0.9 glutamate	3 - 5 ml/min/g liver
0.9 glutamine	
0.6 alanine	oxygen input:
0.5 glycine	300 - 500 µatoms O/h/g liver
0.3 serine	
0.2 threonine	oxygen consumption:
0.1 aspartate	200 - 300 µatoms O/h/g liver
70 g/L dextran (MW 40 000)	
"Rheomakrodex" of Knoll AG., Ludwigshafen, Germany	

* Supported by grants of the Squibb Institute for Medical Research, New Brunswick, New Jersey.

Many setbacks, however, have demonstrated that a homogenous distribution of oxygen throughout the tissue is not achieved easily. Systematic investigations of oxygen tensions on the liver surface were carried out together with D. W. Lübbers and his colleagues (1) and it was recognized that a sufficient perfusion to all parts of the organ may be provided by setting a back pressure of 5-10 cm water in the effluent. This procedure has the effect of increasing the liver volume to about 170 per cent. Histologically, a considerable widening of the pericapillary space is observed. It has been shown, however, that such a preparation, in spite of its rather non-physiological appearance maintains a steady state in the system of energy metabolism over a considerable period of time. However, deviations from the "normal state" caused by anoxia or by the addition of metabolic inhibitors are reversible and reproducible. These results encouraged us to make use of the hemoglobin-free system for a more detailed investigation of metabolic interdependences in liver.

The first portion of this paper describes various possibilities of experimental approach in demonstrating metabolic changes during a "cycle of anoxia" that occur during the sequence normoxia → anoxia → normoxia.

Lactate-pyruvate ratio during a cycle of anoxia. As shown earlier, regulation of the lactate-pyruvate ratio is not only found to be a significant contribution of the liver to the homeostasis of plasma constituents *in vivo*, but also a sensitive indicator of the metabolic fitness of the perfused organ (2,3,4). Reading Figure 1 from left to right, we see that our hemoglobin-free system in the normoxic state very nearly exhibits the physiological ratio of lactate to pyruvate of about 10 in the perfusate. Then, switching over from oxygen-saturated to argon-saturated perfusion fluid, the lactate-pyruvate ratio in the perfusate increases rapidly. Under these conditions, pyruvate is consumed by the organ and lactate is released. After restoration of the oxygen supply these events are reversed and the normoxic state is completely regenerated, with respect to both the lactate-pyruvate ratio as well as the absolute levels of lactate and pyruvate. The rapidity and reversibility of the events exceeds even that found with the blood-perfused liver. This suggests a high degree of homogeneity of perfusion. Moreover, the absence of metabolic interactions by erythrocytes may also contribute.

Surface fluorometry during a cycle of anoxia. The application of the fluorometric technique of Chance *et al.* (5) to the hemoglobin-free perfused liver under conditions similar to those described in the previous section are shown in Figure 2.

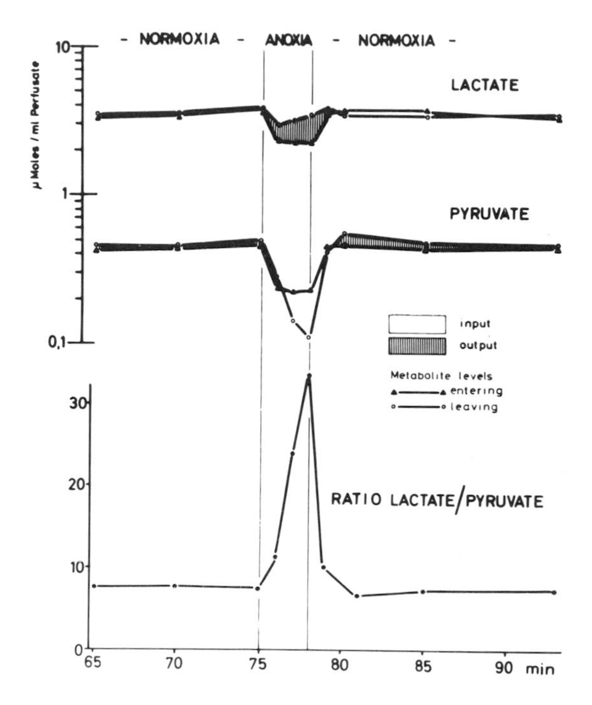

Figure 1. Effect of anoxia on the levels of lactate and pyruvate in the perfusion fluid, entering and leaving the liver (37).

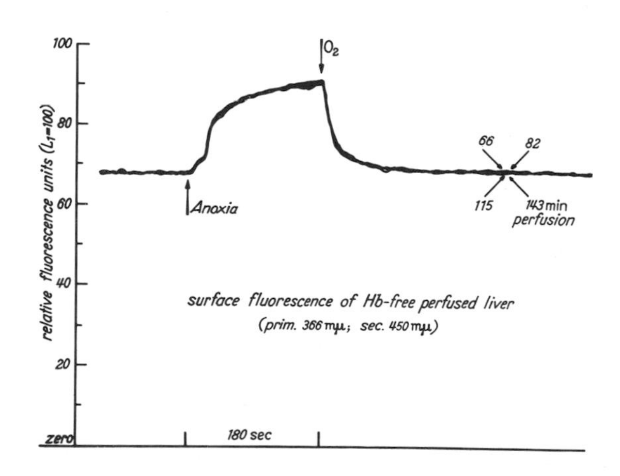

Figure 2. Superimposed fluorescence traces of four anoxic cycles in perfused rat liver (see ref. 1).

Four fluorescence traces have been recorded on the same area of liver surface, but at different times within three hours of perfusion. These traces have been superimposed with respect to the onset of anoxia.

Different sections of the fluorometric trace can be distinguished: first, we find a latent phase of about 5 seconds; then a slow increase is observed, which at 20 seconds after the onset of anoxia is followed by a fast increase ("20 second jump"); and finally, at 35 seconds, the fluorometric trace inclines to a smaller slope, levelling off very slowly. A few seconds after switching over to oxygen-saturated perfusion fluid, the fluorescence intensity decreases sharply and the original level is reached within two minutes.

Again we see the rapidity and reversibility of changes in the anoxic cycle which are similar to changes observed in the "ischemic cycle" caused by stopping the perfusion (1). Furthermore, the experiment demonstrates an outstanding reproducibility of the data found. Absence of hemodynamic effects, which interfere essentially in fluorometric observations of the liver *in vivo* (1) contribute to the high degree of reproducibility. Also the overshoot observed in the *in vivo* experiments during the phase of restitution (6,7) is not observed in the hemoglobin-free system and must be ascribed therefore, to hemodynamic effects.

As shown by Chance and co-workers on various tissues (8, 9,10) and as discussed below for our preparation, the fluorometric changes during a cycle of anoxia are mostly due to corresponding changes in the amount and state of the reduced pyridine nucleotides. It must be mentioned, however, that in the hemoglobin-free perfused system, a long-term change of the base fluorescence is observed: immediately after adjusting the light-spot of the fluorometer to the liver surface, an increase of fluorescence intensity is seen, which reaches a maximum after about 8 minutes. Then follows a gradual levelling off with a 50 per cent value at 40 minutes. About 3 hours after the onset of irradiation, the final level is reached. At every state of this movement of the base fluorescence, a cycle of anoxia could be achieved which is similar in shape qualitatively as well as quantitatively. Thus, the base fluorescence originates from an as yet unknown component which is probably independent of reduced pyridine nucleotides. This portion does not seem to take part in the rapid metabolic changes induced by anoxia or by the addition of the metabolic inhibitors, as used in our measurements.

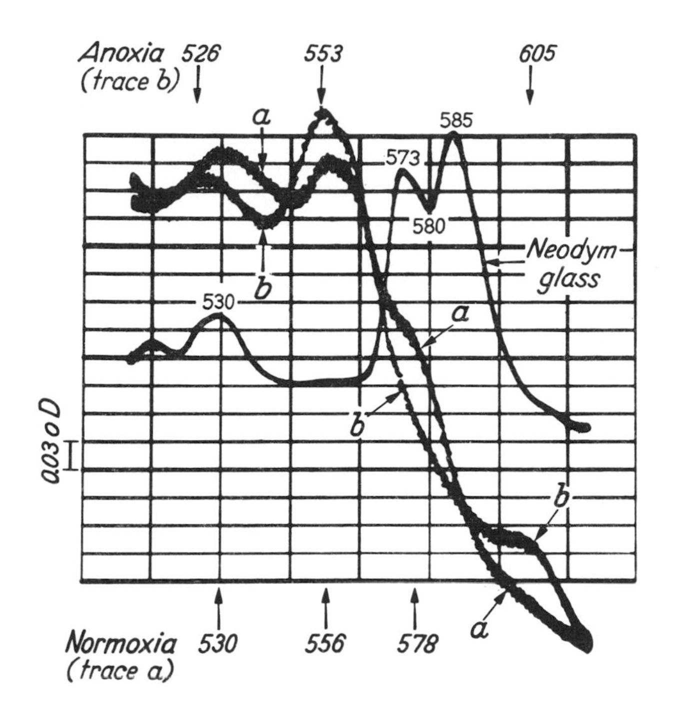

Figure 3. Reflection spectra of perfused rat liver against a reference surface of magnesium oxide. Trace "a", normoxic state; trace "b", anoxic state. (See ref. 13).

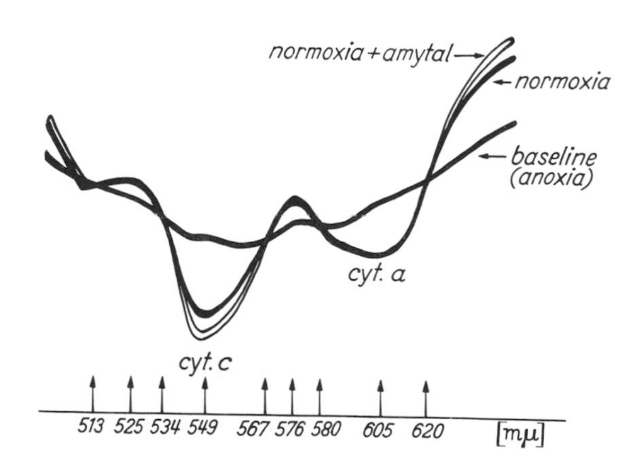

Figure 4. Reflection spectra of perfused rat liver against a reference surface of liver homogenate, treated with dithionite. (See ref. 1).

Reflection spectra during a cycle of anoxia. Since hemoglobin is avoided in our preparation, direct investigation of respiratory pigments by reflection photometry is possible for the first time on the liver surface. The traces shown in Figures 3 and 4 are oscilloscope records of the "Rapidspectrometer" of Lübbers and Niesel (11,12), an instrument which renders 100 reflection difference spectra per second. The spectra in Figure 3 are recorded from the liver surface against a white reference surface. The absorption spectrum of a neodymium glass has also been recorded for checking the wavelength scale. Trace "a" represents a spectrum under normoxic and trace "b" under anoxic conditions (13).

Higher sensitivity is gained by using a liver homogenate reduced by dithionite as a reference. Such difference spectra recorded in normoxia, anoxia and in normoxia under the influence of amytal are seen in Figure 4. Peaks corresponding to cytochromes a and c are observed. With amytal the extinction of cytochrome c increases, whereas cytochrome a stays unaltered. From these spectra it may be concluded that in the normoxic stationary state cytochrome a is nearly oxidized, while cytochrome c is reduced up to 20 per cent (see below).

The kinetics of the spectral changes at 552 and 607 mμ (corresponding to cytochromes c and a) during a cycle of anoxia are shown in Figure 5 together with a simultaneous record of the fluorescence changes. We notice that the time of 50 per cent reduction of the cytochromes is in agreement with the onset of the "20 second junp" of fluorescence mentioned in the preceding section. After 35 seconds of anoxia, spectral changes of cytochromes a and c are complete, while the fluorescence

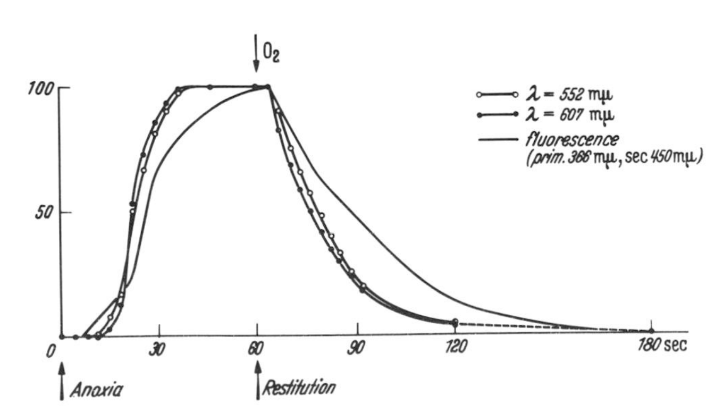

Figure 5. Comparison between changes of reflection at 552 mμ and 607 mμ (cytochrome c and a peak) and the fluorescence intensity during a cycle of anoxia (see ref. 13).

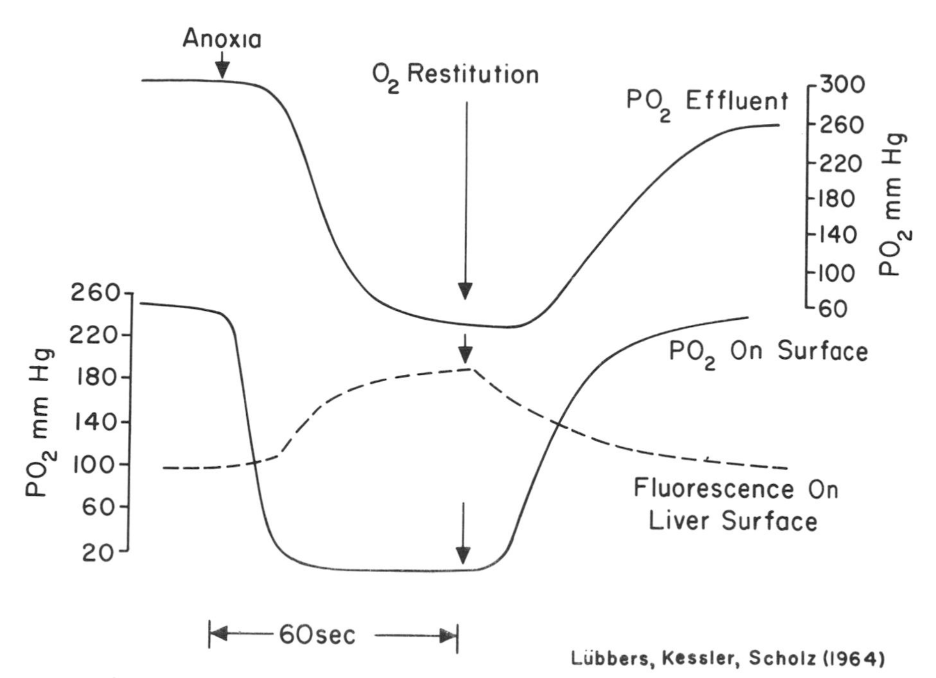

Figure 6. Synchronous registration of oxygen pressure and fluorescence intensity (14).

still increases slowly.

By comparing Figures 5 and 6 with the help of simultaneous fluorescence measurements we may also correlate the kinetics of cytochrome reduction with the corresponding oxygen tension at the tissue surface (14). Figure 6 shows such synchronous recordings from the same liver lobe. The "20 second jump" starts when oxygen reaches the critical value of nearly 10 mm mercury. At this moment the rapid reduction of cytochromes a and c also begins (see Figure 5). On interpreting these data, however, it must be considered that very strict correlations are not possible, because all the cells in the tissue under observation are not necessarily simultaneously subjected to the same changes in oxygen supply.

Cytochrome b_5 during a cycle of anoxia. In contrast to the observations on cytochromes a and c shown above, there are no changes in the α-band of cytochrome b_5 during a cycle of anoxia. The well known α-band at 556 mμ of reduced cytochrome b_5 is already present in the normoxic state (see Figure 3). Almost no changes in this band can be detected in the difference spectra of normoxic against anoxic liver (13). On the basis of spectroscopic observations on liver slices, Chance and Hollunger

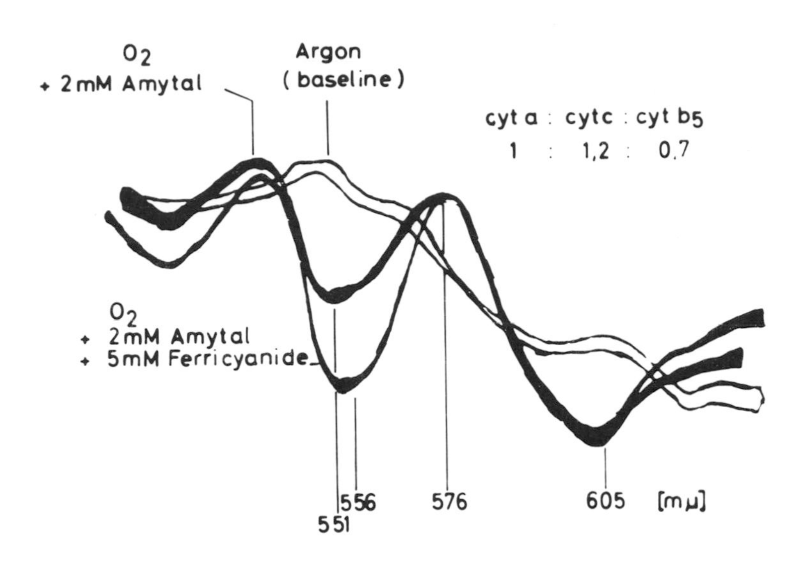

Figure 7. Reflection spectra of perfused rat liver against a reference surface of a liver homogenate, treated with dithionite. The curves shown correspond to treatment of the normoxic liver with 2.0 mM amytal and with 2.0 mM amytal plus 5.0 mM ferricyanide, compared with the anoxic state (argon-saturated perfusion fluid) (14).

(15) have already suggested that cytochrome b_5 does not participate in redox changes of the respiratory chain. The situation is now clarified. Cytochrome b_5 is essentially reduced even in the state of sufficient oxygen supply to the respiratory chain.

One may achieve oxidation of cytochrome b_5 by addition of ferricyanide to the perfusion solution. Figure 7 demonstrates three difference spectra (reference: dithionite-treated liver homogenate) of the liver surface: 1) anoxic conditions (argon-saturated perfusion fluid); 2) normoxic conditions in the presence of amytal; and 3) normoxic conditions in the presence of amytal and ferricyanide in the perfusion fluid (14). If we evaluate these reflection spectra as absorption spectra, a ratio of cytochrome a to cytochrome c + c_1 to cytochrome b_5 of 1.0 / 1.2 / 0.7 is found. These values agree with measurements of the cytochrome a to cytochrome c + c_1 ratio in rat liver given by Klingenberg (16,17), and also with measurements of the cytochrome b_5 content of rat liver by the Osaka group (18) and Scandanavian colleagues (19) related to the content of cytochrome c + c_1 of rat liver measured by Klingenberg (17).

Respiratory rate during a cycle of anoxia. Another advantage of the hemoglobin-free perfusion is that the oxygen consumption of the organ can be easily recorded. Figure 8

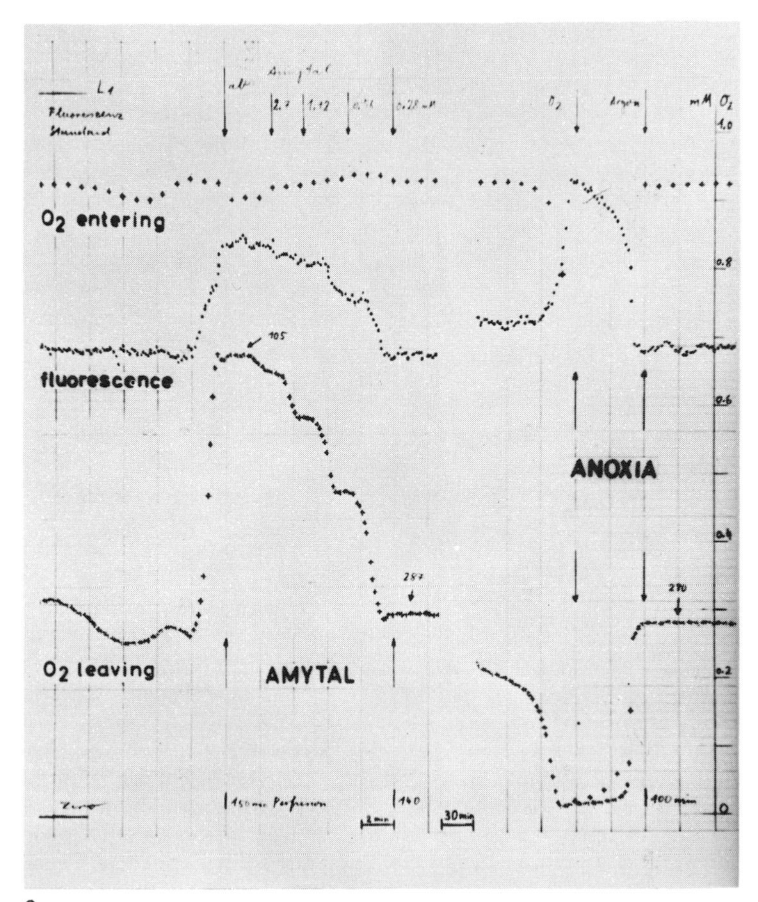

Figure 8. Experimental record showing the oxygen tension (amperometric measurement, using the platinum electrode of Lübbers (39,40)) of perfusion fluid entering and leaving the liver, and the tissue fluorescence during a cycle of anoxia (induced by perfusion with argon-saturated fluid) and during amytal additions. Note time running from right to left. Increases of fluorescence intensity and oxygen tension are denoted by upward deflections of the traces (37).

represents the original record of a perfusion experiment with simultaneous measurements of fluorescence and oxygen tensions in the perfusion fluid entering and leaving the liver. Since the flow rate of the perfusion fluid is constant, the distance between the two traces of oxygen tensions is proportional to the respiratory rate of the liver. For instance, at the beginning of this record, steady state respiration amounts to 290 µatoms oxygen per hour per gram tissue (calculated as fresh weight of the liver before the onset of perfusion).

On the right hand side of Figure 8 a cycle of anoxia is first demonstrated. After switching the perfusion to an oxygen-free solution the oxygen tensions before and after the liver decrease to the zero level. Fluorescence increases in the manner discussed earlier. It must be mentioned that the perfusion fluid passing the liver in anoxia is recirculated into the reservoir used under normoxic conditions. Thus, the lactic acid formed during anoxia is offered to the organ again with the restitution of oxygen supply. After switching the perfusion again to an oxygen-saturated solution, the fluorescence decreases rapidly. A maximal respiratory rate of about 450 µatoms oxygen per hour per gram is then measured. After 10 minutes, the respiration becomes constant at a value of 287 µatoms per hour per gram. At this point the fluorescence also reaches its original level of intensity. The liver recovers from an oxygen debt of about 8 µatoms oxygen per gram tissue. This value is in the range of the amount of lactate produced during 4 minutes of anoxia.

Fluorescence and respiratory rate during an "amytal cycle". In the experiment demonstrated in Figure 8, after a further recovery period of about 20 minutes, amytal was added to the perfusion solution, increasing the molarity stepwise. At the same time the recirculation of the solution was interrupted to avoid an accumulation of amytal. Corresponding to increasing molarities of amytal in the perfusion fluid, we observe a stepwise diminution of the respiratory rate to a final amount of 105 µatoms per hour per gram, i.e., 37 per cent of the respiratory rate in the steady state. In the same manner, the fluorescence intensity mounts up to about 70-80 per cent of the fluorescence increase measured after 4 minutes of anoxia. When amytal is washed away, the effects are rapidly reversible.

Effects of barbiturates. In order to compare the effect of several barbiturates, the concentrations of half-maximal inhibitions of the steady state respiration as well as of half-maximal fluorescence increase, are given in the last columns of Table II (37). These data may be compared with similar measurements reported by Chance and Hess (20) on ascites tumor cells and by Aldridge and Parker (21,22) on isolated liver mitochondria

Cell specific sensibilities for barbiturates are probably responsible for the difference of concentrations for half-maximal effects on liver and ascites cells. With respect to the liver we notice two types of agreements: first the barbiturate concentrations for half-maximal effect on isolated mitochondria (Table II, column 3) is nearly the same as for half-maximal effect on the hemoglobin-free perfused organ (column 4 and 5). Second, the effect on the oxygen uptake of the perfused liver is paralleled by an increase of fluorescence intensity (Figure 8)

TABLE II

Barbiturates as inhibitors of respiration. The figures in the table denote barbiturate concentration (mM) for half-maximal effects.

DRUG	ASCITES TUMOR CELLS	LIVER MITOCHONDRIA	RAT LIVER PERFUSED	
			O_2 UPTAKE	FLUORESCENCE INCREASE
AMYTAL AMYLOBARBITONE	0.8	0.21	0.31	0.30
EVIPAN HEXOBARBITONE	0.2	0.71	0.85	0.91
THIOPENTAL THIOPENTONE		0.21	0.34	
LUMINAL PHENOBARBITONE	1.9	1.0		
VERONAL DIETHYLBARBITONE			1.22	1.77
NEMBUTAL			0.31	0.30
AUTHORS	CHANCE + HESS (1959)	ALDRIDGE + PARKER (1960)	SCHWARZ + SCHOLZ (unpubl.)	

Half-maximal concentrations for both effects agree within the range of experimental errors (column 4 and 5 of Table II). These facts will be of importance for the following discussion of cell physiological problems.

The data given in Table II are also of pharmacological importance in that the effective concentrations of many barbiturates used therapeutically are in the range of these half-maximal concentrations. For instance, the plasma levels of evipan in anesthetized rats (23) would inhibit the respiration in perfused rat liver by about 20-30 per cent.

Mitochodrial and non-mitochondrial respiration. Table III summarizes the effects of various inhibitors on the respiratory rate of the hemoglobin-free perfused liver. Stationary respiration amounts to about two thirds of the maximal respiratory capacity after anoxia or after uncoupling by dinitrophenol, while 20 per cent of the stationary oxygen uptake is cyanide resistent, i.e., it does not pass through the respiratory chain. Thus, 20 per cent of respiratory chain dependent oxygen uptake in the steady state cannot be inhibited by amytal, i.e., it probably does not involve mitochondrial DPNH.

TABLE III

Respiratory rates (μatoms of oxygen per hour) of isolated mitochondria (per 60 mg of protein) and of perfused rat liver (per gram of initial fresh weight).

MITOCHONDRIA (per 60 mg Protein)		PERFUSED LIVER (per 1 g fresh weight)		
SUCCINATE	550	NORMOXIC STATIONARY		250 - 300
ISOCITRATE	180	RECOVERY FROM ANOXIA		450
β-HYDROXYBUTYRATE	180	+ DNP	0.1 mM	400
CAPRONATE	200	+ AMYTAL	1.0 mM	100
PYRUVATE + MALATE	140	+ KCN	0.5 mM	50
GLYCERINE - 1 - P	15			
KADENBACH (1964) rat liver mitochondria, state 3		SCHOLZ + SCHWARZ (unpubl.)		

We may compare these values to the respiratory capacities of liver mitochondria in the presence of ADP (state 3), carefully measured by Kadenbach in Klingenberg's group. In Kadenbach's thesis (24) respiratory rates are given per mg of mitochondrial protein. The figures in Table III are based on a tissue content of 60 mg of mitochondrial protein per gram fresh weight of liver (see also next section). At present we hesitate to give a detailed quantitative evaluation of these figures. Further experimental information would be needed for that. In general, however, the rather important conclusion seems to be justified that mitochondria in the intact organ must use their respiratory capacity vigorously during stationary respiration of the liver.

Redox state of respiratory carriers. Proceeding from this conclusion, we may consider the redox state of the respiratory carriers in the tissue under stationary respiration.

With respect to cytochromes a and c the following may be obtained from the reflection spectra: amytal, inhibiting at least 80 per cent of mitochondrial respiration, when applied under normoxic conditions, does not change the 605 mμ peak of the reflection spectra (see Figure 3). Therefore, cytochrome a is probably entirely oxidized in the normoxic stationary state. The 549 mμ peak does not change when amytal is applied. The difference against the anoxic state increases to about 25 per cent. Since no difference of the 605 mμ peak is visible, it may be allowed to neglect changes of the "background", (light scattering, absorption of the organ, etc.). Accordingly, cytochrome c appears to be reduced to about 20 per cent in the normoxic stationary state (Table IV, lower part).

With respect to the state of pyridine nucleotides the question arises which information can be obtained from the fluorometric recordings:

In the liver parenchyme cell DPN- and TPN-systems are reacting in at least 3 (mitochondrial, ergasto- and hyaloplasmatic) compartments. Hence, the fluorometric recording reflects the changes of at least 6 variables. Moreover, the fluorescence enhancement (28) due to the binding of reduced pyridine nucleotides at various sites comes into play, as well as possible changes of the "background".

As described above (see Figure 2) we distinguish several phases in the fluorescence trace affected by anoxia: a latent phase, an initially slight increase, a "jump" at 20 seconds, and finally a slower levelling off. Clues as to the meaning of these phases may be obtained in various ways. We noticed already (see Figure 6) that the "20 second jump" is started when oxygen tension of the tissue reaches the critical value of 10 mm mercury. Also, reduction of respiratory pigments coincides with the "20 second jump" of the fluorescence trace (see Figure 5). Hence, the "20 second jump" may be interpreted as the transition of the mitochondrial pyridine nucleotide system from the normoxic to the anoxic state, (transition from state 3, resp. 4, to state 5, corresponding to the classification given by Chance _et al._ (25, 26)).

The lower portion of Figure 9 shows analyses of pyridine nucleotide contents in the state of normoxia and during the transition to anoxia, compiled from 36 perfusion experiments (38). With respect to the end of the process the tissue contents of DPNH and TPNH have been divided into a mitochondrial and an extramitochondrial fraction. Recent nucleotide analyses of isolated rat liver from Klingenberg's group have been used for this calculation (27). These values are referred to mitochondrial protein (biuret): DPN + DPNH = 2.6 μmoles per gram; TPN + TPNH = 4.1 μmoles per gram. The DPN- and TPN-systems were assumed to be 70 per cent, resp. 96 per cent reduced in anoxia (state 5)(29). Consequently an assumption on the tissue content of mitochondrial protein was necessary. As in the preceding section (see Table III) an amount of 60 mg mitochondrial

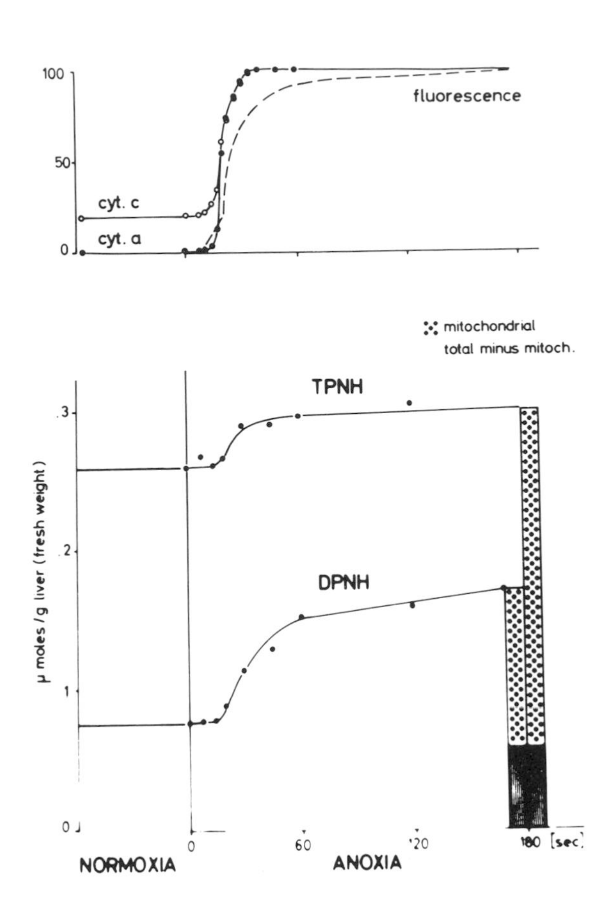

Figure 9. Kinetics of tissue content of reduced pyridine nucleotides during an aerobic to anaerobic transition in perfused rat liver. Also shown are the calculated distribution of DPNH and TPNH between the mitochondrial and extramitochondrial compartments 3 minutes after the start of anaerobiosis. The contents are referred to the weight of the liver before the onset of perfusion (multiplication with 1.75) (38).

protein per gram fresh weight of liver was used. This value originates from two different approaches (24): a) determination of cytochrome a in isolated mitochondria and in tissue homogenates ("cytochrome factor" (17)), and b) determination of glutamate dehydrogenase activity at the cellular and mitochondrial level. The value of 60 mg is somewhat lower than earlier published data (72 mg, (17)). Nevertheless, the possibility cannot be excluded that the real content of mitochondrial protein in liver is even lower. According to these uncertainties criticism may arise with respect to the mitochondrial-extramitochondrial distribution of reduced pyridine nucleotide as suggested by the bars in Figure 9.

The kinetics shown in Figure 9 confirm once more that changes of the cellular level of the reduced pyridine nucleotides are reflected indeed in the fluorescence trace, (see also ref. 10). Mitochondrial DPNH is the main participant. TPNH appears to be located mainly in the mitochondria. About 30 per cent of the total increase of reduced pyridine nucleotides during the aerobic to anaerobic transition may be attributed to TPNH. The contribution of TPNH to the fluorescence increase is even lower, since the fluorescence of mitochondrial DPNH is considerably more enhanced (28) than that of TPNH.

The experiments with amytal (see Figure 8 and Table II) furnish another approach to our problem. In normoxia with added amytal, the increase of fluorescence amounts to 70-80 per cent of the increase after 4 minutes of anoxia. The effects of amytal at the low concentrations used are well defined and yield a striking argument in favor of the assumption that mitochondrial DPNH contributes to two thirds or even more of the fluorescence changes in a cycle of anoxia, corresponding to the "20 second jump".

From these data and arguments we may now estimate the redox state of the mitochondrial DPN-system in the perfused liver during stationary normoxic conditions. The DPN-system appears to be essentially oxidized. The value in the lower part of Table IV (20 per cent of reduction) was derived from the "downward" deflection of the fluorometric trace under the influence of dinitrophenol using the "upward" deflection induced by amytal as a reference. The evaluation of dinitrophenol effects, however, is complicated by light absorption in the primary and secondary fluorometric beam. We believe that the true value is even lower on account of the following argument: the respiratory enhancement following after the anaerobic to aerobic transition does not exhibit any "downward" deflection of the fluorometric trace. For instance, in the first experiment of Figure 8 (right hand; cycle of anoxia) after the restitution of normoxic conditions the respiratory rate overshoots to 450 μatoms oxygen (stationary: 290 μatoms) per hour per gram. But no corresponding overshoot of fluorescence is observed. As explained above rapid changes of the fluorescence intensity represent mainly redox changes of the mitochondrial DPN-system. Hence if we were to assume that a considerable fraction of mitochondrial DPN is reduced during stationary normoxic respiration, a "downward" overshoot of the fluorometric trace should be observed shortly after the anaerobic to aerobic

TABLE IV

States of respiratory chain in isolated mitochondria under different conditions and in perfused rat liver during stationary respiration.

	STATE	RATE LIMITING	PERCENTAGE REDUCTION Cyt.a	Cyt.c	DPN
Isolated Mitochondria	2	Substrate	0	0	0
	3	Respiratory chain	>4	6	8
CHANCE + WILLIAMS (1956) KLINGENBERG + SLENCZKA (1959)	4	ADP	0	14	40
	5	Oxygen	100	100	70
Hb-free perf. rat liver LUBBERS, SCHOLZ, BUCHER (1965)	Normoxia		0	20	<20

transition. Instead of this, the trace falls down to a slightly elevated plateau, then levelling off slowly to the original plateau within 10 minutes, (oxidation of extramitochondrial DPNH?).

State of mitochondria in the perfused liver. A comparison can be made with states in liver mitochondria defined in Philadelphia ten years ago (25,26). The redox values of respiratory carriers in isolated mitochondria of different states (Table IV, upper part) are taken from Chance and Williams (cytochromes a and c)(25) and from Klingenberg and Slenczka (DPN-system)(29,30). The percentage of DPN-reduction depends somewhat on the type of metabolites added, being lowest with isocitrate and being highest with succinate as substrate. The values in Table IV have been established with β-hydroxy-butyrate, α-keto-glutarate and pyruvate plus malate.

With respect to cytochromes a and c the state 4 of isolated mitochondria approaches to the state in the stationary respiring liver. From this statement we might draw the rather important conclusion that the respiratory chain of the perfused liver is controlled by the phosphate potential in the same manner as in the experiments on isolated mitochondria. In contrast, the DPN-system, which would be expected to exhibit the largest changes in the redox state under the control of ADP, is distinctly less reduced, (less than 20 per cent of reduction in the normoxic liver as opposed to 40 per cent in state 4 of isolated mitochondria). We have to notice, however, that mitochondria *in vitro* have been offered just one or a few substrates at one time. *In vivo*, on the other hand, a variety of substrates is always present. The respiratory chain is amply supplied at the site of the flavoproteins as well as at the site of pyridine nucleotides. Furthermore, we know from the work of Plaut (31) and of Goebell and Klingenberg (32) that ADP acts as a modifier of DPN-specific isocitrate dehydrogenase. "Activity control" (41) may be responsible for control of the flow rate within the citrate cycle and consequently for the relatively high degree of oxidation of the mitochondrial DPN-system found in the perfused liver. It must be mentioned in this connection that the perfusion fluid used in these experiments is of restricted complexity in supplying only glucose and amino acids for the organ. Since the perfusion was running for at least one hour before the measurements were made, the contribution of fatty acid combustion to the metabolic state may be negligible.

Adenylate system. The controlling action of ADP would lead us again to the centrally coordinating factor, i.e., the state of the adenylate system.

Figure 10 shows in the top portion the already known time course of the cytochrome and pyridine nucleotide (i.e., changes in fluorescence intensity) redox states in the perfused liver. The lower part exhibits the movements of ATP, ADP and AMP (38). The columns at the beginning and at the end phase of the process are divided into a mitochondrial and an extramitochondrial fraction of the ATP and ADP content of the tissue. In the same manner as described above the mitochondrial contents of the nucleotides were calculated from analyses of Klingenberg's group (27). Also, the tissue contents of DPNH are shown again. This may help us to realize the stoichiometric proportions of the main nucleotide system. These stoichiometric proportions are related to the proportions of the turnover within the systems. Hence, they may also lead to a better understanding of the functional correlations of the fluorescence changes observed.

Secondly, we notice the speed of breakdown of high energy phosphate in anoxia, which is essentially complete within 30 seconds (see also ref. 2 and 6). This breakdown appears to be synchronous with the so-called "20 second jump" of the fluorescence and the reduction of the cytochromes. These measurements have the technical advantage of being taken under fluorometric control. The nucleotide analyses in the extracts of freeze stopped liver (34) was performed by automatic chromatography (33).

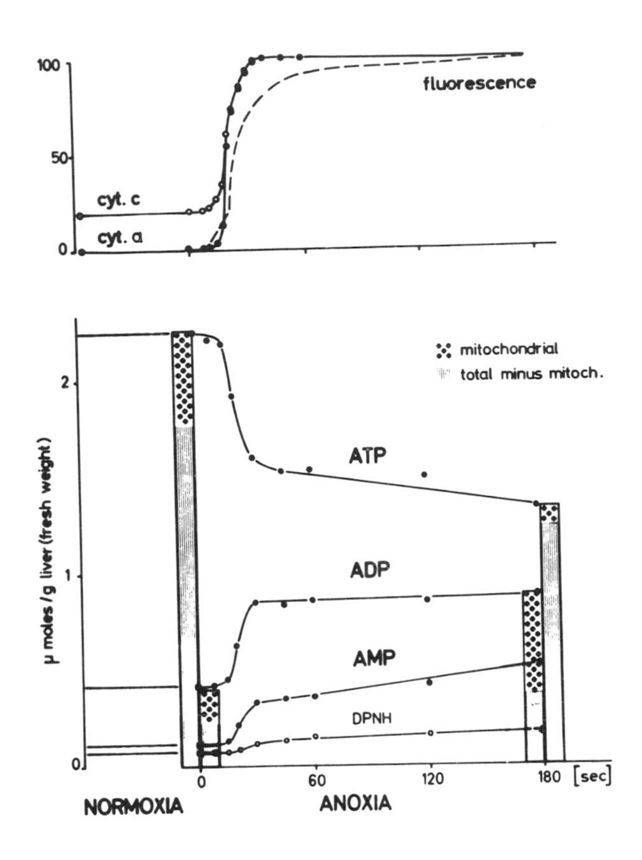

Figure 10. Changes of adenine nucleotides during an aerobic to anaerobic transition, calculated in the same way as for Figure 9. Note that DPNH changes are also given in this figure to demonstrate the relative scales of the changes of the pyridine and adenine nucleotides (38).

With isolated liver mitochondria Chance and Williams (35, 42,43) observed maximal enhancement of respiration when extra-mitochondrial ADP was available at a concentration of about 50 μmolar. ("K_m" = 20 to 30 μmolar ADP, (42)). The ADP content of the normoxic perfused liver is considerably higher, (0.4 μmoles ADP per gram tissue, as can be seen in Figure 10). It is evident, however, that these values are not concentrations but represent the sum of free and bound nucleotide in at least two compartments. As shown by the bars, the ADP content in the two main compartments is about equal. Thus, the extra-mitochondrial content amounts to about 0.2 μmoles per gram of tissue. Which fraction of this ADP content may be assumed to be "free" is an open question (see also next section).

Furthermore, we may ask if the mitochondrial affinity for ADP might be affected by the ATP concentration. We may gather from Figure 10 that a large fraction of the ATP content in normoxic liver is extramitochondrial (about 1.8 μmoles ATP per gram tissue). Chance and Williams excluded an influence of extramitochondrial ATP levels on the mitochondrial ADP affinity under two conditions: first, titrating the respiratory chain with ADP under varying conditions of electron flow activity, (state 3 to state 4 transition, (43)); second, recording the "shut off" of respiratory activity with absence and presence of ATP (42). In these experiments succinate and glutamate, resp. succinate and β-hydroxy-butyrate as substrate have been applied at 10° and 26° C. On the other hand, Klingenberg, using α-ketoglutarate as substrate (at 25° C) demonstrated significant influences of ATP (36). In these experiments half-maximal respiration was obtained with 100 μmolar ADP in the presence of 2500 μmolar ATP and with 250 μmolar ADP in the presence of 5000 μmolar ATP. The experiments of the two groups are not strictly contradictory since different substrates have been used. We should also consider that usually _in vitro_ experiments are performed at unphysiological temperatures. Further research is necessary to clarify the situation, as well with respect to the data of _in vitro_ systems as with respect to the energetic potential of the adenylate system _in vivo_.

Cytidine phosphate system. Other nucleotides, especially the cytidine phosphate system, may perhaps yield a better insight in these energetic potentials. As shown in Figure 11, the ratio of CTP to CDP of about 30 in the normoxic stationary state of perfused liver drops drastically by one order of magnitude within a few seconds after the onset of anoxia in the tissue. Perhaps, cytidine phosphate is qualified as an indicator of the true controlling concentrations in the adenylate system, since it is not phosphorylated directly by the respiratory chain. Unfortunately, tissue levels of the cytidine nucleotides are low, causing analytical problems especially in the normoxic state. Solution of these problems might facilitate quantitative statements about the state and the control of energy metabolism in liver in the future.

Summary

Further investigations on behalf of the characterization of a new system for studies in liver metabolism are presented. Rat liver was extracorporally perfused by a hemoglobin-free fluid of restricted complexity. Hormones were absent. Glucose and amino acids were offered. Surface fluorometry, reflection photometry, measurements of surface oxygen tensions and of respiratory rates have been coordinated with enzymatic and

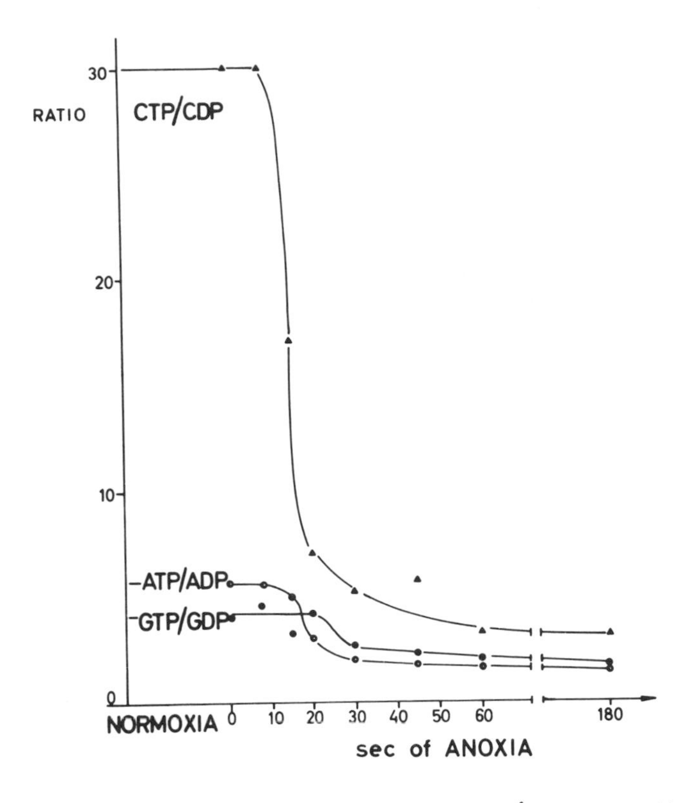

Figure 11. Comparison of the ratio of CTP/CDP with the ATP/ADP and GTP/GDP ratios in rat liver during aerobic to anaerobic transition.

chromatographic analyses of metabolite contents. Normoxic-anoxic and anoxic-normoxic transitions (cycles of anoxia) as well as changes under the influence of classical respiratory inhibitors have been studied in order to obtain further insight into the compartmentation and coordination of hydrogen-, electron-, and phosphate-carriers at the cellular level. The predominant role of the mitochondria with respect to the control of the redox- and phosphate-networks in the liver results from the presented data.

REFERENCES

1. Schnitger, H., Scholz, R., Bücher, Th., and Lübbers, D. W., Biochem. Z., 341, 334 (1965).

2. Hohorst, H. J., Kreutz, F. H., and Bücher, Th., Biochem. Z., 332, 18 (1959).

3. Schimassek, H., Biochem. Z., 336, 460 (1963).
4. Bücher, Th., and Rüssmann, W., Angew. Chemie (Inter. Ed.), 3, 426 (1964).
5. Chance, B., and Jöbsis, F. F., Nature (London), 184, 195 (1959).
6. Chance, B., Schoener, B., Krejci, K., Rüssmann, W., Wesemann, W., Schnitger, H., and Bücher, Th., Biochem. Z., 341, 325 (1965).
7. Chance, B., and Schoener, B., Biochem. Z., 341, 340 (1965).
8. Chance, B., Cohen, P., Jöbsis, F. F., and Schoener, B., Science, 136, 325 (1962).
9. Chance, B., Jöbsis, F. F., Cohen, P., and Schoener, B., Science, 137, 499 (1962).
10. Chance, B., Williamson, J. R., Jamieson, D., and Schoener, B., Biochem. Z., 341, 357 (1965).
11. Lübbers, D. W., and Niesel, W., Pflügers Arch. ges. Physiol., 268, 286 (1959).
12. Niesel, W., Lübbers, D. W., Schneewolf, D., Richter, R., and Botticher, W., Rev. Sci. Instru., 35, 578 (1964).
13. Lübbers, D. W., Kessler, M., Scholz, R., and Bücher, Th., Biochem. Z., 341, 346 (1965).
14. Lübbers, D. W., Scholz, R., Kessler, M., and Brauser, B., unpublished data.
15. Chance, B., in Proc. of Intern. Symp. on Enzyme Chemistry, Tokyo and Kyoto, 1957, Maruzan Co., Ltd., p. 9.
16. Klingenberg, M., and Bücher, Th., Ann. Rev. of Biochem., 29, 669 (1960).
17. Schollmeyer, P., and Klingenberg, M., Biochem. Z., 335, 426 (1962).
18. Omura, T., and Sato, R., J. Biol. Chem., 239, 2370 (1964).
19. Dallner, D., Acta Path. Microbiol. Scand. Suppl., 166 (1963).
20. Chance, B., and Hess, B., J. Biol. Chem., 234, 2404 (1959).
21. Aldridge, W. N., in Ciba Foundation Symposium on Enzymes and Drug Action, London, 1962, p. 155.
22. Aldridge, W. N., and Parker, V. H., Biochem. J., 76, 47 (1960).
23. Sproegel, E., Thesis Medical Faculty, University of Marburg (1962).
24. Kadenbach, B., Thesis Faculty of Science, University of Marburg (1964), Biochem. Z., in the press.

25. Chance, B., and Williams, G. R., J. Biol. Chem., 217, 409 (1955).

26. Chance, B., and Williams, G. R., Adv. in Enzymol., 17, 65 (1956).

27. Pfaff, E., Thesis Faculty of Science, University of Marburg (1965).

28. Estabrook, R. W., and Nissley, S. P., in "Funktionelle und morphologische Organisation der Zelle" Berlin, Göttingen, Heidelberg, 1962, p. 119.

29. Klingenberg, M., and Slenczka, W., Biochem. Z., 331, 486 (1959); Slenczka, W., Thesis, Medical Faculty, University of Marburg (1960).

30. Klingenberg, M., Slenczka, W., and Ritt, E., Biochem. Z., 332, 47 (1959).

31. Chen, R. F., and Plant, G. W. E., Biochemistry, 2, 1023 (1963

32. Klingenberg, M., Goeball, H., and Wenske, G., Biochem. Z., 341, 199 (1965).

33. Schnitger, H., and Bücher, Th., in preparation.

34. Bücher, Th., Krejci, K., Rüssmann, W., Schnitger, H., and Wesemann, W., in "Rapid Mixing and Sampling Techniques in Biochemistry", New York, Academic Press, 1964, p. 255.

35. Chance, B., in Ciba Foundation Symposium on the Regulation of Cell Metabolism, London, 1959, p. 91.

36. Klingenberg, M., Angew. Chemie, 75, 900 (1963).

37. Schwarz, F., Scholz, R., and Bücher, Th., unpublished data.

38. Grunst, J., Scholz, R., and Bücher, Th., unpublished data.

39. Lübbers, D. W., Pflügers Arch. ges Physiol., 265, 172 (1957).

40. Gleichmann, U., and Lübbers, D. W., Pflügers Arch. ges. Physio 271, 431 (1960).

41. Klingenberg, M., this volume, p. 149.

42. Chance, B., and Williams, G. R., J. Biol. Chem., 217, 383 (1955).

43. Chance, B., and Williams, G. R., J. Biol. Chem., 221, 477 (1956).

CONTROL OF ENERGY METABOLISM IN MITOCHONDRIA

Britton Chance

Johnson Research Foundation, University of Pennsylvania
Philadelphia, Pennsylvania

Introduction

The glycolytic pathway of energy metabolism operates in the absence of oxygen and was aptly termed "la vie sans l'air" by Louis Pasteur some years ago. Glycolysis has been reconstructed in solution from purified enzymes and carries out metabolic functions nearly identical to those of the living tissue according to the work of Warburg (1), Meyerhof (2), Cori (3) and others. The aerobic way of life employs a process of energy conservation called oxidative phosphorylation and cannot be reconstructed in solution; apparently, a structural organization of the enzymes is required. This structure is supported by the mitochondrion, called by some, the power-house of the cell. The identification of the mitochondrial structure with the function of oxidative phosphorylation and ion accumulation, with the succinate and DPNH oxidase system, and with electron transport via the cytochromes evolved in different laboratories with different perspectives. Thus, generalizations on the relationship of structure and function in mitochondria were overlooked for many years. For example, D. Keilin (4) who identified MacMunn's histohematins (5) as cytochromes and studied them in detail in intact cells and in subcellular fractions surely recognized the importance of biologucal structure, but he did not recognize that the structures in succinate and DPNH oxidase were derived from mitochondria. Otto Warburg (1), who emphasized the role of iron in cellular oxidation and whose photochemical action spectra provided an indisputable identification of the role of hematins in cytochrome oxidase, was not greatly influenced by the possible role of cytochromes in electron transport or the importance of structure in biological reactions. Belitzer (6), Kalckar (7) and others who identified the process of oxidative phosphorylation did not consider their systems to be mitochondrial or to be related to Keilin's succinate or DPNH oxidizing system and its cytochrome chain. The concepts of oxidative phosphorylation, electron transport and mitochondrial structure were without close analogy in other biochemical systems and thus over 20 years passed before current viewpoints were generally recognized and accepted. While many developments were involved, some of them helped particularly to provide a unity of viewpoint: 1) that electron transport involves the cytochromes (4); 2) that homogeneous suspensions of mitochondria carry out oxidative phosphorylation (8,9); 3) that oxidative phosphorylation in mitochondria proceeds through the cytochrome chain (10); 4) that oxidative phosphorylation exerts a control over the oxidation-reduction state at particular sites in the cytochrome chain (10); 5) that oxidative phosphorylation capability is present in submitochondrial particles (11,12) including the original succinate and DPNH oxidizing particles studied by Keilin and Hartree (13,14).

Energy conservation as it occurs in the mitochondrion is a biological process indispensible to the continuity of life, particularly in the daily maintenance of biological structures. This symposium has considered two biological functions, bioelectricity and muscular contraction, in which energy expenditure is involved. The energy demands for these functional processes may be provided either by oxidative phosphorylation in the mitochondrial structure or by glycolytic phosphorylation in the soluble enzyme system. This paper describes control mechanisms for oxidative phosphorylation and shows how particular kinetic properties of this system allow it to exert a supervisory control over energy metabolism in the cell in general and to regulate the energy supply in accordance with the availability of oxygen in particular.

The Cytochromes

A remarkable property of the cytochrome chain in mitochondria is their distinctive absorption spectra. Those cytochromes that absorb in the region of the visible spectrum can be observed with low dispersion spectroscopes, as indeed was done first by MacMunn who termed them histohematins (5) and later by Keilin (4) who clarified their functions and identified their spectra by visual observation of many cells and tissues. Figure 1 shows the absorption band of the cytochromes as Keilin saw them through the microspectroscope. These absorption bands (indicated by the dark lines in the figure) appear at great intensity when the cytochromes are in the reduced or ferrous state because of the expenditure of oxygen in the system. The absorption bands are labelled a, b, and c, letters which have been traditionally used to identify different enzymes of the respiratory chain.

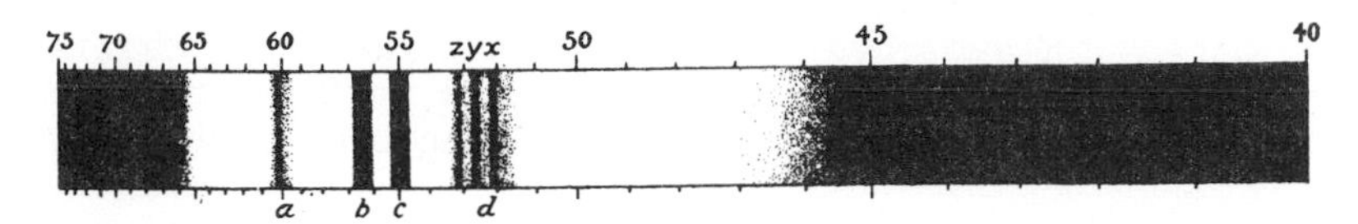

Figure 1. The absorption bands of reduced cytochrome as seen through the microspectroscope (4).

With more modern instruments it is possible to delineate the cytochromes of Keilin's electron transfer chain more accurately, not just as the darker portion of the spectrum spread out before the eye, but as actual absorption maxima on a recorder chart (see Figure 2). In the visible region Figure 2 shows that the cytochrome a and c peaks are recorded sufficiently accurately to afford a quantitative determination. In addition, the spectrophotometer reveals the Soret or γ bands in the cytochromes (in the region 400-500 mμ). Also discernible

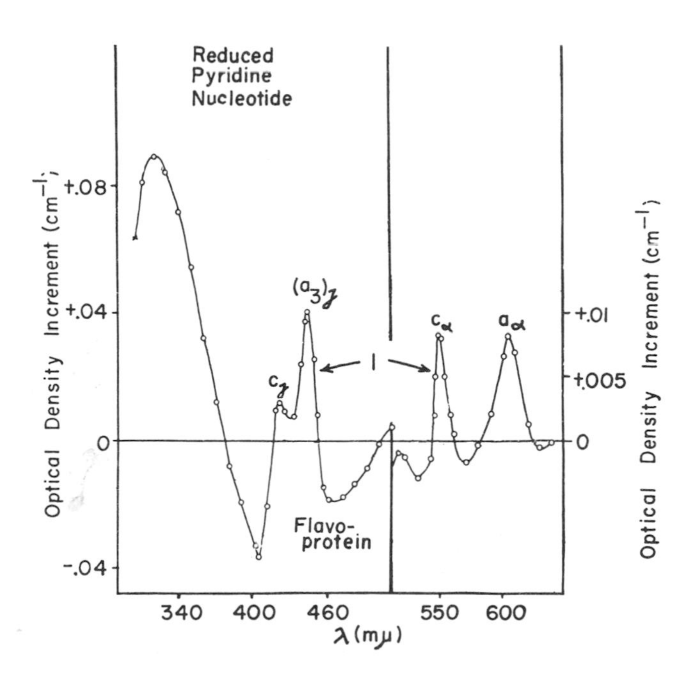

Figure 2. The absorption difference spectrum of cytochrome of rat liver mitochondria as recorded by sensitive spectrophotometric techniques (reduced cytochrome, flavoproteins and pyridine nucleotides). (432 d II)

are two bands which had not previously been observed by visual methods, namely, flavoprotein, indicated by the disappearance of its oxidized band at 465 mμ, and reduced pyridine nucleotide, indicated by the appearance of its absorption band at about 340 mμ.

Quantitative measurements of these peaks now permit precise studies of the cytochrome reactions with oxygen in a special flow apparatus developed for the study of highly turbid suspensions of cells and mitochondria. This apparatus enables a quantitative measurement of the times at which the absorption bands of the cytochromes disappear on suddenly adding oxygen to the anaerobic system. Figure 3 gives the time sequence of the dissapearance of the bands of $\underline{a}_3$ (445 mμ), $\underline{a}$ (605 mμ), $\underline{c}$ (550 mμ), $\underline{b}$ (560 mμ), flavoprotein (465 mμ) and DPNH (340 mμ). These times are the kinetic sequence in which oxidations occur in the respiratory chain and therefore a sequence in which the proteins interact with one another. The kinetic method has allowed us for the first time to draw definitive conclusions concerning the sequence of the action in the cytochromes. The optical method indicates the relative amounts of cytochromes to be approximately 1:1. This conclusion led us to formulate the hypothesis that the entire function of electron transport could be accomplished with one each of the cytochromes (15). Associated with the cytochromes were 2 to 3 molecules of flavoprotein and 10 to 20 molecules of reduced pyridine nucleotide (10). Figure 3 indicates the number of cytochromes and flavoproteins by the number of circles (the number of pyridine nucleotides, 10-20, is indicated numerically). This basic unit for a respiratory assembly competent for electron transport in oxidative phosphorylation has been given the name "oxysome" (16).

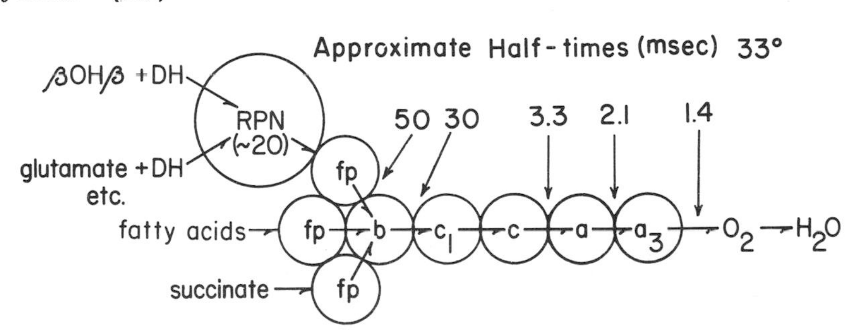

Figure 3. The sequence of cytochromes of the respiratory chain indicating the half times for the oxidation of the reduced cytochrome on the addition of 15 μM oxygen. (MD 82A)

The potentialities of the electron transfer chain for high speed reactions is indicated by the shortness of the intercarrier electron transfer times (shown in Figure 3 in milliseconds). But electron transfer in the steady state of biological oxidation is much slower, usually 10 to 20 electrons per second per carrier. Furthermore, this flow can be slowed nearly to a halt when the energy supply exceeds the energy demand and high energy intermediates accumulate and limit the speed of electron transfer processes to rates of less than one electron per second per carrier.

In order to provide a chemical basis for the inhibition of electron transfer in the phosphorylating system, we have postulated that ligands bind the cytochromes and impede electron flow. These ligands are essential to the process of converting from electron flow to chemical bond energy. The role of these intermediates is indicated by the more complicated diagram of the respiratory chain shown in Figure 4, which indicates by $\sim I_3$ the inhibitory ligand, for example, for the cytochromes c and a. The figure also indicates that the compound $X \sim I_3$ can further be utilized in the phosphorylation of ADP, in the reversal of electron transport causing DPN reduction by succinate, or in the accumulation of cations as described later.

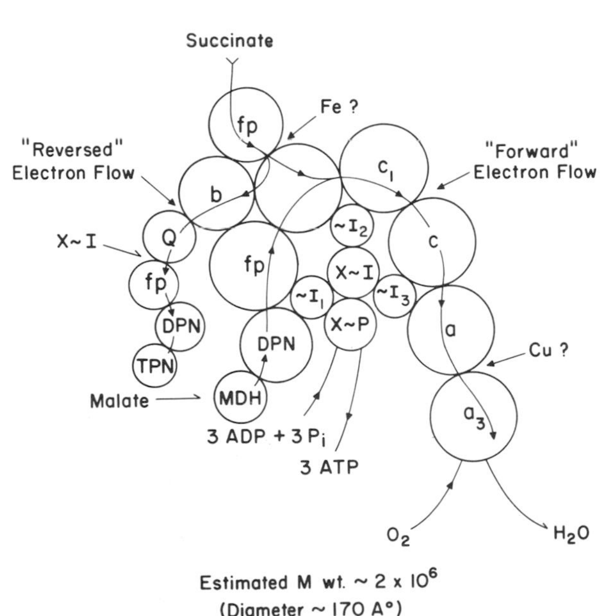

Figure 4. Pathways of electron transport and energy transfer in the "oxysome". (MD 138 L)

Location of the respiratory assembly. The intimate relationship of energy conservations in mitochondria and energy utilization in biological function is best illustrated in muscle where ATP breakdown in the contractile elements is counterbalanced by ATP formation in the mitochondria. The regular vertical bands in Figure 5 (see p. 433) represent the myofibrils, and the masses of darker material represent the mitochondria. The dark osmium-tetroxide-stained portions of the mitochondria are the protein-containing crista with a thickness of about 100 Å (which may be somewhat distorted in the preparation for the electron micrographic studies. Simple calculations on the amount of cytochrome in mitochondria suggest that the only portions of the mitochondrion in which sufficient space is available for the cytochromes is in these crista. The calculations further show that approximately 20,000 assemblies of the respiratory enzymes such as those shown in Figure 3, can be accomodated in a single mitochondrion of average size (17). The relation of the mitochondria to the myofibrils of the muscle is shown in Figure 6 (see p. 433), in which the crista are also more clearly indicated by the greater magnification.

A more effective way of examining the detailed structure of the mitochondrial membrane is the method of phosphotungstic acid staining which, when combined with surface spreading, reveals a very different picture (Figure 7, see p. 434). The surface spread mitochondria exhibit projecting subunits (inner membrane subunits = IMS) or knobs termed "elementary particles" by Fernandez-Moran (18) and Green (19), presumably identifying the particle with the elementary process of electron transport and implying that the particle contained whatever was necessary for the elements of this function. Also identified in the figure is the base membrane where the cytochromes are believed to exist, and the intracristal spaces (ICS). A crucial test of the hypothesis that the projecting subunits contain the entire respiratory chain is provided by removing them and determining whether or not any cytochromes were left in the membranes stripped of their IMS. This can be accomplished by violently shaking the mitochondria in an ultrasonic apparatus. As indicated in Figure 8 (see p. 434), the extruded crista of rat liver mitochondria stained with phosphotungstic acid showed numerous projecting subunits. On the right hand side, following treatment with ultrasound the same preparation exhibits smooth surfaces on which no visible IMS remain. Nevertheless, enzymatic and optical assays showed that the electron transport activity and concentration per unit weight has, if anything, increased (20). Thus, the theory that the projecting subunits contain the electron transport system lacks experimental foundation.

Work in collaboration with Dr. Parsons in Toronto, Dr. Racker in New York and Drs. Estabrook and Tyler of the Johnson Foundation, led to the identification of the enzymatic nature of the projecting macromolecule (21). Some of the proteins by which Dr. Racker has been able to reconstitute oxidative phosphorylation activity were found to reconstitute the biological structure of IMS as well. Figure 9 (see p. 435) shows, on the left hand side, a mixture of the protein cofactor of oxidative phosphorylation, F_1, and the stripped membranes in the absence of magnesium. This protein cofactor is shown in the middle left hand portion of the diagram and has a size very similar to that of the projecting subunits (100 Å). Nevertheless, under these experimental conditions the particles lie on the background of the figure and have not become attacted to the "knob-free membrane." If magnesium and another cofactor (F_2) are added, particles attach themselves to the membranes in numerous cases and reconstitute the knob-like structure observed in the initial material (see arrow). This reconstitution is not perfect, but neither is the reconstitution of the enzymatic activity. The observation that the projecting subunits are identified with the terminal step of oxidative phosphorylation and not with an electron transport function represents a definite step toward increasing our knowledge of the macromolecular structure of the mitochondrial membrane.

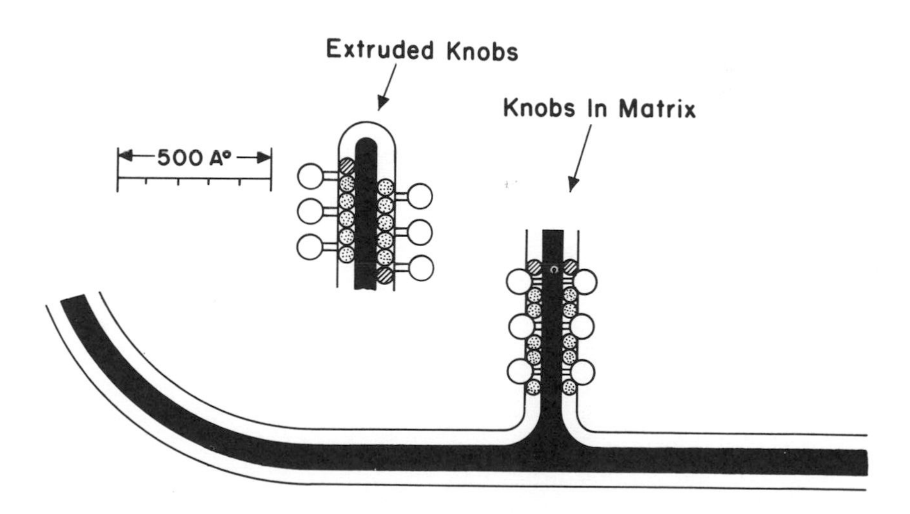

Figure 10. Schematic localization of respiratory chain in mitochondrial membranes. The shaded circles represent electron transport components and the open circles represent IMS. (RWE 21M)

We may summarize our knowledge of the structure of the membrane in Figure 10 where we indicate schematically, by an extension of Dr. Estabrook's ideas, the way in which the enzymes of the respiratory process may be nestled together to constitute the bulk of the mitochondrial membrane (knobs and matrix -- open circles represent the knobs imbedded in the matrix; the shaded circles represent the electron transport components). With phosphotungstic acid staining the knobs are readily observed, and according to the view represented left of center in this figure, are "extruded" from the membrane. The electron transport components remain in the membrane (shaded circles). Ultrasound removes the projecting subunits and recombination of the membranes with the phosphorylation cofactor re-establishes the structure labelled "extruded knobs."

Control properties of the mitochondrion. So far, we have considered the structural and biochemical properties of the respiratory chain; now it is appropriate to consider its biophysical properties and to determine how it can be controlled. For these purposes, it is sufficient to represent the respiratory chain as a black box (see Figure 11) where the three sites at which energy is accumulated in the form of a high energy intermediate (~ I) are pointed out. The diagram indicates the

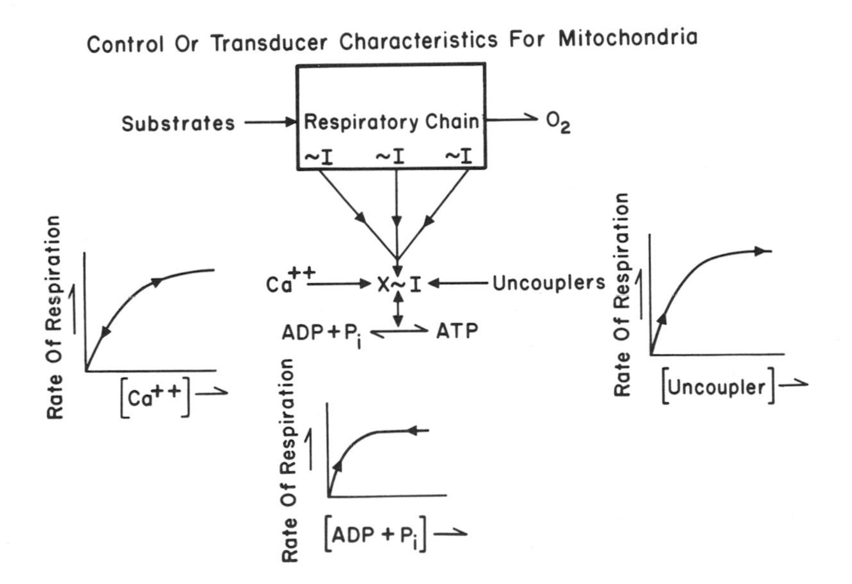

Figure 11. Control characteristics for the mitochondrion illustrating responses to ADP, to calcium, and to uncoupling agents. (MD 137 L)

transfer compound X ~ I and the three points at which the system can be controlled. Shown directly below the box is its control by ADP where a rise in this concentration increases the rate of respiration over 10-fold in an approximately hyperbolic relationship. A second control is indicated on the left where cations, for example, calcium, can interact with the intermediate and thereby be accumulated within the mitochondria again. There is a hyperbolic relationship between calcium concentration and the rate of respiration and we can conclude that cations characteristically stimulate the respiration to a higher level than that obtained with ADP and phosphate. The third control is on the right, where uncoupling agents activate respiration maximally.

An important difference between the control of respiration by uncouplers and that by cations or ADP plus phosphate, is indicated by the arrows on the traces of Figure 11. In the case of uncouplers, it is a "one-way steet"; respiration activated by uncouplers continues unabated until the uncoupler is removed; there is no stoichiometric relationship between the concentration of oxygen expended and the concentration of uncoupler added. In the extreme left and middle traces, however, the situation is different. Here we see that the effects are reversible, the amount of oxygen consumed being proportional to the amount of substrate. The stoichiometric ratio can be calculated and it gives the efficiency of cation uptake and of oxidative phosphorylation. According to this mechanism the intermediate X ~ I has twice the valency towards calcium as it has for ADP.

An illustration of these three control properties of the mitochondria is afforded by Figure 12 where four basic parameters of mitochondrial function are recorded. The overall reaction, or utilization of oxygen is recorded on the two bottom traces as oxygen concentration and oxygen rate (as a function of time), the latter being obtained with a simple differentiating circuit. The sequence of addition of chemicals stimulates the three controls of the previous figure (Figure 11), namely the addition of ADP to activate oxidative phosphorylation, of calcium to activate ion uptake, and of dicumarol to result in uncoupling of the mitochondria. We shall consider the response to ADP first.

Response to ADP. The cyclic rise and fall of the respiratory rate shown by the differentiated oxygen trace, indicates ADP control of substrate flow. The addition of ADP gives an increase in rate. After a steady state interval, ADP is expended and respiration falls to the initial level. The ratio of rates is 3:1. Calcium and dicumarol will activate the system to a greater extent. These changes in rate have an impact on the electron transfer system and alter the oxidation-reduction ratio of the respiratory carriers. Two of the components of the respiratory chain are recorded in the first two traces. The top trace indicates cytochrome c which is recorded by an absorbancy decrease at 550 mμ with 540 mμ as the reference wavelength. This component jumps to a more

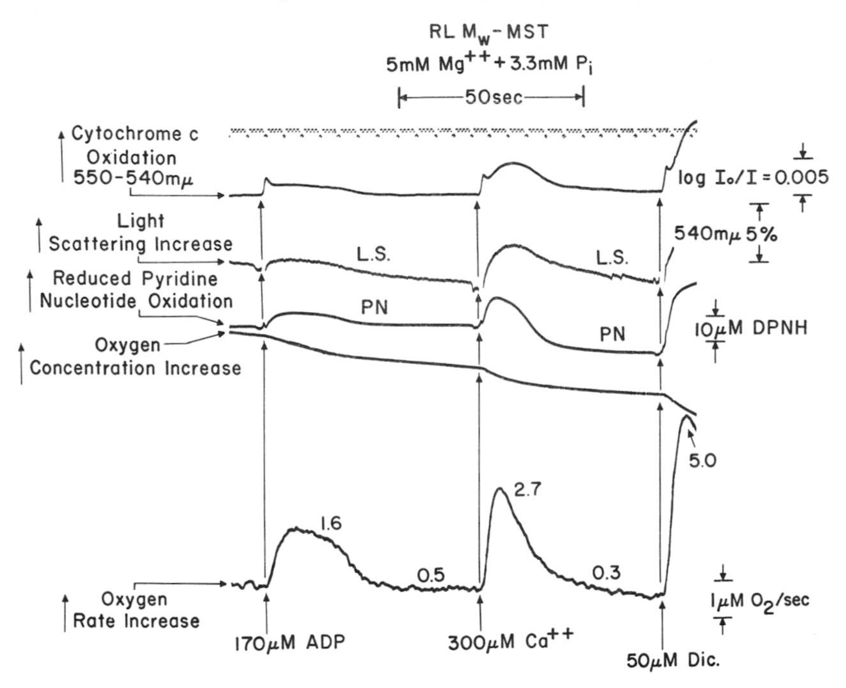

Figure 12. Response in rat liver mitochondria to ADP, calcium, and dicumarol. Top trace, cytochrome c; 2nd trace, pyridine nucleotide; 3rd trace, light scattering; 4th trace, oxygen rate; 5th trace, oxygen concentration. (937-23 IV)

oxidized level when ADP is added (upward deflection of the top trace) and this altered level lasts as long as the rate of accelerated respiration, thereafter subsiding to the initial level. Similarly, the reduced pyridine nucleotide component (measured by the emission at 450 mμ; excited by radiation at 366 mμ), also shows a jump to a higher oxidation state with the increased electron transport rate, and gradually subsides with the decreased rate.

Accompanying these changes of electron flow are characteristic changes of mitochondrial structure evidenced by a small increased light scattering recorded as a decrease of light transmission at 540 mμ. Here also the response follows the changes of respiratory rate. Thus, the mobilization of electron transport activity in mitochondria alters both the oxidation-reduction level of the electron transfer agents and the conformation of the mitochondrion.

Response to calcium. The control of electron transfer in mitochondria by calcium is indicated next on the traces; the respiration increases more than 5-fold. Similar responses are observed in the electron transport components, cytochrome c and DPNH, but to a greater extent with calcium than with ADP, commensurate with the greater degree of respiratory stimulation. The largest change is that of the conformation of the mitochondria where the light scattering trace shows increased scattering during the active accumulation of the cation. As in the case of ADP, when the cation concentration external to the mitochondria is expended, the respiratory rate drops abruptly to the initial level, as do the responses to the cytochromes. The light scattering response drops to the initial level at a significantly slower rate in this case for reasons that are not yet fully understood.

Response to dicumarol. The irreversible activation of respiration is indicated by the third addition (50 μM dicumarol). The initial phases of this reaction are shown on the right hand portion of the figure. The respiration rate is accelerated 17-fold to 0.5 μM per second. Cytochrome c, pyridine nucleotide, and light scattering show even larger responses than with calcium. These responses continue indefinitely.

The whole chart, therefore, demonstrates the three responses of mitochondria: 1) a response to energy demands for the phosphorylation of ADP; 2) a response to energy demands for the accumulation of cations; and 3) the complete release of their energy-conserving potentialities.

Control of energy metabolism in vivo. The electron micrographs of Figures 5 and 6 illustrate the relations of the energy conservation in mitochondria to the energy utilizing myofibrils. The time relationships between the energy demands made upon the mitochondria by muscle contractions and the mitochondrial response to the rise in the level of ADP and phosphate can be studied by the same means as in Figure 12. Technical difficulties do not allow the measurement of the change of oxygen concentration, not is it an easy matter to measure changes of cytochromes, although this has been done for perfused muscle (22,23). The fluorescence method used for measuring reduced pyridine nucleotide in mitochondrial suspensions in Figure 12 can be readily applied to the exposed surface of

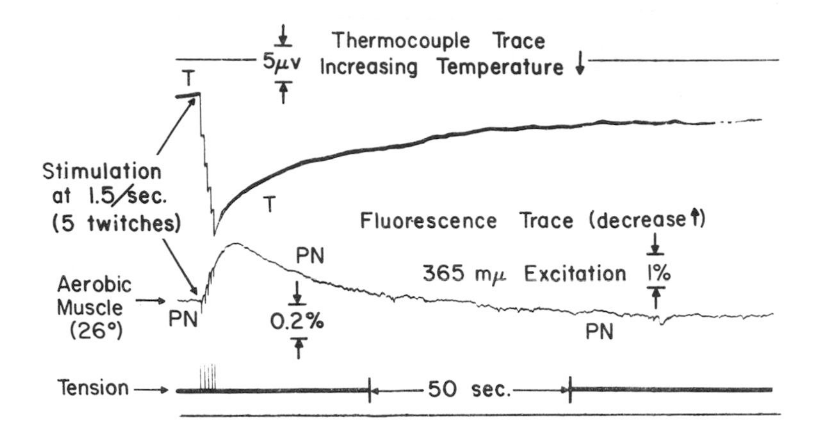

Figure 13. Response of frog sartorius muscle. Stimulation measured fluorometrically and calorimetrically. (50e,45a)

a contracting muscle, indicating changes in the oxidation-reduction level of this component of the mitochondria. Figure 13 indicates an experiment of this type on excised frog sartorius muscle carried out in collaboration with Xavier Aubert of the University of Louvain. Here the increases of tension caused by electrical stimulation are indicated as an upward deflection on the bottom trace. A thermocouple placed next to the muscle registers the rise of temperature due to energy utilization during muscle contraction, as mentioned by Dr. Davies (p. 383). The middle trace registers the oxidation of reduced pyridine nucleotide as a series of steps, one for each twitch. A steady state level of oxidation very similar to the response of mitochondria to ADP and calcium is observed. Both the calcium released in the contractile process and ADP plus phosphate may affect the mitochondria, as in Figure 12. The response of pyridine nucleotide subsides as the energy deficit is made up by oxidative phosphorylation, and the muscle cools to the initial temperature as the recovery heat diminishes.

The transition from mitochondrial function to glycolytic function -- the Pasteur reaction. The release of metabolic control observed by Pasteur, that is, the increase rate of glucose utilization of an anaerobic cell, has been under intensive study for a number of years in order to determine the nature of the metabolic controls involved. The possibility of continuously monitoring the reduced pyridine nucleotide level in cells and tissues, together with the greatly increased time resolution of sampling methods (24) and the elegance of the enzymatic assay of tissue metabolites (25), now allows a mcuh more accurate study of the Pasteur reaction. The method is illustrated in Figure 14 (see p. 435). Here, the perfused heart is contained in a small thermostatic jacket and illuminated at 366 mμ. The reduced pyridine nucleotide fluorescence can be measured by a photomultiplier. This technique gives a continuous readout of the oxidation state of the reduced pyridine nucleotide in the spontaneously beating heart; the beat itself does not appreciably affect the traces if the optics are appropriately arranged. Dr. Williamson has used this apparatus extensively to measure the kinetics of the metabolite changes, and Figure 15 gives an example of such a transition caused by changing from oxygen-saturated perfusate to carbon monoxide-saturated perfusate. Carbon monoxide rapidly blocks the respiratory processes and causes a

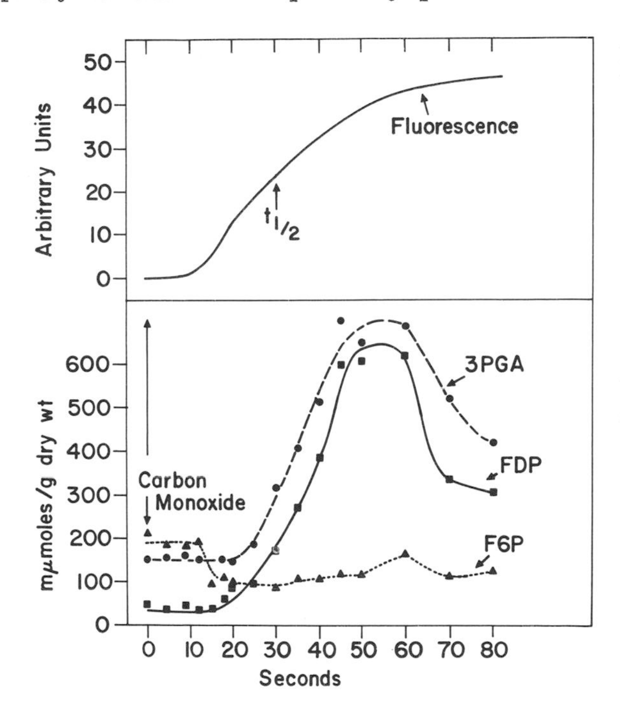

Figure 15. Correlation of fluorescence changes with metabolite assays in perfused heart. (JRW 105)

rapid conversion from mitochondrial to glycolytic control, a transition to true anoxia.

The top trace of Figure 15 shows a rise of fluorescence which begins 7 to 10 seconds after the perfusate has been changed from oxygen- to carbon monoxide saturated. The increase of reduced pyridine nucleotide occurs continuously for about a minute, and half-maximal reduction is reached 30 seconds after perfusion with carbon monoxide is begun. The trace registers the time interval in which the interesting biochemical changes are occurring. Metabolite assays are made on a series of hearts rapidly frozen at various times after the initiation of perfusion with carbon monoxide. In the middle traces the control chemicals ADP, AMP and phosphate begin to rise about 15 seconds after perfusion with carbon monoxide. This rise of the adenine nucleotides and possibly of phosphate as well, triggers the glycolytic system to replace the loss of energy of oxidative phosphorylation and to prevent any further fall of ATP. The activation of glycolysis causes a sharp fall of fructose-6-phosphate (F-6-P) and a sharp rise of fructose diphosphate (FDP) between 12 and 18 seconds. An overshoot in the concentration of FDP is observed which subsides to a lower level in about one minute, while the adenine nucleotides rise monotonically to their new levels. Thus, the switch of metabolic control from the highly efficient process of oxidative phosphorylation to the less efficient but kinetically competent process of glycolysis occurs rapidly and effectively. These controls maintain the ATP level but allow rises of ADP and AMP.

Oscillating enzyme reactions. The fact that the aerobic-anaerobic transition gives an overshoot in the concentration of an intermediate has attracted our attention ever since we first observed this phenomenon in Baker's yeast cells (26). More, recently, we have found that the overshoot of intermediates in the anaerobic system is the first portion of a damped oscillation which is now well documented in yeast cells (27). Since these oscillations give a considerable insight into the mechanisms of metabolic control, particularly the role of the ATP/ADP ratio, it has been of great interest to determine

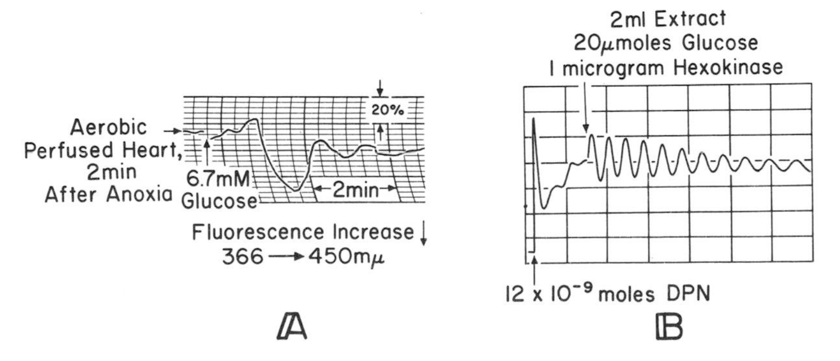

Figure 16. Oscillations in perfused heart, left; cell-free extract obtained from heart, right. (662D-3-IV)

whether they could be observed in heart. Figure 16 indicates on the left hand side, reduced pyridine nucleotide fluorescence in the perfused heart under conditions similar to those in Figure 15. In this case, the heart is perfused with oxygen, following an interval of two minutes anoxia with nitrogen in order to deplete the glycogen store of the heart. At this time the reduced pyridine nucleotide is in a highly oxidized state, and glucose addition to the perfusate causes an abrupt increase of fluorescence reaching a maximum one minute later, a recovery from the maximum, and thereafter a cyclic response similar to a highly damped form of the oscillation observed in Baker's yeast cells. It is apparent that the metabolic control system of the heart is capable of the same types of feedback as the yeast system, which may lead to damped, or under special conditions, to continuous oscillations (28). As evidence that this oscillation can be observed in an extract contained in the glycolytic enzymes of the heart, we include Figure 16B where the heart extract, supplemented with DPN and with glucose and hexokinase, bursts into a nearly continuous chain of sinusoidal oscillations of the DPNH level. Corresponding fluctuations of the metabolite intermediates occur as well (Y. Cassuto, unpublished observations). Thus, we see not only the action of metabolic control causing a transition monotonically from one state to another, but also an oscillatory tendency of the feedback system under appropriate conditions.

Computer simulation of metabolic control. The understanding of the dynamic changes of many intermediates in multi-enzyme systems requires the use of the modern digital computer initially developed at this University. By such simulation we can test incisively our representation of the metabolic pathway and its control, by making the computer simulate the biochemical system (29,30). Such simulation involves a number of differential equations and may require many hours, even to simulate a half minute of the cell life, but such a solution can give the essential agreement -- or disagreement -- of current hypotheses on metabolic control and biochemical observations on the living system. We do not see any other effective way of assembling the vast range of experimental data on metabolite assays in a form that can be effectively used in the examination of mechanisms of metabolic control. For this and other reasons, we envisage a greatly increased employment of computer simulation in biomedical research.

Summary

It has been the purpose of this review to emphasize the controls which equilibrate the supply and demand for energy metabolism in tissues. The controls exerted over electron flow in the respiratory chain are demonstrated, and the relationship of their function to the structure of the mitochondria emphasized.

The oxidative phosphorylation system of mitochondria exhibits control characteristics in response to the phosphorylation of ADP and to the accumulation of cations, and examples of this control are afforded by techniques which allow the continuous monitoring of reduced pyridine nucleotide in skeletal muscle of perfused beating heart. These monitoring methods, coupled with frequent sampling of the tissue and complete assays, give a better understanding in chemical terms of the sparing of metabolites in the switch from anaerobic to aerobic energy conservation. Increased knowledge of metabolic controls give not only an understanding of the regulatory process but possibly the power of interacting with such control systems in a way that will ultimately be fruitful in the solution of problems in medicine and biology.

References

1. Warburg, O., Stoffwechsel du Tumoren, Springer, Berlin, 1926.
2. Meyerhof, O., Biochem. Z., 178, 395 (1926).
3. Cori, C. F., Harvey Lectures, 41, 253 (1945-46).
4. Keilin, D., Proc. Roy. Soc. (London), B98, 312 (1925).
5. MacMunn, C. A., Phil. Trans, 177, 267 (1886).
6. Belitzer, V. A., and Tsibakowa, E. T., Biokhimiya, 4, 516 (1939).
7. Colowick, S. P., Kalckar, H. M., and Cori, C. F., J. Biol. Chem., 137, 343 (1941).
8. Hogeboom, G. H., Schneider, W. C., and Palade, G. H., J. Biol. Chem., 172, 619 (1948).
9. Lehninger, A. L., Harvey Lectures, 49, 176 (1954-55).
10. Chance, B., and Williams, G. R., Advances in Enzymology (F. F. Nord, ed.), Interscience, New York, 1956, p. 65.
11. Racker, E. F., and Conover, T., Fed. Proc., 22, 1088 (1963).
12. Green, D. E., Beyer, R. E., Hansen, M., Smith, A. L., and Webster, G., Fed. Proc., 22, 1460 (1963).
13. Keilin, D., and Hartree, E. F., Proc. Roy. Soc. (London), B127, 167 (1939).

14. Lee, C-P., and Ernster, L., Biochem. Biophys. Res. Comm., 18, 523 (1965).

15. Chance, B., Nature, 169, 215 (1952).

16. Chance, B., Estabrook, R. W., and Lee, C-P, Science, 140, 379 (1963).

17. Estabrook, R. W. and Holowinsky, A., J. Biophys. Biochem. Cytol., 9, 19 (1961).

18. Fernandez-Moran, H., Science, 140, 380 (1963).

19. Green, D. E., Sci. Am., 210, 63 (1964).

20. Chance, B., Parsons, D. F., and Williams, G. R., Science, 143, 136 (1964).

21. Chance, B., Racker, E. F., Tyler, D. D., Estabrook, R. W., Conover, T. E., and Parsons, D. F., in Oxidases and Related Oxidase Systems (T. E. King, H. S. Mason, and M. Morrison, eds.), John Wiley and Sons, Inc., New York, in the press.

22. Chance, B., and Weber, A. M., J. Physiol., 169, 263 (1963).

23. Chance, B., and Jöbsis, F. F., Nature, 184, 195 (1959).

24. IUB/IUBS Rapid Mixing and Sampling Techniques in Biochemistry (B. Chance, Q. H. Gibson, R. Eisenhardt, and K. K. Lonberg-Holm, eds.), Academic Press, New York, 1964.

25. Estabrook, R. W., this volume, p. 125.

26. Chance, B., Harvey Lectures, 49 (1953-54).

27. Betz, A., and Chance, B., Arch. Biochem. Biophys., 109, 579 (1965).

28. Pye, E. K., personal communication.

29. Chance, B., Hess, B., Garfinkel, D., and Higgins, J. J., J. Biol. Chem., 235, 2426 (1960).

30. Garfinkel, D., and Hess, B., J. Biol. Chem., 239, 971 (1964).

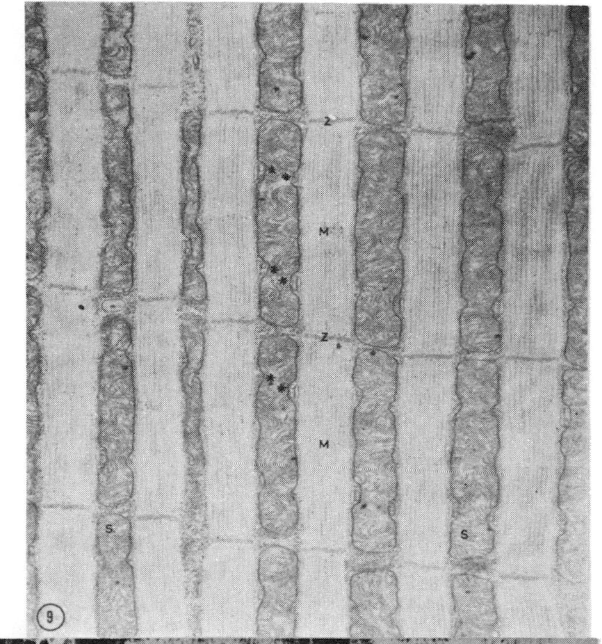

Figure 5.
Arrangement of mitochondria in relation to myofibrils in the flight muscle. (DS 8) Courtesy, David Smith, University of Virginia.

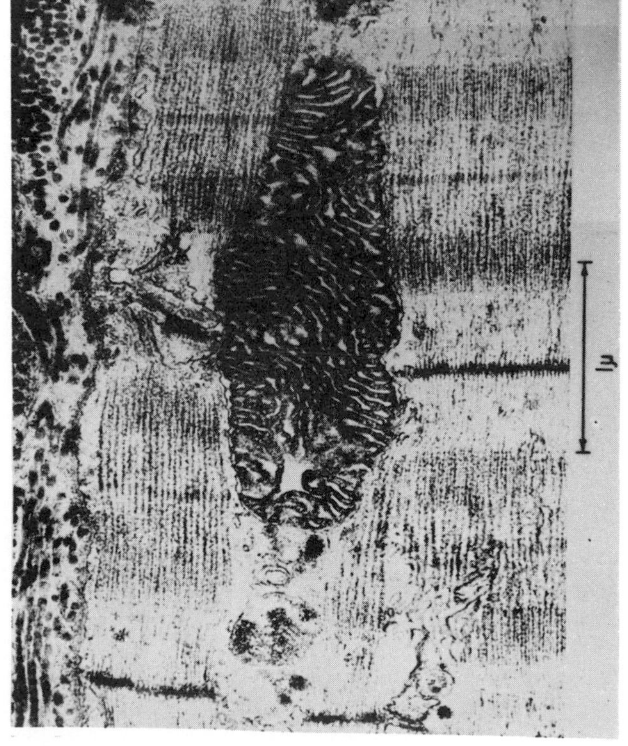

Figure 6.
Enlarged view of the internal structure of the mitochondrion showing crista. (O 103)
Courtesy, R. Birks and H. Huxley.

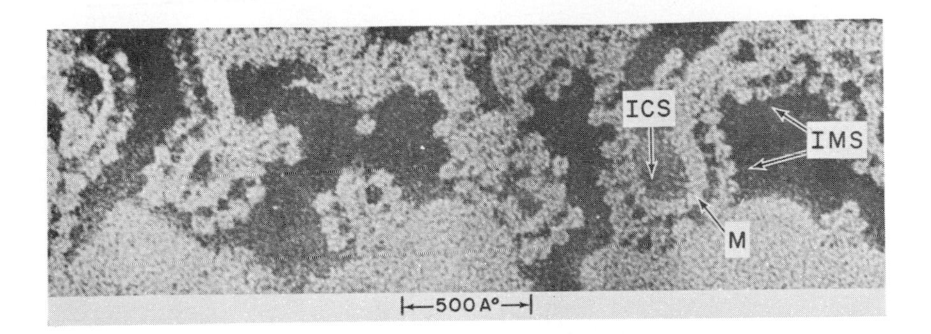

Figure 7. Phosphotungstic acid stained electron micrograph showing the inner membranes of the IMS. (P 6255b) Courtesy, Donald F. Parsons.

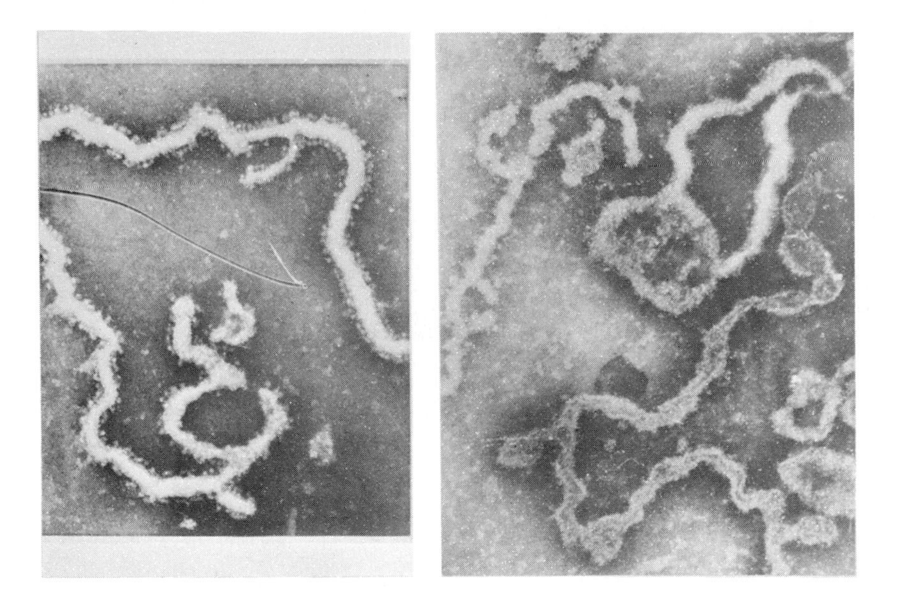

Figure 8. Electron micrograph of rat liver mitochondria befor and after stripping of the IMS by ultrasound. (P 53a) Courtesy, Donald F. Parsons.

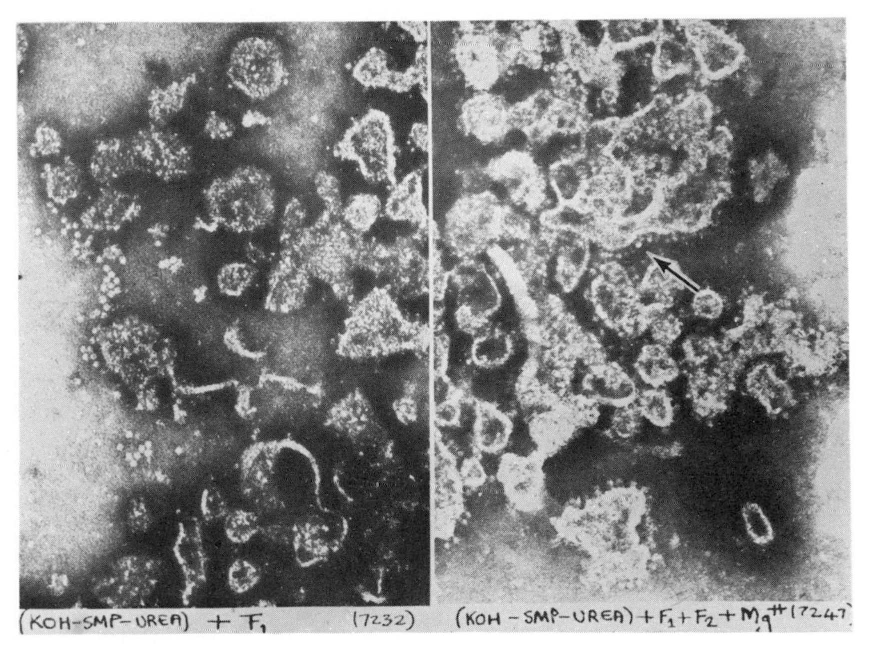

Figure 9. The combination of the cofactor F_1 with the stripped membranes of beef heart mitochondria (left) to form the projecting subunits (IMS)(right). (P 61) Courtesy, D.Parsons, E. Racker.

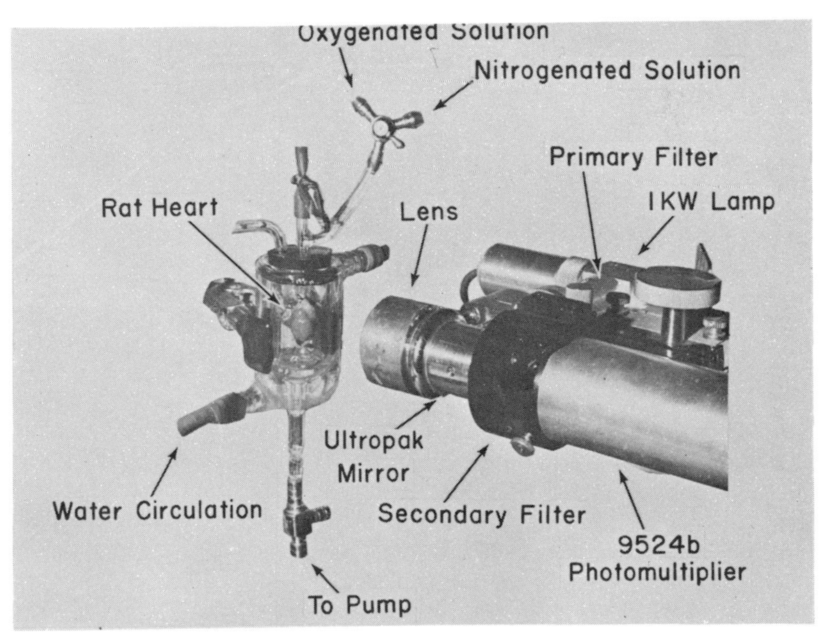

Figure 14. Apparatus for measuring reduced pyridine nucleotide in the beating perfused heart. (JRW 1)

SUBJECT INDEX

A

Absolute control plane, 37, 38
Acetate, effects on rat heart, 339
Activation of hexokinase in stimulated muscle, 308
  of phosphorylase, 302
Active carrier mediated transport, 221
Activity control, 150
Actomyosin filaments in muscle, 385
Adenine nucleotides in liver, 409
Adenylate kinase, 153
ADP, activation of respiration, 167
  control of, 9
  control respiration chain, 10
  K_m, 9
ADP control, 196
ADP and Pi control, ascites metabolism, 159
Aminoisobutyric acid transport, 221
  effect insulin, 225, 228
  effective concentration, 225
  ion inhibition, 225, 227
Amytal, effects in liver, 402
ATP/ADP ration, 167
ATP compartmentation, 158, 170, 198
  pools, 183
Aldolase, phosphate effect on, 56
Allosteric activation, 111
γ, aminobutyric transaminase, glycerophosphate shuttle, 199, 301
Anaerobic glycolysis, 163
Analogue computer, 13
Anesthesia, effect on metabolites in brain, 323
Anoxia, adenine nucleotide changes, 409
  effect on *E. coli*, 361
  effects on metabolites in brain, 322
  on rat heart, 336, 339
Antimycin A, 10
Ascites cells, metabolite content, 161
Availability of ADP, 194

B

Back activation, 42
Barbiturates, effect on respiratory inhibition in liver, 402
Biochemical imprinting, 249
Biochemical switch, 113
Biochemical systems, simulation, 49
Bioelectricity, 375
  coupling with metabolism, 378
Brain, level of Krebs cycle intermediates in, 321
Brain mitochondria, 203

C

Caffeine, effect on phosphorylase, 304
Calcium concentration in muscle, 384
Calcium transport, effect anion, 211
  effect Pi, 211
Cardiac glycosides, effects on ion movements, 380
Cellular levels, AMP, 198
Chain branching, 12
Characteristic time T, 14, 21
Chemical relaxation, 57
Citrate cleavage enzyme, 261
  cellular locus, 261
  induction of, 261
Citrate control of PFK, 338, 357
Citric acid cycle intermediates, determination of, 328
$^{14}CO_2$ Fixation in rat heart, 359
Compartmentation, 52, 53, 125, 127, 283
  of metabolites in tissue, 369, 370
Computer based analysis, 49
Computer simulation of control, 429
Control anaerobic glycolysis, 187
Control by adenine nucleotides, 149
  during transient, 49
  of glycolysis,
    effect of pH, 287
    in *E. coli*, 360
  multi-site, 55, 56
Control plane diagram, 36

Control points, 55
in citric acid cycle, 324
Control site, 111
in *E. coli*, 362
Control transfer, 40
Coordination of glycolytic activity, 296
Co-repressor, 242
Crossover sites of glycolytic intermediates in rat heart, 338, 341
Crossover theorem, 10, 12, 55
diagram, 12
reversal crossover, 12, 56
Cybernetic coupling, 111
Cyclic AMP
control of PFK, 366
in rat heart, 345, 363
Citidine phosphate changes in liver, 411
Cytochromes, 416, 418
organization, 418, 424
stoichiometry, 418
Cytosol, 245

D

Damped oscillations, 243
γ-Deoxyglucose, penetration and phosphorylation in muscle, 309
Diffusion of chemicals, 13
DPN kinase, 267
DPN of liver, oxidation-reduction state of, 246
DPNH, effect 144
2,4-Dinitro fluorobenzene, effects in muscle, 316
Displacement from equilibrium, 118
Dynamical state level, 16
characteristics, 30
diagram, 18, 19, 22

E

Effective cellular concentration pi, 192
Effect-substrate concentration, 21
Efficiency of muscular contraction, 390
Electron transfer times, 419
Electron transport, effect of anesthetics on, 326
Elementary particles, 420
Energy control, 150
Energy-linked hydrogen transfer, 275
Energy-linked reduction PN, 274, 275
effect of hyperbaric oxygen, 274
Energy-linked transhydrogenation, 276
Enzyme profiles, 113
heart extract, 123
yeast, 114
Enzyme repression, 241
Enzymes, structural organization, 415
Epinephrine, effects on rat heart, 341
identification of control sites in glycolysis, 343
Equation of motion, 18
Equilibrium control, 150
Equilibrium state, 15, 16
Essential fatty acids, effect on TPN dehydrogenases, 254
liver composition 254

F

F_1, 421
Fatty acid,
chain lengthening, 257
desaturation, 256
metabolism in rat heart, 357
Feedback, 111
Feedback control of glycolysis, 158
Feedback inhibition, 239, 243
Feedback interaction, 12
Feedback properties, 41
Feedforward control, 119
Fertilization, effect
on pyridine nucleotides, 267
on respiration, 267
Flavoproteins, 418
Fluoroacetate, effect on metabolites in brain, 326
Fluorometry in liver, 394
Flux control, 34
control strength, 34, 39, 40
Flux profiles, 115
Forward control, 57
Forward inhibition, 42
Fructokinase, 263
Fructolysis, 263
Functional readiness, 55

G

Glucokinase, 205, 262
Gluconeogenesis, 245
effect of fasting, 246
of hydrocortisone, 246
of insulin, 246
of mannoheptulose, 246
Glucose transport in rat heart, 347

Glucose uptake in rat heart
effects of anoxia, 349
of insulin,
of tension development, 352
of work, 349
GAPDH, de-inhibition, 197
DPNH inhibition, 141
inhibition, 196
by 1, 3, Di-PGA, 144
pyruvate inhibition, 141
product control, 168
Glyceraldehyde-3-P dehydrogenase, control of, 364
Glycerol extracted muscle, 388
Glycolysis, activation of, 287
ascites cell, 50
increased rate caused by hyperthermia, 324
reconstitution, 127
Ground state, 18

H

Heteroexchange diffusion, 222
Hexokinase, ADP control, 197
ascites, 128, 177
ATP K_m, 178
bound, 177
brain, 202
control point, 52
effect G-6-P, 177, 181
effect Pi, 205
G-6-P control of, 170
G-6-P inhibition, 128, 131
Pi effect, 128
Hexokinase, product inhibition, 201
Hexokinase effect, Pi, 178, 181, 182
Hyperlysogenesis, 253
Hyperthermia, effect on metabolites in brain, 323

I

Inhibition of PFK, effect of pH, 292
Induction of microsomal enzymes, 253
Inner membrane subunits, 420
Insulin, effect on metabolites in brain, 326
Intracellular DPNH, redox state, 277
Iodoacetamide, effects on rat heart, 337
Ion accumulation, 209, 217
Ion compartments, 210, 230, 236
Ion translocation, 150
Ion transport,
ATPase, 217
carrier hypothesis, 376
cation flux, 209, 217
Conway's redox pump theory, 377
effect pH, 209
effect parathyroid hormone, 213
energy-linked, 209
Ion transport yield, 235
Isocitrate dehydrogenase, ADP activation, 153
effect of DPN, 153
Isoenzymes, 58

K

K^+ permeability, 212
Kinesine hypothesis, 171
Kinetic control, 150

L

L-Arabinose transport in rat heart, 351
Lactate-pyruvate ratio in liver, 396
Law of Guildberg and Waage, 13, 23, 24
Laws of Quantum Mechanics, 23
Lipogenesis, 245
effect of HMP dehydrogenase, 252
Liver, respiratory rate, 400

M

Mg^{++} permeability, 212
Malate synthesis, effect of insulin, 246
Mass action ratio, 55, 115
Membrane hyperpolarization, 232
Membrane potential, 235
Metabolic couples, 55
Metabolic limit line, 18
Metabolic overshoot, 239
Metabolite load line, 115
Metabolite patterns, perfused heart, 428
Metabolite pools, 116
Metabolite profiles, 111
Michaelis Menton, 21, 27
Michaelis kinetics, 117
Microsomal ATPase, 217
Mitochondria, structural organization, 9
Mitochondrial compartmentation, 152
Mitochondrial contraction, 211
Mitochondrial pools of nucleotides, 153
Mitochondrial swelling, 212

Mitochondrion, control charcteristics, 422
effect ADP, 422
effect uncouplers, 425
ion uptake, 422, 425
metabolic state in liver, 408
Multiple control sites, 163
Multisite control of glycolysis, 334
Muscle contraction, theory of, 387
Muscle twitch, energy changes, 389
Myokinase mass action ratio, 198

N

Na^+ Electrochemical gradients, 227
Na^+ K activated ATPase, 217
Na^+ pump, 221, 231
Na/~P ratio, 218, 235
Negative feedback, 42
Net flux, 27, 30, 39
diagrams, 41

O

Oligomycin, effect on phosphorylase, 305
Oliver Wendell Holmes, 136
Oscillation cycles, 197
Oscillations, 172
glycolytic, 50
heart extract, 429
synchrony, 145
yeast, 428, 429
Oscillatory glycolysis, 114, 143
Oscillatory system, 44
Ouabain, 217
Oxidative phosphorylation, 415
control, 9
reversibility, 150
Oxygen/cation ratio, 213
Oxysome, 419

P

pH changes *In vivo*, effect on phosphorylase, 291
PK, ATP inhibition, 143
effect of FDP, 119
FDP activation, 143
Parathyroid hormoe, 210
effect on succinate oxidation, 213
Pasteur effect, 127, 136, 178, 183, 191, 193
influence ADP, 193
influence Pi, 193
Pasteur quotient, 193
Pasteur reaction, 172, 426, 427
Periodic cell division, 243
Phosphate, control by, 161
Phosphate control, 167, 196
Phosphate control glycolysis, 134
Pi, critical level, 160
inhibition of phosphorylation, 167
Phosphate potential, 169
PFK, absorption spectrum, 74
activation, 82, 296
activity, 115
activity ratio, 77
ATP activation, 84, 165
ATP cleavage, 94
ascites cells, 87
backward reaction, 77, 78
bound nucleotide, 74, 75
cellular localization, 71
computer study, 101
conformation change, 92
control, 168
of glycolysis, 133
of nucleotides in rat heart, 345
deviation from equilibrium, 337
dissociation, 67
effect EDTA, 92
effective ionic strength, 73, 84
forward reaction, 77
ITP effects, 132
inactivation, 105
inactive form, 73
interconversion of active and inactive forms, 69
kinetic activation, 81
kinetic properties, 63
ATP inhibition, 63, 87, 90, 97, 128, 143
citrate inhibition, 63, 102
Mg inhibition, 63, 90
NH_4 activation, 63
Pi activation, 63, 87
5′ AMP activation, 63, 79, 98, 99, 102
F-6-P activation, 63, 82, 98
K^+ activation, 63
cyclic AMP, 63, 81
pyruvate kinase,
FDP activation, 57, 58
phosphate control, effect on K_m, 56
phase plane, 14
plots, 17, 44
pool sizes, 9, 171
lag period, 88
mechanism of action, 93
model, 94

multiple forms, 81, 84
phosphorylase b, 65
purification, 65, 71
sedimentation properties, 67, 70, 85
stabilization by dithiothreitol, 69
yeast, 97
Phosphorylase, effect of nucleotides, 306, 307
in smooth muscle, 313
Phosphorylation potential, 152
Product inhibition, 171
Pyridine nucleotides, cellular distribution, 273
content of liver, 405
intact tissue, 425
Pyruvate decarboxylase, 144

R

Rat heart, metabolite patterns, 335
Rate constants, 19
Rate controlling steps, 38, 45
Rate laws, 25
Reactions, classification, 26
Reaction frequency, 18
Reconstituted oscillating glycolytic system, 139
Redox potentials, 153
Redox state of respiratory carriers in liver, 404
Reflection spectra in liver, 398
Regulation of oxidative metabolism in brain, 321
Relaxation time, 14
Repression, 111
Respiratory assembly, 420
Respiratory chain, velocity constant, 9
inhibitors, 10
Reversible oxidative phosphorylation, 273

S

Self-consistent control approximation, 37
Sodium efflux, 218
Sodium transport, effect of concentration, 218
effect Na, 221
Stationary states, 19
Stationary state motions, 24
Steady state, 14
steady state flux, 114
Stimulation of muscle, 299
Stimulation on muscle
effects on glycolysis, 300
Structural control variables, 22, 31, 33
Substructure reactives, 30
Sulfate ion transport, 239

T

Thermal measurements, 426
Thermodynamic equilibrium, 55
TPN malic enzyme, 249
effect of thyroxine, 249
of estrogen, 249
of DNP, 249
TPNH, effect on protein synthesis, 267
Time constants, 57
Time partner reactives, 118
Transient metabolite profiles, 120

U, V, Y

Ubiquinone, 9
Valinomycin, 235
Yeast oscillations, phase differences, 121